Electrical Heats at Low Temp...

Specific Heats at Low Temp...

High Magnetic Fields

...conductivity for Engineers

...c Laboratory Equipment

...ctivity in Elements, 'Compounds

...y Equilibria

...paration

H. J. Goldsmid
G. T. Meaden
E. S. R. Gopal

D. H. Parkinson
J. L. Ol...
A. J. Croft and p...

THE INTERNATIONAL CRYOGENICS MONOGRAPH SERIES

General Editors

Dr. K. Mendelssohn, F. R. S.
The Clarendon Laboratory
Oxford, England

Dr. K. D. Timmerhaus
University of Colorado
Boulder, Colorado

Thermoelectric Refrigeration, 1964

...istance of Metals, 1965

...eratures, 1966

SPECIFIC HEATS
AT LOW TEMPERATURES

E. S. R. Gopal

Department of Physics, Indian Institute of Science
Bangalore, India

PLENUM PRESS

NEW YORK

1966

CHEMISTRY

Library of Congress Catalog Card Number 65-11339

Preface

This work was begun quite some time ago at the University of Oxford during the tenure of an Overseas Scholarship of the Royal Commission for the Exhibition of 1851 and was completed at Bangalore when the author was being supported by a maintenance allowance from the CSIR Pool for unemployed scientists. It is hoped that significant developments taking place as late as the beginning of 1965 have been incorporated.

The initial impetus and inspiration for the work came from Dr. K. Mendelssohn. To him and to Drs. R. W. Hill and N. E. Phillips, who went through the whole of the text, the author is obliged in more ways than one. For permission to use figures and other materials, grateful thanks are tendered to the concerned workers and institutions.

The author is not so sanguine as to imagine that all technical and literary flaws have been weeded out. If others come across them, they may be charitably brought to the author's notice as proof that physics has become too vast to be comprehended by a single onlooker.

E. S. RAJA GOPAL

Department of Physics
Indian Institute of Science
Bangalore 12, India
November 1965

v

Contents

Introduction

Investigations at temperatures below room temperature have advanced our knowledge in many ways. Toward the beginning of the present century, physical chemists evolved their reference state for chemical equilibria and thermodynamic properties on the basis of such studies. Later, physicists realized that a clear manifestation of quantum effects was possible at low temperatures. In recent times, superconductors, rocket fuels, cryopumping and a multitude of other developments have lifted low-temperature studies out of academic cloisters and into the realm of technology.

In any practical attempt to study low-temperature phenomena, the question of specific heats crops up immediately, in connection with the refrigeration needed to take care of the thermal capacity of the apparatus. Apart from its significance in this perennial problem of cooling equipments to desired low temperatures, knowledge of specific heats forms a powerful tool in many other areas, such as lattice vibrations, electronic distributions, energy levels in magnetic materials, and order-disorder phenomena in molecules. No better evidence for the usefulness of specific-heat studies is needed than the presence of the Debye characteristic temperature θ in so many branches of solid state studies. This monograph is basically a descriptive introduction to the different aspects of specific-heat studies.

Historically, the need for measuring specific heats at low temperatures arose in conjunction with the formulation of the third law of thermodynamics. Nernst realized that the specific heat of all substances should vanish as the absolute zero of temperature is approached. Einstein demonstrated the quantum effects that come into play in specific heats at low temperatures. This opened up the prospect of checking the energy states of all substances with the help of calorimetric measurements. Whatever theory of solid, liquid, and gaseous states is developed, it leads in the first place to a set of energy levels which the particles can occupy. By using suitable statistical methods, it is possible to compute the mean energy of the system and from it the specific heat. Any such calculation requires a minimum of extra theoretical assumptions. This is both a strength

1

and a weakness of specific-heat studies. The heat capacity provides a direct and immediate test of the theoretical model of the system, but because it is a measure of a mean quantity it cannot shed light on the finer details of the model. It is wise not to lose sight of this limitation—which, incidentally, holds true to some extent for the study of any phenomenological property of substances.

The reduction of specific heats at low temperatures is of tremendous significance in the practice of cryogenic techniques. For the ordinary materials used in the construction of apparatus, the specific heat is about 6 cal/gram-atom·degK at room temperature (300°K), approximately 4 units at liquid-air temperature (80°K), and only 10^{-2} units at liquid-helium temperature (4°K). The rapid fall in specific heats in the liquid hydrogen–helium temperature range makes itself felt in several ways. Once a large apparatus has been cooled to liquid-air temperature, relatively small amounts of refrigeration (measured in terms of, say, the latent heat of the liquid helium that is boiled away) are sufficient to cool it to about 4°K. It is, in fact, a standard practice to conserve liquid helium by precooling the cryostats with liquid air, and if possible liquid hydrogen, so that little helium is boiled away in reducing the temperature to the vicinity of 4°K. Secondly, if a part of the cold apparatus is thermally insulated from the main heat sink, its temperature may rise considerably because of small amounts of heat influx. Such situations commonly arise in the measurement of specific heats. For the same reason, when very low temperatures ($<1°K$) are achieved by adiabatic demagnetization, it is of utmost importance to cut out as much stray heat input as possible. Thirdly, because of the small heat capacity at low temperatures, thermal equilibrium among the various parts of an apparatus is established very quickly. Typically, a system which takes about an hour to come to internal equilibrium at room temperature will do so in about a minute at 4°K.

It was mentioned above that the energy levels of the particles specify the mean energy of the system, which in turn determines the specific heat of the system. These energy levels may be in the form of translational, rotational, or vibrational motions of molecules in gases, vibrations of atoms about their lattice sites in solids, the wandering of electrons free to move in metals, and so on. The enumeration of the possible modes of energy can be continued further, and it is obvious that a discussion of the specific heats of substances must inevitably cover a very wide field, since any temperature-dependent phenomenon can contribute to specific heats. In a monograph such as this, it is both unnecessary and impossible to be comprehensive in the description of all phenomena which bear some slight relationship to specific heats. The solution attempted here is to provide a reasonably comprehensive description of the various aspects of specific-heat studies at low temperatures, leaving the discussion of allied phenomena to various other texts.[1] It has been a difficult task to steer between the Scylla of encyclopedic completeness and the Charybdis of shallow banality.

This compromise has been chosen to serve two purposes. For the interested neophyte, the monograph should be a simple survey and a stepping-stone to an understanding of the problems of specific heats. Thus, in discussing the basic principles, no attempt at rigor is made. In citing references, preference is given, if possible, to elementary texts rather than to advanced treatises. If in this process several authors feel themselves overlooked, it is because the choice is not meant to be a judgment of the scientific value of such works, but is only a didactic device for elucidating the basic questions. Further, the normal behavior of solids, liquids, and gases is treated first before taking up, in Chapter 7, abnormalities in the specific heat of some substances. No doubt, the reader will find that some instances of specific-heat anomalies are introduced surreptitiously in Chapters 3 to 6, but the present arrangement has the added advantage that by Chapter 7 enough anomalies have been mentioned to focus attention on classification of such behavior. For those actively engaged with cryogenic problems, a description of the many facets of specific-heat studies, with adequate references to the sources of more detailed analyses of any single aspect, should make the book useful.

The task of listing all the references, especially to the early literature on the subject, has been rendered superfluous by the monumental work of Partington.[2] Therefore, references to early papers are seldom given, and anyone interested can trace such papers from either the above treatise[2] or the recent reviews and books cited at the end of each chapter. Moreover, the description of cryogenic techniques has been limited to a minimum because of the availability of excellent books on the subject.[3]

REFERENCES

1. C. F. Squire, *Low Temperature Physics*, McGraw-Hill, New York, 1953. K. Mendelssohn, *Cryophysics*, Interscience, New York, 1960. L. C. Jackson, *Low Temperature Physics*, Methuen, London, 1962. R. W. Vance and W. M. Duke, *Applied Cryogenic Engineering*, Wiley, New York, 1962. H. M. Rosenberg, *Low Temperature Solid State Physics*, Clarendon, Oxford, 1963. M. McClintock, *Cryogenics*, Reinhold, New York, 1964.
2. J. R. Partington, *Advanced Treatise on Physical Chemistry*, Longmans-Green, London; *Vol. I, Properties of Gases* (1949); *Vol. II, Properties of Liquids* (1951); *Vol. III, Properties of Solids* (1952).

3. G. K. White, *Experimental Techniques in Low Temperature Physics,* Clarendon, Oxford, 1959. R. B. Scott, *Cryogenic Engineering,* Van Nostrand, New York, 1959. F. Din and A. H. Cockett, *Low Temperature Techniques,* Newnes, London, 1960. F. E. Hoare, L. C. Jackson, and N. Kurti, *Experimental Cryophysics,* Butterworth, London, 1961. A. C. Rose-Innes, *Low Temperature Techniques,* English University Press, London, 1964.

Chapter 1

Elementary Concepts of Specific Heats

1.1. DEFINITIONS

The specific heat of a substance is defined as the quantity of heat required to raise the temperature of a unit mass of the substance by a unit degree of temperature. To some extent, the specific heat depends upon the temperature at which it is measured and upon the changes that are allowed to take place during the rise of temperature. If the properties x, y, ..., are held constant when a heat input dQ raises the temperature of unit mass of the substance by dT, then

$$c_{x,y,...} = \lim_{dT \to 0} \left(\frac{dQ}{dT} \right)_{x,y,...} \tag{1.1}$$

The specific heat, sometimes called the *heat capacity*, is in general a positive quantity. In the absence of any rigid convention, it seems best to use the term *specific heat* when referring to 1 g of the material and the term *heat capacity* when a more general amount of the material, i.e., a gram-atom or a gram-molecule, is involved.

In expressing the numerical values of specific heats, the MKS system, based on kilogram units of the substance, is not yet widely used in current literature, and so cgs units will be used throughout the book. By convention, $c_{x,y,...}$ refers to the specific heat per gram and $C_{x,y...}$ to the heat capacity per gram-molecule of the substance. The $c_{x...}$ value is usually expressed in cal/g·degK or in J/g·deg, the present conversion factor being 1 thermochemical calorie = 4.1840 J. In engineering literature, it is still not uncommon to find specific heats in BTU/lb·degF, which luckily has almost the same value in cal/g·degK.

1.2. THERMODYNAMICS OF SIMPLE SYSTEMS

All processes in which quantities of heat and work come into play are governed by the fundamental laws of thermodynamics. Some properties of specific heats follow immediately from these laws, and it is therefore appropriate to consider them first. A discussion of the principles of thermodynamics is given in several well-known texts.[1] If a quantity of heat dQ is supplied to a substance, a part of it goes to increase the internal energy E of the system and a part is utilized in performing external work W. In accordance with the first law,

$$dQ = dE + dW \tag{1.2}$$

If the heat exchange is reversible, the second law of thermodynamics permits calculation of the entropy S of the system from the relation

$$dQ = T\,dS \tag{1.3}$$

Apart from the special conditions to be discussed in Section 8.5, E and S are proportional to the mass of the substance; that is, they are extensive variables.

It is instructive to start with a simple substance, namely, the ideal fluid. In gases and liquids, the pressure P at a point is the same in all directions, and any work done by the system dW is an expansion against the pressure. Then dW must be of the form

$$dW = P\,dV \tag{1.4}$$

Moreover, fluids obey an equation of state

$$f(P, V, T) = 0 \tag{1.5}$$

This means that any one of P, V, T can be expressed in terms of the other two and that only two of the three quantities can be arbitrarily varied at the same time. Hence, during the change of temperature, either P or V can be kept constant, and correspondingly there are two principal heat capacities:

$$\begin{aligned}
C_p &= \left(\frac{dQ}{dT}\right)_p = T\left(\frac{\partial S}{\partial T}\right)_p \\
C_v &= \left(\frac{dQ}{dT}\right)_v = T\left(\frac{\partial S}{\partial T}\right)_v
\end{aligned} \tag{1.6}$$

The case for solids is somewhat more complicated. Unlike ordinary fluids, which require forces only for changing their volume, solids require forces both to change their linear dimensions and to alter their shape. It is shown in the texts on elasticity[2] that dW is of the form

$$dW = \sum_i t_i \, de_i \qquad (i = 1, 2, ..., 6)$$

where t_i are the stresses and e_i are the strains. Obviously, it is possible in principle to define a large number of specific heats, allowing only one stress or strain component to change during the heating. In practice, however, such experiments are hardly feasible, and only C_p, C_v are of importance. It can be shown[3] that they obey the same thermodynamic relations as the C_p, C_v of liquids and gases, so there is no significant loss of generality in restricting the discussion to the simple case of fluids.

Combining (1.2) and (1.3), one can write the change in internal energy as

$$dE = T \, dS - P \, dV \qquad (1.7)$$

Often it is convenient to handle the other principal thermodynamic functions of the system, namely, enthalpy H, Helmholtz function A and Gibbs' function G, whose variations are

$$dH = d(E + PV) = T \, dS + V \, dP \qquad (1.8)$$

$$dA = d(E - TS) = -S \, dT - P \, dV \qquad (1.9)$$

$$dG = d(E - TS + PV) = -S \, dT + V \, dP \qquad (1.10)$$

These four functions are nothing but measures of the energy content of the substance under various conditions, and the changes in these must depend only upon the initial and final states. Mathematically equivalent is the statement that the differentials (1.7) to (1.10) are perfect differentials; this condition leads to the four Maxwell's relations

$$\left(\frac{\partial T}{\partial V}\right)_S = -\left(\frac{\partial P}{\partial S}\right)_v \qquad \left(\frac{\partial T}{\partial P}\right)_S = \left(\frac{\partial V}{\partial S}\right)_p$$

$$\left(\frac{\partial S}{\partial V}\right)_T = \left(\frac{\partial P}{\partial T}\right)_v \qquad \left(\frac{\partial S}{\partial P}\right)_T = -\left(\frac{\partial V}{\partial T}\right)_p \qquad (1.11)$$

The four relations are useful in expressing thermodynamic formulas in terms of quantities which are experimentally measured.

1.3. DIFFERENCE BETWEEN C_p and C_v

As an illustration of the use of equation (1.11), the important expressions for $C_p - C_v$ may be calculated. Take T and V as the independent variables in describing the entropy of a mole of substance

and write

$$dS = \left(\frac{\partial S}{\partial T}\right)_v dT + \left(\frac{\partial S}{\partial V}\right)_T dV$$

or

$$\left(\frac{\partial S}{\partial T}\right)_p = \left(\frac{\partial S}{\partial T}\right)_v + \left(\frac{\partial S}{\partial V}\right)_T \left(\frac{\partial V}{\partial T}\right)_p$$

Replacing $(\partial S/\partial V)_T$ by $(\partial P/\partial T)_v$ and using equations (1.6) yields

$$C_p - C_v = T\left(\frac{\partial S}{\partial T}\right)_p - T\left(\frac{\partial S}{\partial T}\right)_v = T\left(\frac{\partial P}{\partial T}\right)_v \left(\frac{\partial V}{\partial T}\right)_p \qquad (1.12)$$

This relation is convenient if the equation of state is known explicitly. For example, a mole of a gas obeys the relation $PV = RT$ under ideal conditions, and so equation (1.12) gives the difference between the molar heat capacities:

$$C_p - C_v = R \qquad (1.13)$$

The gas constant R has a value 8·314 J/mole·deg, or 1.987 cal/mole·deg. For liquids and solids, $(\partial P/\partial T)_v$ is not easy to measure and is best eliminated from the equations. To do this, consider P as a function of T and V:

$$dP = \left(\frac{\partial P}{\partial V}\right)_T dV + \left(\frac{\partial P}{\partial T}\right)_v dT$$

At constant pressure, $dP = 0$, and

$$\left(\frac{\partial P}{\partial T}\right)_v = -\left(\frac{\partial P}{\partial V}\right)_T \left(\frac{\partial V}{\partial T}\right)_p$$

Now the coefficient of cubical expansion $\beta = V^{-1}(\partial V/\partial T)_p$ and the isothermal compressibility $k_T = -V^{-1}(\partial V/\partial P)_T$ are amenable to experimental measurements. In terms of β, k_T, and the molar volume V,

$$C_p - C_v = \frac{TV\beta^2}{k_T} \qquad (1.14)$$

The mechanical stability of a substance requires $k_T > 0$. Therefore, C_p is always greater than C_v. They are equal when $\beta = 0$, as in the case of water near 4°C, liquid ^{4}He near 1.1°K, and liquid ^{3}He near 0.6°K. The reason for $C_p \geqslant C_v$ is easy to see. Heating the substance at constant pressure causes an increase in the internal energy and also forces the substance to do external work in expanding against the pressure of the system. On the other hand, in heating at constant volume there is no work done against the pressure and all the heat goes to raise the internal energy. Hence, in the latter case the temperature rise is larger for a given dQ. In other words, C_v is less than C_p.

The difference between C_p and C_v is about 5% in most solids at room temperature. It decreases rapidly as the temperature is lowered. Table 1.I gives the values for copper, and the behavior of other solids is very similar. However, to calculate $C_p - C_v$ exactly, a tremendous amount of data is needed. The complete temperature dependence of molar volume, volume expansion, and isothermal compressibility, besides C_p, should be known, and this knowledge is not always available. Under such conditions, approximate relations are used. The most successful one is the Nernst–Lindemann relation based on Grüneisen's equation of state:

$$C_p - C_v = \frac{V\beta^2}{k_T C_p^2} C_p^2 T = A C_p^2 T \tag{1.15}$$

The parameter A is nearly constant over a wide range of temperature. For example, in copper $A = 1.54 \times 10^{-5}$ mole/cal at 1000°K and 1.53×10^{-5} at 100°K, if the mechanical equivalent of heat is taken as 4.184×10^7 ergs/cal. If A is calculated at any one temperature from the values of V, β, and k_T, it may be used to calculate $C_p - C_v$ over a wide range of T without serious error.

In gases at low pressures, $C_p - C_v$ is equal to R [equation (1.13)], but at high pressures small corrections for nonideality are needed.[1] The values of C_p or C_v are not dramatically changed at low temperatures. The behavior of nitrogen is typical: C_p is about 6.95 cal/mole·deg at 300°K and about 6.96 at 100°K.

The ratio of specific heats C_p/C_v is nearly unity for solids and liquids, but not for gases. The value $C_p \sim \frac{7}{2}R$ for nitrogen shows that $C_v \sim \frac{5}{2}R$, and so $C_p/C_v \sim 1.4$. It is 1.67 for monatomic gases such as helium or argon, and becomes approximately 1.3 for polyatomic

Table 1.I. C_p and C_v for Copper

T	C_p	V	β	k_T	$C_p - C_v$	C_v	C_p/C_v
1000	7.04	7.35	65.2	0.976	0.778	6.27	1.12
300	5.87	7.06	49.2	0.776	0.157	5.71	1.03
100	3.88	7.01	31.5	0.721	0.023	3.86	1.00
4	0.0015	7.00	0.0	0.710	0.0	0.0015	1.00

T in degK; C_p, C_v in cal/mole·deg; V in cm^3/mole; β in 10^{-6}/deg; k_T in 10^{-12} cm^2/dyne.

gases. In general, the ratio C_p/C_v depends upon the state of the substance and is useful in converting adiabatic elastic data to isothermal data. For example, it is a simple exercise to show that

$$\frac{k_T}{k_S} = \frac{C_p}{C_v} \tag{1.16}$$

where k_T is the isothermal compressibility and k_S is the adiabatic value. The ratio has greater significance for gases, where, besides being involved in the adiabatic equation $PV^{C_p/C_v} = $ constant, it also gives information about the number of degrees of freedom of the molecules constituting the gas.

1.4. VARIATION OF SPECIFIC HEATS WITH TEMPERATURE AND PRESSURE

It was mentioned in Section 1.1 that the specific heats depend to some extent upon the state of the substance, and Table 1.I shows how C_p, C_v in a solid are affected by temperature. The full details of such temperature dependences are very complicated, and their elucidation is the major task of the whole book. Here, only some simple consequences of general thermodynamic considerations are pointed out.

The use of Maxwell's relations (1.11) shows that

$$\left(\frac{\partial C_v}{\partial V}\right)_T = T\left(\frac{\partial^2 P}{\partial T^2}\right)_v$$

$$\left(\frac{\partial C_p}{\partial P}\right)_T = -T\left(\frac{\partial^2 V}{\partial T^2}\right)_p \tag{1.17}$$

The prime use of these relations is in reducing the measured specific heats of gases to the ideal values at zero pressure with the help of the equation of state. For a perfect gas, C_p and C_v are independent of pressure.

The third law of thermodynamics specifies the behavior of specific heats at very low temperature. According to it, the entropy of any system in thermodynamic equilibrium tends to zero at the absolute zero. Since $S = 0$ at $T = 0$ and S is finite at higher temperatures, the difference in entropy at constant volume between $T = 0$ and $T = T_0$ may be obtained from equation (1.6) as

$$S(T_0) = \int_0^{T_0} \left(\frac{C_v}{T}\right) dT$$

For the integral to converge, i.e., remain finite definite, at the lower limit $T = 0$, C_v/T must be a finite number (including zero) as $T \to 0$. In other words, when absolute zero is approached, the specific heat must tend to zero at least as the first power of T.

The vanishing of specific heats at $T = 0$ is of great importance because it permits the use of $0°K$ as a reference for all thermodynamic calculations. For instance, the entropy at any temperature T may be uniquely expressed as

$$S(T) = \int_0^T C_v \, T^{-1} \, dT \qquad (1.18)$$

without any undetermined additive constants. Since C_v is known to vanish at $0°K$, it is enough to measure it to a sufficiently low temperature from where it may be safely extrapolated to zero. Unfortunately, the laws of thermodynamics do not give any indication of how low this temperature should be. For many solids, measurements down to liquid-helium temperature are adequate, whereas for some paramagnetic salts measurements well below $1°K$ are needed before a safe extrapolation is possible.

Figure 1.1 shows the specific heats of some materials near absolute zero. Dielectric solids (Figure 1.1a) have a low-temperature specific heat proportional to T^3, while metals (Fig. 1.1b) obey a relation $c = A_1 T^3 + A_2 T$. These variations are simple enough to permit a ready extrapolation of the observations to $0°K$. However, if the material contains paramagnetic ions—and such materials are important in adiabatic demagnetization techniques—the behavior is often quite anomalous. The specific heat of chromium methylamine alum,[6] shown in Fig. 1.2, is not falling off to zero even at $0.1°K$. Instead it appears to be increasing as the temperature is lowered! No doubt the specific heat will eventually tend to zero as $T \to 0$, but it is quite impossible to guess its behaviour from, say, $0.5°K$. It is also noteworthy that because of the low temperatures the entropy associated with these anomalous variations is often large (of the order of R per mole).

1.5. STATISTICAL CALCULATION OF SPECIFIC HEATS

The examples of Fig. 1.1 and 1.2 serve to illustrate the fact that while thermodynamics is powerful in specifying the general laws governing a phenomenon it does not give any clue about the detailed behavior. This belongs to the realm of statistical mechanics, and in the following chapters it will become abundantly clear that a variety of effects observed in the behavior of specific heats may indeed be satisfactorily explained. In statistical thermodynamics, the general

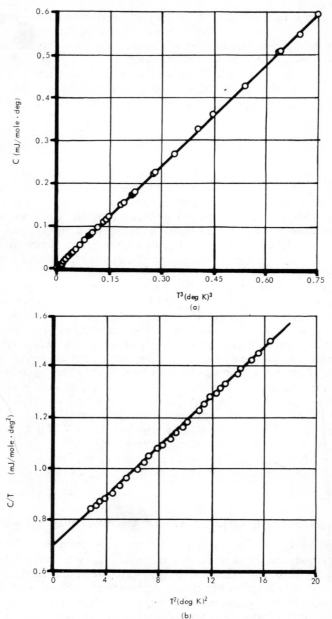

Fig. 1.1. Well-behaved heat capacities near 0°K: (a) potassium bromide,[4] (b) copper.[5]

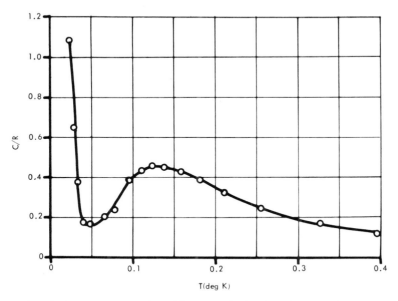

Fig. 1.2. Anomalous variation of heat capacity in chromium methylamine alum.[6]

scheme for deducing the thermal properties is quite simple, although its derivation should be left to the texts on statistical mechanics.[7]

The systems that are of interest in practical problems consist of a very large number of basic constituents, for convenience called *particles* even if they are identified as atoms, molecules, or quanta of energy. The interaction among the particles can be analyzed on the basis of theoretical models to yield the energies E_i of the various possible levels of, say, a mole of the system. Once this is done—and it is in this process that the complex physical systems have to be judiciously represented by simple mathematical models—the thermodynamic quantities are contained in the partition function of the system

$$Z = \sum_i \exp\left(\frac{-E_i}{kT}\right) \qquad \sum_i \text{ over all levels of the system} \qquad (1.19)$$

which is related to the Helmholtz free energy per mole by the relation

$$A = -kT \ln Z \qquad (1.20)$$

Here, k is Boltzmann's constant, equal to 1.3805×10^{-16} erg/degK.

It is now a simple matter to get from A

$$S = -\left(\frac{\partial A}{\partial T}\right)_v \qquad E = kT^2\left(\frac{\partial \ln Z}{\partial T}\right)_v \qquad C_v = T\left(\frac{\partial^2 (kT \ln Z)}{\partial T^2}\right)_v \quad (1.21)$$

These are the thermodynamic quantities of interest, and they are easily calculated if the partition function is set up in a convenient form.

Clearly, the specific heat at constant volume is the quantity that arises naturally in the theoretical analysis. The experimental measurement of C_v is possible in gases under favorable conditions because the pressures encountered, of the order of atmospheres, can be balanced by the walls of the container. For liquids and solids, on the other hand, the pressures needed to keep the volume constant run into thousands of atmospheres, and normally balancing such pressures is not practicable. Therefore, measurements are ordinarily done at constant pressure and C_v is calculated from equation (1.14). The difference $C_p - C_v$ is usually less than a few percent at low temperatures, unless the substance is near a phase transition.

1.6. DIFFERENT MODES OF THERMAL ENERGY

The above discussion underlines the fact that the heat capacity of a substance is governed by the manner in which the internal energy is distributed among its constituents. The molecules in a gas can have translational, rotational, vibrational, and electronic energy levels, and each type of thermal motion contributes its share to the specific heat of a gas. The atoms in a solid are usually held fixed at their lattice sites and can at most vibrate about their mean positions. This motion is called the *lattice mode of thermal excitation*. If the lattice consists of molecules, there are motions of atoms within the molecules besides the vibrations involving molecules as units. These internal vibrations may be described as *molecular modes*. There may be free electrons wandering through the lattice, as in metals, and the *electronic contribution* to C_v arises from the thermal excitation of these electrons. In some cases, the energy levels of bound electrons may be split into discrete levels. The transitions among the levels are known as *excitation modes*. Yet another complication is that in some cases the probability of exciting some mode of thermal agitation depends strongly upon the number of particles already excited. Excitations of the particles therefore increase extremely rapidly, as though by positive feedback, once the first of such modes are excited; these snow-balling processes are called *cooperative phenomena*.

The contributions from all these modes have to be added together to get the total heat capacity. This may be easily seen, since to a first approximation the energy of a system is the sum of the energies due to the various modes of motion. An inspection of equation (1.19) shows that the partition function is the product of factors associated with each mode. For example, the partition function Z of a gas is the product

$$Z = Z_t Z_r Z_v Z_e \qquad (1.22)$$

of the translational, rotational, vibrational, and electronic functions. A involves $\ln Z$, which is the sum of $\ln Z_t$, $\ln Z_r$, etc., and it is clear that the thermodynamic quantities are the sums of the contributions from the various modes.

While all these possible types of thermal agitation give their share to the heat capacity of the substance, the observed specific heat depends also upon their variation with temperature. Some of the modes are excited over the entire temperature range and so contribute observable specific heat at all temperatures. The atoms in a lattice can vibrate at all temperatures, and the lattice contribution to heat capacity is significant at all temperatures. It falls off as T^3 when 0°K is approached, as shown in Fig. 1.1a. The free electrons in a metal have very high heat content, but this varies so little with temperature that its contribution to specific heats is overshadowed by the lattice term at room temperature. However, the electronic specific heat, varying as the first power of T, becomes important at liquid-helium temperature, as was seen in Fig. 1.1b.

In contrast to these types of thermal excitation, there are some modes which are excited over a restricted range of temperatures and so contribute an appreciable specific heat over that small range only. Typical is the excitation of energy in a system with two levels approximately kT_0 apart. At temperatures much below T_0, the thermal energy is insufficient to cause many excitations, as $T \sim T_0$ transitions can occur freely, while at much higher temperature the levels are equally populated and little change in energy is possible. Hence, the specific heat is significant only in the region $T \sim T_0$ and is usually detected as a sharp bump superimposed on the other specific-heat contributions. Such behavior is called a *specific-heat anomaly*; Fig. 1.2 shows a good example. The hump at about 0.1°K is due to the transitions among the energy levels of the paramagnetic ions. The substance chrome methylamine alum, $Cr(NH_3CH_3)(SO_4)_2 \cdot 12H_2O$, is peculiar in showing another nearby anomaly. The sharp peak at 0.02°K is caused by a cooperative transition from a paramagnetic state to an ordered antiferromagnetic state.

Any theory of solids, liquids, or gases must take into account the different types of thermal agitation, and so must lead in the first place to the energy levels of the system. The calculation of heat capacities involves no further assumptions. It is thus a special feature of the specific-heat studies that they provide a first ready test of the theory. However, the specific heat is only an averaged quantity; consequently, the full details of the energy levels are not usually elucidated unless the measurements are supplemented by the investigations of other properties of the substance. This interplay among the different properties of the systems will become evident in the later chapters, where the heat capacity due to the various modes of thermal agitation will be analyzed with the help of suitable simple models. Before proceeding to this, it is convenient to indicate how the specific heats are experimentally determined. Only an outline of the experimental methods will be given here, since the matter is taken up comprehensively in a forthcoming monograph in this series.

1.7. CALORIMETRY

At the turn of the present century, the vacuum calorimeter was introduced by Nernst for the determination of specific heats at low temperatures; subject to minor modifications, it is still the method widely used. In its simple form, Fig. 1.3a, it consists of the block B, over which an insulated coil W of platinum wire is wound. The block B may be either a piece of the solid to be studied or merely a container for some solid, liquid, or gas. B is suspended by the leads LL in a vacuum-tight container C, which is cooled in a dewar D containing liquid air, hydrogen, or helium, as the case may be. Initially, C is filled with helium gas at a low pressure of about 1 mm of mercury, and the block B is cooled to the temperature of the bath by the heat transfer through the gas. After B has been cooled, the gas is pumped away. Thereafter, B is thermally isolated. Known quantities of heat are applied to the coil W by passing known currents for definite intervals of time, and the resulting rise of temperature is measured by the change in resistance of the platinum wire. It is now common to have separate heaters and sensitive thermometers. It is sometimes advantageous to supply heat continuously and to derive the specific heats from a continuous record of the temperatures.

The vacuum space C avoids any heat transfer by gas conduction or convection. At temperatures above 20°K, heat transfer by radiation, varying as T^4, becomes significant. This difficulty is avoided in adiabatic calorimetry, introduced at low temperatures by Lange, Southard, and Andrews,[8] although at room temperature it has been brought to a high degree of refinement by Richards and many other earlier workers. The adiabatic shield S (Fig. 1.3b) contains a separate heater, and is made to follow the temperature of B accurately. This can be done either manually or by suitable electronic devices making

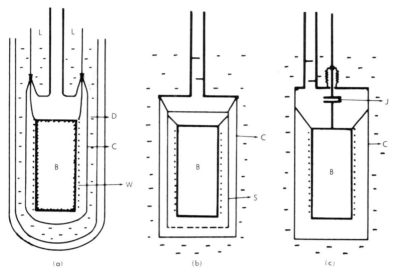

Fig. 1.3. Vacuum calorimeter and its modifications.

use of differential thermocouples between B and C to observe any temperature difference between them. In the liquid-helium range, a different problem arises because the helium gas used for precooling B is strongly absorbed on the surfaces of B and C. The vacuum is thereby spoiled, and even with fast pumps it may take a few hours to dislodge all the helium gas. So it is preferable to avoid the helium exchange gas altogether, though this necessitates alternative provisions for cooling the block B to low temperatures. In a simple form, a polished metal plate J (Fig. 1.3c), which can be operated from outside the cryostat and which is in good thermal contact with C, is made to press firmly against a similar polished metal disk attached to B. C remains evacuated throughout the operation. The drawback in this technique is that when the difference in temperature between B and C is small, especially at low temperatures, heat transfer across the mechanical contact becomes very inefficient. Several cryostats, ingeniously designed to minimize these and other difficulties, are described by White[9] and Hill.[10] These and other books[11,12] contain a full account of the general cryogenic techniques.

The above method is useful for measuring the specific heat above about 1°K. Below this temperature, one has to use the ^{3}He isotope as a coolant (up to about 0.3°K), or use adiabatic demagnetization to attain low temperatures. The details of these refrigeration techniques are described in several texts.[9,10,12] Mention need be made here only of some special methods of finding specific heats in particular cases. Below 1°K, the heat capacity of the demagnetization pill used to cool the specimen becomes large compared to the heat capacity of the specimens. One way of avoiding this interference is to pass a periodic heat-wave through the specimen and to derive C_p as in the Ångstrom method of finding diffusivity at room temperatures.[13] For magnetic materials, specific heats may be obtained from studies of paramagnetic relaxation or demagnetization from various magnetic fields (Chapter 4).

In the case of gases, measurements made by having the gas in a closed container, as originally done by Eucken and others for hydrogen, yield C_v directly, because the volume change under such conditions is very small. The specific heat at constant pressure can be determined by continuous-flow methods as at room temperatures. Information about C_v in gases may be obtained from the heat conduction when the mean free path becomes comparable to the dimensions of the measuring apparatus. Moreover, the ratio of specific heats C_p/C_v may be determined from the velocity of sound in gases (Section 8.3). A good survey of the measurement of specific heat in gases is given by Rowlinson.[14]

There are many problems associated with thermometry and heat leakages, the details of which are discussed in several reviews.[15,16,17] A point often overlooked is the need for pure specimens. Parkinson[16] has listed a number of anomalous results originally reported in such common materials as sodium, mercury, beryllium, germanium, etc., which had been puzzling and which have now proved to be not characteristic of the pure materials. When it is realized that at 0.1°K chrome methylamine alum has a molar heat capacity nearly 40,000 times that of copper, it is obvious that even traces of impurities may sometimes vitiate calorimetric measurements.

REFERENCES

1. M. W. Zemansky, *Heat and Thermodynamics*, McGraw-Hill, New York, 1957. J. K. Roberts and A. R. Miller, *Heat and Thermodynamics*, Blackie, London, 1960.
2. H. B. Huntington, *Solid State Phys.* 7, 213 (1958). R. F. S. Hearmon, *Introduction to Applied Anisotropic Elasticity*, Oxford University Press, Oxford, 1961.
3. R. Viswanathan and E. S. Raja Gopal, *Physica* 27, 1226 (1961).
4. H. R. O'Neal, Ph.D. thesis (unpublished), University of California, 1963.
5. J. A. Rayne, *Austral. J. Phys.* 9, 189 (1956). K. G. Ramanathan and T. M. Srinivasan, *J. Sci. Industr. Res.* **16B,** 277 (1957).
6. W. E. Gardner and N. Kurti, *Proc. Roy. Soc. (London)*, Ser. A **223**, 542 (1954).
7. C. Kittel, *Elementary Statistical Physics*, Wiley, New York, 1958. D. K. C. MacDonald, *Introductory Statistical Mechanics for Physicists*, Wiley, New York, 1963.
8. F. Lange, *Z. Phys. Chem.* **110**, 343 (1924). J. C. Southard and D. H. Andrews, *J. Franklin Inst.* **209**, 349 (1930).

9. G. K. White, *Experimental Techniques in Low Temperature Physics*, Clarendon, Oxford, 1959.

10. F. E. Hoare, L. C. Jackson, and N. Kurti, *Experimental Cryophysics*, Butterworth, London, 1961.

11. F. Din and A. H. Cockett, *Low Temperature Techniques*, Newnes, London, 1960.

12. A. C. Rose-Innes, *Low Temperature Techniques*, English University Press, London, 1964.

13. D. H. Howling, E. Mendoza, and J. E. Zimmerman, *Proc. Roy. Soc.* (*London*), *Ser. A* **229**, 86 (1955). N. V. Zavaritsky, *Progr. Cryogenics* **1**, 207 (1959).

14. J. S. Rowlinson, *The Perfect Gas*, Pergamon, Oxford, 1963, chapter 2.

15. P. H. Keesom and N. Pearlman, *Handbuch der Physik*, *XIV* (*I*), 282 (1956).

16. D. H. Parkinson, *Rept. Progr. Phys.* **21**, 226 (1958).

17. R. W. Hill, *Progr. Cryogenics* **1**, 179 (1959). W. P. White, *The Modern Calorimeter*, Chem. Pub. Co., New York, 1928. J. M. Sturtevant, in: A. Weissberger (ed.), *Physical Methods of Organic Chemistry*, Part I, Interscience, New York, 1959, chapter 10.

Chapter 2

Lattice Heat Capacity

2.1. DULONG AND PETIT'S LAW

One of the earliest empirical generalizations concerning the specific heat of solids was enunciated by Dulong and Petit in 1819. Its theoretical justification was advanced by Boltzmann in 1871, and in 1907 Einstein showed why it failed at low temperatures. These dates are among the principal landmarks in the study of specific heats. To appreciate the significance of these developments, consider the specific heats of several common elements at room temperatures, as collected in Table 2.I. The specific heat per gram of the element varies considerably, being small for the elements of high atomic weight and large for those of low atomic weight. However, the heat capacity per gram-atom of all of them is nearly equal to 6.2 cal/mole·deg,

Table 2.I. Specific Heat of Solid Elements at Room Temperature[1]

	Element						
	Bi	Pb	Au	Pt	Sn	Ag	Zn
c_p	0.0299	0.0310	0.0309	0.0318	0.0556	0.0559	0.0939
Atomic weight	209.0	207.2	197.0	195.1	118.7	107.9	65.4
C_p	6.22	6.43	6.10	6.21	6.60	6.03	6.14
	Cu	Fe	Al	Si	B	C(gr)	C(di)
c_p	0.0930	0.110	0.218	0.177	0.26	0.216	0.12
Atomic weight	63.6	55.9	27.0	28.1	10.8	12.0	12.0
C_p	5.92	6.14	5.83	5.00	2.84	2.60	1.44

C_p in cal/mole·deg, Sn = grey tin, C(gr) = graphite, C(di) = diamond.

Table 2.II. Molar Heat Capacity of Compounds[1]
(in cal/mole·deg)

	Compound								
	NaCl	KBr	AgCl	PbS	CuS	Ag_2S	$PbCl_2$	CaF_2	Fe_2O_3
C_p	11.93	12.25	12.15	12.01	12.33	17.83	18.05	16.56	27.2

which is the rule found by Dulong and Petit in 1819. A closer inspection shows that for "light and hard" elements (silicon, boron, and carbon) the atomic heat capacity falls much below the Dulong–Petit value.

Subsequent experiments by several workers during the period 1840 to 1860 revealed an important extension of the Dulong–Petit rule. The molar heat capacity of a compound is equal to the sum of the atomic heat capacities of the constituent elements. Table 2.II illustrates this rule, which is sometimes called the *law of Neumann and Kopp*. Diatomic solids have a molar specific heat of approximately 12cal/mole·deg, while triatomic solids have $C_p \sim 18$ units. As in Table 2.I, there are many substances that deviate greatly from this simple behavior, but on the whole there is enough evidence for taking the atomic specific heat to be about 6 cal, irrespective of the chemical structure of the substance. Since the gas constant $R = Nk$ has a value of approximately 2 cal/mole·deg, this statement implies that each atom in a solid contributes about $3k$ to the specific heat.

2.2. EQUIPARTITION LAW

The empirical results of the previous section can be readily interpreted on the basis of the theorem of equipartition of energy developed by Boltzmann. A derivation of this theorem may be found in the texts on statistical mechanics or in other places.[2,3] In classical mechanics, a system executing small oscillations may be described in terms of normal coordinates; its energy is then expressed as the sum of several squared terms. For example, the energy of a linear harmonic oscillator is made up of kinetic and potential energies $(2m)^{-1}p^2 + \frac{1}{2}m\omega^2q^2$, where p is the momentum and q the coordinate. For a three-dimensional oscillator there are three p_x^2, p_y^2, p_z^2 terms and three q_x^2, q_y^2, q_z^2 terms. Each such square term in the energy expression is said to arise from a degree of freedom of the system, which is nothing more than an enumeration of the independent variables needed to describe the system. The equipartition law states that in thermal equilibrium each degree of freedom contributes $\frac{1}{2}kT$ to the energy of the particle. Thus, a three-dimensional oscillator has an internal energy $3kT$ when a system of such oscillators is in thermal equilibrium.

The atoms in a solid are arranged in a regular lattice and held in their lattice sites by interatomic forces acting on them. A simple model of a lattice would be a set of mass points connected to one another by elastic springs. The atoms can vibrate about their mean positions under the influence of the forces acting on them, and if the amplitude of oscillation is small, the atoms may be considered as harmonic oscillators. Each (three-dimensional) oscillator has six degrees of freedom, and by the equipartition theorem has an internal energy $3kT$. In a gram-atom of the element there are N atoms and the internal energy is $3NkT$. Therefore, the heat capacity is $C_v = \partial E/\partial T = 3R \approx 5.96$ cal/mole·deg. For a compound with r atoms per molecule, the molar heat capacity is $3rR$.

Classical statistical mechanics is thus able to justify the empirical observation of Dulong and Petit and others. The successful theoretical explanation of the heat capacity of solids (and of gases, which will be discussed in Chapter 6) was, at that time, partly instrumental in the acceptance of molecular mechanisms not only for mechanical properties but also for thermal properties of matter, a fact which is taken for granted nowadays.

A perusal of Table 2.I shows, however, that for some substances the heat capacity is much less than the equipartition value. Experiments performed above room temperature revealed that at high temperatures the heat capacity of even these substances increases to 3R. For example, diamond, which had $C_p \sim 1.4$ cal/mole·deg at 300°K, had $C_p \sim 5.5$ units at 1200°K. On the other hand, when cryogenic experiments were performed, it was found that the specific heat of all materials decreased at low temperatures. Illustrative is the behavior of copper with $C_p \sim 5.9$ cal/deg at 300°K and ~ 3.9 units at 100°K. At 4°K, its value is only 1/4000 of the equipartition value! Classical statistical mechanics could offer no cogent explanation whatsoever for such large temperature variations of specific heats. The clarification had to await the development of quantum theory.

2.3. QUANTUM THEORY OF SPECIFIC HEATS

In 1901, Planck was forced to conclude from his studies on the spectral distribution of blackbody radiation that the energy of an oscillator of frequency v must change in discrete steps of hv, and not continuously, as had been assumed in classical mechanics. The constant h, called *Planck's constant*, has a value of 6.626×10^{-27} erg-sec.

Einstein soon realized that electromagnetic radiation travels in packets of energy hv and momentum h/λ; these wave packets have come to be called *photons*. Finally, in 1907, Einstein took the bold step of applying quantum theory outside the field of electromagnetic radiation to the thermal vibrations of atoms in solids. The floodgates had been opened for quantum concepts to pervade the whole of our physical knowledge.

Before going into the details of the theory, it is best to grasp the simple implications of the quantization of energy. It was known even in 1907 that the atomic vibrations in a solid have frequencies of the order of 10^{13} cps. The energy hv needed to excite such a vibration is approximately 6.6×10^{-14} erg. In a naïve way, if this is equated to the classical energy of an oscillator $3kT_0$, then T_0 comes out to be 150°K. At high temperatures, the atomic vibrations will be excited fully, but below about 150°K the vibrations cannot be excited because the minimum energy needed for this process is not available. Hence, the specific heat should drop from its classical equipartition value to zero below about 150°K. In practice, the reduction will not be so abrupt as in this naïve picture, because at any temperature above 0°K there is a statistical probability of exciting some vibrations, given by the Boltzmann factor $\exp(-hv/kT)$. The effect of lowering the temperature is to reduce the number of excitations, and in this manner the quantization of energy levels brings about a reduction of specific heats at low temperatures.

The formal way of handling the problem, as outlined in Section 1.5, is to calculate the partition function Z and the Helmholtz free energy A:

$$A = -kT \ln Z \qquad Z = \sum_i \exp\left(\frac{-E_i}{kT}\right) \qquad (2.1)$$

An atom in a lattice vibrates under the influence of the forces exerted on it by all the other atoms of the system. If the amplitude of the vibrations is small, classical mechanics shows that the vibrations can be resolved into normal modes, i.e., into a set of independent one-dimensional harmonic oscillations. In a mole of the substance, the molecules of which contain r atoms, there are $3rN$ such independent modes. The total energy is the sum of their energies, and the total partition function is the product of the $3rN$ modes:

$$Z_{\text{system}} = \Pi z_{\text{mode}}$$

Detailed quantum-mechanical considerations show that the energy levels of a linear oscillator are given by $\varepsilon_n = (n + \frac{1}{2})hv$, the $\frac{1}{2}hv$ being the zero-point energy. Then, summing up the geometrical series,

$$z = \sum_{n=0}^{\infty} \exp\left(\frac{-\varepsilon_n}{kT}\right) = \frac{\exp(-\frac{1}{2}hv/kT)}{1 - \exp(-hv/kT)} = \frac{1}{2}\operatorname{csch}\left(\frac{\frac{1}{2}hv}{kT}\right) \quad (2.2)$$

Now the number of modes in a crystal is so large, of the order of $10^{23}/cm^3$, that it is advantageous to write

NUMBER OF MODES BETWEEN FREQUENCIES v AND $v + dv = 3rNg(v)\, dv$
$$\text{(2.3)}$$

Obviously, the total number of modes is $3rN$, so that

$$\int_0^{\infty} g(v)\, dv = 1 \tag{2.4}$$

With the distribution of frequencies $g(v)$, equation (2.1) becomes

$$\begin{aligned}
A &= 3rNkT \int_0^{\infty} \ln\left[2\sinh\left(\frac{\frac{1}{2}hv}{kT}\right)\right] g(v)\, dv \\
&= E_0 + 3rNkT \int_0^{\infty} \ln\left[1 - \exp\left(\frac{-hv}{kT}\right)\right] g(v)\, dv
\end{aligned} \tag{2.5}$$

where

$$E_0 = \frac{1}{2}3rN \int_0^{\infty} hvg(v)\, dv$$

is the zero-point energy of the solid. The calculation of the specific heat is now straightforward, and it may be verified that

$$C_v = -T\left(\frac{\partial^2 A}{\partial T^2}\right)_v = 3rNk \int_0^{\infty} \left(\frac{\frac{1}{2}hv}{kT}\right)^2 \operatorname{csch}^2\left(\frac{\frac{1}{2}hv}{kT}\right) g(v)\, dv \quad (2.6)$$

This general introduction serves several purposes. For the sake of simplicity, the later calculations of specific heats will start from a discussion of the mean energy of the particles. In satisfying the didactic exigencies, it should not be forgotten that a pedestrian derivation from first principles is possible. Secondly, in some of the discussions it will not be obvious whether P or V is held constant, that is, whether C_p or C_v is calculated, mainly because there is no thermal expansion if harmonic vibrations are assumed. The above derivation makes it clear that only C_v is calculated. Thirdly, the thermodynamics of crystals has been reduced to the evaluation of the distribution of frequencies $g(v)$. The determination of $g(v)$ is a dynamical problem of great complexity, and it is best to introduce the subject with the simple models proposed by Einstein (1907), Debye (1912), and Born and Von Kármán (1912).

2.4. EINSTEIN'S MODEL

Einstein, in his fundamental paper, considered a very simple model of lattice vibrations, in which all the atoms vibrate independently of one another with the same frequency v_E. In a substance such as copper, for instance, an atom has the same environment as any other atom, and it is plausible to suppose as a first approximation that all atoms vibrate with the same frequency v_E. If that were so, $g(v)$ would be zero for $v \neq v_E$ and nonzero for $v = v_E$. Then equation (2.6) immediately gives

$$C_v = 3rNk\left(\frac{\frac{1}{2}hv_E}{kT}\right)^2 \operatorname{csch}^2\left(\frac{\frac{1}{2}hv_E}{kT}\right) \tag{2.7}$$

which is Einstein's well-known relation.

It is, however, instructive to derive the same relation by a different method. The atoms in a solid vibrate about their mean positions, and for such localized particles Maxwell–Boltzmann statistics is applicable. This means that the probability of exciting an energy ε at an equilibrium temperature T is proportional to $\exp(-\varepsilon/kT)$. According to quantum theory, the energy levels of an oscillator v are given by $\varepsilon_n = (n + \frac{1}{2})hv$. In thermal equilibrium, the probability that a given oscillator will be in the energy state ε_n is proportional to the Boltzmann factor $\exp(-\varepsilon_n/kT)$, and so the average energy of the oscillator is

$$\bar{\varepsilon} = \frac{\sum\limits_n \varepsilon_n \exp(-\varepsilon_n/kT)}{\sum \exp(-\varepsilon_n/kT)} = \tfrac{1}{2}hv + hv\frac{\sum ne^{-nx}}{\sum e^{-nx}}$$

where $x = hv/kT$. Now

$$\frac{\sum ne^{-nx}}{\sum e^{-nx}} = -\frac{d}{dx}\ln\sum e^{-nx} = -\frac{d}{dx}\ln\frac{1}{1-e^{-x}} = \frac{1}{e^x - 1}$$

Therefore, at a temperature T, the mean energy of the oscillator is

$$\bar{\varepsilon} = \tfrac{1}{2}hv + \frac{hv}{\exp(hv/kT) - 1} \tag{2.8a}$$

On differentiating this, the specific-heat contribution from the oscillator is seen to be

$$\frac{\partial \bar{\varepsilon}}{\partial T} = \frac{kx^2 e^x}{(e^x - 1)^2} \qquad \left(x = \frac{hv}{kT}\right) \tag{2.8b}$$

In the Einstein model, all the $3rN$ independent vibrations have the same frequency ν_E. Hence, the total internal energy is

$$E = 3rRT\left[\tfrac{1}{2}x_E + \frac{x_E}{e^{x_E} - 1}\right] \qquad \left(x_E = \frac{h\nu_E}{kT}\right) \qquad (2.9a)$$

and the molar heat capacity is

$$C_v = 3rR\frac{x_E^2 e^{x_E}}{(e^{x_E} - 1)^2} = 3rR(\tfrac{1}{2}x_E)^2 \operatorname{csch}^2(\tfrac{1}{2}x_E) \qquad (2.7)$$

The molar entropy is

$$S = 3rR\left[\frac{x_E}{e^{x_E} - 1} - \ln(1 - e^{-x_E})\right] \qquad (2.7a)$$

The quantity $h\nu_E/k$ plays the role of a scaling factor for temperature and is called the *Einstein temperature* T_E. The Einstein functions $E(T_E/T)$ and $C_v(T_E/T)$ are tabulated in several places[4,5] (see also the appendices at the end of Chapter 8). A consideration of the values of exponentials in equation (2.7) at very high and very low temperatures shows that

$$C_v = 3rR\left[1 - \tfrac{1}{12}\left(\frac{T_E}{T}\right)^2 + \dots\right] \qquad \text{(high temperature, } T \gg T_E)$$

$$(2.10)$$

$$= 3rR\left(\frac{T_E}{T}\right)^2 \exp\left(-\frac{T_E}{T}\right) + \dots \qquad \text{(low temperature, } T \ll T_E)$$

The Einstein theory leads to the Dulong–Petit value at high temperatures, and shows how at low temperatures the quantization of lattice vibrations results in a reduction of heat capacity. The theory contains one unknown parameter T_E, which may be approximately related to the compressibility and density of the solid. For many materials, $T_E \sim 200°K$, which accounts for the success of the Dulong–Petit law at room temperature. For diamond, with a value $T_E \sim 1326°K$, Einstein was able to explain quantitatively the variation of C_v then available over a range of 200 to 1200°K (Fig. 2.1). The simplicity of the theoretical analysis and the qualitative correctness of the conclusions left no doubt that the decrease of specific heats of low temperature was indeed a quantum phenomenon.

In order to check Einstein's theory in some detail, systematic calorimetric measurements were undertaken at low temperatures by Nernst, Eucken, and others. The qualitative features of Einstein's theory were confirmed very well, but the quantitative agreement was not satisfactory. In particular, equation (2.10) shows that below $T/T_E \sim 0.1$, the specific heat should become extremely small, of the

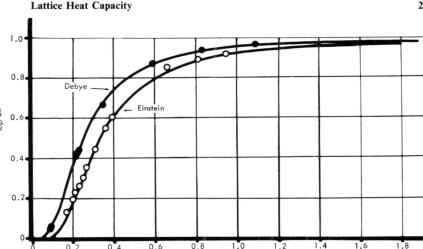

Fig. 2.1. Temperature variation of heat capacity in Einstein and Debye models. Original comparison of Einstein for diamond ($T_E = 1326°K$) and of Debye for aluminum ($\theta_D = 396°K$) are shown.

order of mJ/mole · deg, whereas experimentally the decrease was much slower (Fig. 2.1). Several workers, including Einstein himself, recognized that the model was oversimplified.[6] In a tightly coupled system, such as a lattice, the motion of one atom affects the vibrations of the others and the atoms can vibrate with several frequencies. Experimentally, Nernst and Lindemann pointed out that the observations could be fitted better if two frequencies v_E and $\frac{1}{2}v_E$ were used instead of v_E alone. In the simple model, there is no provision for vibrations of low frequencies, which alone can be fully excited in the region of small energies, i.e., at low temperatures. These ideas culminated in the calculations (1912) of Debye and Born and Von Kármán, who used a better description of lattice vibrational frequencies. Debye's model is the simpler and will be taken up in the following section.

Despite the cursory dismissal usually accorded to Einstein's oversimplified model, the calculation was a fundamental step in enlarging the field of application of quantum ideas. A great deal of experimental and theoretical work on the specific heats of solids and gases was inspired by it. Indeed, even today Einstein's calculation remains useful as a very simple approximation in many problems of the solid state and in discussion of molecular vibrations.

2.5. DEBYE'S MODEL

The quantization of vibrational energy implies that at low temperatures only the low-frequency modes of lattice vibrations will be appreciably excited. Now the usual very-low-frequency vibrations of a solid are its acoustic oscillations. They have wavelengths much larger than atomic dimensions, and so in discussing their behavior the ideas of an elastic continuum may be borrowed. Debye calculated the distribution of frequencies which result from the propagation of acoustic waves of permitted wavelengths in a continuous isotropic solid and assumed the same distribution to hold good in a crystal, also. The use of such a $g(v)$ turned out to be so extraordinarily successful in explaining the thermal behavior of solids that it merits discussion in some detail.

A plane wave propagating with velocity c in an isotropic medium satisfies the equation

$$c^2 \nabla^2 \phi = \frac{\partial^2 \phi}{\partial t^2}$$

For convenience, take a rectangular parallelopiped of sides L_1, L_2, L_3, on the faces of which the displacement amplitude is zero. Then the wave equation has a standing-wave solution of the form

$$\phi = A \sin q_1 x \sin q_2 y \sin q_3 z \sin 2\pi v t$$

where the orders of the overtones n_i are related to the wave vectors $q_i = 2\pi/\lambda_i$ by

$$q_i = \frac{n_i \pi}{L_i} \qquad (n_1, n_2, n_3 = 0, 1, 2, ...)$$

An enumeration of the values of n_i which give a frequency between v and $v + dv$ solves the problem of finding $g(v)dv$. In a practical case, the number of modes, approximately $10^{23}/cm^3$, is so large that the n_i may well be treated as continuous variables. The number of allowed values of n_i in the range n_i to $n_i + dn_i$ is then equal to

$$\Delta n_1 \Delta n_2 \Delta n_3 = \frac{L_1 L_2 L_3}{\pi^3} \Delta q_1 \Delta q_2 \Delta q_3 = \frac{V}{\pi^3} \Delta q_1 \Delta q_2 \Delta q_3$$

where V is the volume of the solid. Now the frequency of the wave is

$$v^2 = \frac{(q_1^2 + q_2^2 + q_3^2)c^2}{4\pi^2} = \frac{q^2 c^2}{4\pi^2}$$

Since the n_i are all positive, this is nothing but the equation for the first octant of a sphere in the $q_1 q_2 q_3$-space. The volume of the shell between q and $q + dq$, equal to $\frac{1}{8}4\pi q^2\, dq$, corresponds to $(V/2\pi^2)\, q^2\, dq$ allowed values of n_i. In terms of frequencies, the number of allowed modes between v and $v + dv$ is

$$n(v)\, dv = \frac{4\pi V}{c^3} v^2\, dv \qquad (2.11)$$

In an elastic solid, three types of waves are possible.[7,8] One is the longitudinal wave with velocity c_L, for which ϕ_L may be taken as the dilatation of a volume element. The other two are transverse shear weaves, and for them ϕ_{T1}, ϕ_{T2} are the components of the rotation of a volume element. In an isotropic solid, which is being considered at first, the transverse waves have the same velocity c_T. Adding the three contributions, the number of frequencies between v and $v + dv$ in an elastic solid is

$$n(v)\, dv = 4\pi V(c_L^{-3} + 2c_T^{-3})v^2\, dv \qquad (2.12)$$

Considerations of simplicity necessitated a derivation of equation (2.12) for a rectangular parallelepiped, but the result is not significantly altered by considering a large body with any shape. The same remark holds good for several other distributions of energy levels considered in this book (Sections 2.8 and 6.3). Mathematical proofs of this assertion have been given in various cases.[9]

Debye suggested that the collective low-frequency oscillations of the solid given by equation (2.12) should be applied even at high frequencies and that the discrete nature of the atomic lattice should be taken into account by setting a minimum to the allowed wavelengths. The corresponding upper limit v_D to the frequency is to be obtained from the normalizing condition, equation (2.4), that the total number of modes is equal to $3rN$ per mole. Thus, taking the molar volume to be V,

$$\frac{4\pi V}{3}(c_L^{-3} + 2c_T^{-3})v_D^3 = 3rN$$

or

$$v_D = \left(\frac{9rN}{4\pi V}\right)^{1/3} (c_L^{-3} + 2c_T^{-3})^{-1/3} \qquad (2.13)$$

For the cut-off procedure to be meaningful, the limiting wavelength should have atomic dimensions. In a typical solid, the minimum possible wavelength is

$$\sim \left(\frac{4\pi V}{9N}\right)^{1/3} \sim \left(\frac{4\pi \times 10}{9 \times 6 \times 10^{23}}\right)^{1/3} \approx 3\text{Å}$$

which is indeed of the same order as the lattice spacing.

The distribution of frequencies may therefore be taken as

$$g(v) = \frac{3v^2}{v_D^3} \qquad \text{for } v \le v_D$$

$$= 0 \qquad \text{for } v > v_D \qquad (2.14)$$

Each wave of frequency v has an energy hv and momentum h/λ. In the quantum formulation, the lattice waves are called *phonons*; equation (2.14) represents the Debye approximation to the phonon spectrum of a crystal lattice (Fig. 2.5b). The characteristic temperature

$$\frac{hv_D}{k} = \theta_D \qquad (2.15)$$

is known as the *Debye temperature*.

It is now a simple matter to check that

$$E = 3rN \int_0^{v_D} \left[\tfrac{1}{2}hv + \frac{hv}{e^{hv/kT} - 1} \right] \frac{3v^2}{v_D^3} \, dv$$

$$= \frac{9rNk\theta}{8} + \frac{9rNkT^4}{\theta^3} \int_0^{\theta/T} \frac{x^3 \, dx}{e^x - 1} \qquad (2.16a)$$

$$S = \frac{9rNk\theta^3}{T^3} \int_0^{\theta/T} \left[\frac{x}{e^x - 1} - \ln(1 - e^{-x}) \right] x^2 \, dx$$

$$= 3rNk \left[\frac{4T^3}{\theta^3} \int_0^{\theta/T} \frac{x^3 \, dx}{e^x - 1} - \ln(1 - e^{-\theta/T}) \right] \qquad (2.16b)$$

$$C_v = 3rNk \int_0^{v_D} \left(\frac{hv}{kT} \right)^2 \frac{e^{hv/kT}}{(e^{hv/kT} - 1)^2} \frac{3v^2}{v_D^3} \, dv$$

$$= \frac{9rNkT^3}{\theta^3} \int_0^{\theta/T} \frac{x^4 e^x}{(e^x - 1)^2} \, dx$$

$$= 9rNk \left[\frac{4T^3}{\theta^3} \int_0^{\theta/T} \frac{x^3 \, dx}{e^x - 1} - \frac{\theta/T}{e^{\theta/T} - 1} \right] \qquad (2.17)$$

These are the famous relations derived by Debye.

Two general remarks are appropriate here before discussing the theory in detail. According to quantum statistics[2,3], the smallest possible cell in the p,q-phase space (momenta p_x, p_y, p_z, coordinates q_x, q_y, q_z) is of volume h^3. In a gas of free particles contained in an enclosure of volume V, the number of allowed cells $n(p) \, dp$ between momenta p and $p + dp$ is $h^{-3} \iiint \iiint dp_x \, dp_y \, dp_z \, dq_x \, dq_y \, dq_z$. The integration over dq is equal to V. Next, converting the integral over

dp into spherical polar coordinates,

$$n(p)\,dp = \frac{4\pi V}{h^3}p^2\,dp \qquad (2.18)$$

Considering phonons as free particles with $p = h/\lambda$, this immediately gives equation (2.11). Secondly, in the preceding derivation, Maxwell–Boltzmann statistics was applied to the vibrations of localized atoms in deriving equation (2.7). Instead, one may consider a set of phonons obeying Bose–Einstein statistics and derive Debye's results. This point of view is adopted in Section 5.4 in treating a closely related problem.

2.6. COMPARISON OF DEBYE'S THEORY WITH EXPERIMENTS

The Debye model has been extremely successful in correlating the specific heats of solids. The temperature variation of C_v given by equation (2.17) is obeyed very well by a variety of substances, a typical example being given in Fig. 2.1. At high temperatures, the integrand in equation (2.17) approaches x^2, so that

$$C_v = 3rR\left[1 - \tfrac{1}{20}\left(\frac{\theta}{T}\right)^2 + \ldots\right] \qquad (T \gg \theta) \qquad (2.19)$$

At very low temperatures, the upper limit of the integral may be taken as infinity, when the integral has a value $12\pi^4/45$. Thus, for $T < \theta/10$,

$$C_v = \tfrac{12}{5}rR\pi^4\left(\frac{T}{\theta}\right)^3 = 464.3\left(\frac{T}{\theta}\right)^3 \text{ cal/mole}\cdot\text{deg} \qquad (2.20)$$

$$= 1944\left(\frac{T}{\theta}\right)^3 \text{ J/mole}\cdot\text{deg}$$

At intermediate temperatures, the Debye function must be evaluated numerically,[10] and several tables exist.[4,11] A comprehensive numerical tabulation is reproduced at the end of Chapter 8.

The T^3-variation at low temperatures was one of the first predictions of the theory. The T^4-variation of the internal energy is the acoustic analog of the well-known Stefan–Boltzmann law that the energy density of a photon gas is proportional to T^4. Debye's prediction was soon verified, and the specific heat of many dielectric solids, such as rocksalt, sylvine, fluorspar, etc., show excellent agreement with the theoretical law. In Fig. 1.1a, an example was given to illustrate the T^3-behavior at sufficiently low temperatures. As a matter of fact, the T^3-law is so universal at very low temperatures that it has found a permanent place in the theory of specific heats, although the range of validity has now been restricted to $T < \theta/50$ on account of more recent theoretical work to be described later.

Apparent deviations are found in some cases for rather obvious reasons. Graphite, boron nitride, and other layered materials, which behave like two-dimensional crystals, show a T^2-variation at some temperatures. Similarly, long-chain molecules such as sulfur and some organic polymers exhibit a variation linear in T at some temperatures, as pointed out by Tarasov and coworkers. Even in these cases, detailed calculations show that at sufficiently low temperatures a T^3-law should be present, and such measurements have been carried out recently.[12]

Over wide ranges of temperature, the Debye theory has the note-worthy and attractive feature of making the specific heat depend upon a single parameter θ. Therefore, with a suitable choice of the temperature scales, the heat capacities of all substances should fall on the same curve. Schrödinger[13] and later Eucken[1] reviewed the specific-heat data available prior to 1928 and found extraordinarily good agreement with Debye's theory. Figure 2.2, adapted from Schrödinger's review, makes the excellence of the agreement self-evident. Striking agreements such as this have resulted in a wide-spread application of Debye's theory to a variety of solid state problems, some of which will be mentioned in Section 2.11.

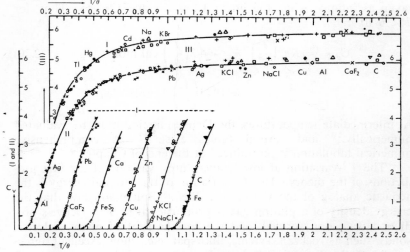

Fig. 2.2. Heat capacities of several substances (in cal/mole·deg) compared with Debye's theory. For the sake of clarity, portions I and III are shown shifted.

It will be seen later that small deviations from the theory are found and that if at each temperature the specific heat is fitted to a Debye term then the resulting values of θ vary slightly with temperature.[14] In a good many cases, the variation of θ from its mean value is less than about 10%, though a few exceptions, for instance, zinc and cadmium, show variations of more than 20%. For a preliminary calculation of specific heats, a list of Debye characteristic temperatures, as given in Table 2.III, can be used with complete confidence. The values given in Table 2.III have been taken at $T \sim \theta/2$, which gives a reasonable fit over most of the specific-heat curve.[10] In Chapter 3, θ values of some metals are given, but there θ refers to θ_0, the value at very low temperatures, since the specific-heat data at very low temperatures are involved.

Table 2.III. Debye Characteristic Temperatures of Some Representative Elements and Compounds (in deg K at $T \sim \theta/2$)

Element	θ	Element	θ	Element	θ	Element	θ
A	90	Dy	155	Mg	330	Sb	140
Ac	100	Er	165	Mn	420	Se	150
Ag	220	Fe	460	Mo	375	Si	630
Al	385	Ga (rhom)	240	N	70	Sn (fcc)	240
As	275	Ga (tetra)	125	Na	150	Sn (tetra)	140
Au	180	Gd	160	Nb	265	Sr	170
B	1220	Ge	370	Nd	150	Ta	230
Be	940	H (para)	115	Ne	60	Tb	175
Bi	120	H (ortho)	105	Ni	440	Te	130
C (diamond)	2050	H (n-D_2)	95	O	90	Th	140
C (graphite)	760	He	30	Os	250	Ti	355
Ca	230	Hf	195	Pa	150	Tl	90
Cd (hcp)	280	Hg	100	Pb	85	V	280
Cd (bcc)	170	I	105	Pd	275	W	315
Ce	110	In	140	Pr	120	Y	230
Cl	115	Ir	290	Pt	225	Zn	250
Co	440	K	100	Rb	60	Zr	240
Cr	430	Kr	60	Re	300		
Cs	45	La	130	Rh	350		
Cu	310	Li	420	Rn	400		

Compound	θ	Compound	θ	Compound	θ	Compound	θ
AgBr	140	BN	600	KCl	230	RbI	115
AgCl	180	CaF_2	470	KI	195	SiO_2 (quartz)	255
Alums	80	$CrCl_2$	80	LiF	680	TiO_2 (rutile)	450
As_2O_3	140	$CrCl_3$	100	MgO	800	ZnS	260
As_2O_5	240	Cr_2O_3	360	MoS_2	290		
$AuCu_3$ (ord)	200	FeS_2	630	NaCl	280		
$AuCu_3$ (disord)	180	KBr	180	RbBr	130		

A fundamental feature of Debye's theory is the connection between elastic and thermal properties of substances. The characteristic temperature θ may be determined from the velocities of longitudinal and transverse sound waves, using equations (2.13) and (2.15). In crystals, a complication arises because the velocity of elastic waves depends upon the direction of propagation in the anisotropic medium. In general, the three modes have different velocities and are not separable into pure longitudinal and pure shear modes.[7,8] It is then convenient to define a mean velocity

$$3(\overline{c^3})^{-1} = c_L^{-3} + 2c_T^{-3} = (4\pi)^{-1} \int \sum_{i=1,2,3} c_i^{-3} \, d\Omega$$

where $d\Omega$ is an element of solid angle in which the velocities are c_1, c_2, c_3. Various approximate procedures for calculating the mean velocity in terms of the elastic constants are reviewed by Blackman[10] and Hearmon.[7] Table 2.IV gives some values of θ originally calculated by Debye from the elastic constants of polycrystalline materials. A comparison with the calorimetric results at moderate temperatures reveals a surprisingly good agreement in spite of the uncertainty in the elastic constants. Equation (2.13) gives a dependence of θ upon the density of the substance; in the case of solid helium-four and solid helium-three, which are highly compressible, θ can be changed by as much as 30% with a moderate pressure of about 150 atm. Another good example is the dependence of θ upon the isotopic mass of the atom, which is easily observable in lithium isotopes of masses 6 and 7. The experimental difference[15] of $9 \pm 2\%$ is in quantitative agreement with the theoretical estimate of 8%. Such a correlation of the thermal and mechanical properties of solids must be considered a great triumph of the theory.

In view of these remarkable successes, the Debye theory has found a permanent niche in solid state physics. It is based on a simple and understandable model. C_v is expressed in terms of a single parameter θ and is in reasonably good agreement with experimental values. The predicted T^3-behavior is verified at low tempera-

Table 2.IV. Comparison of θ-Values from Calorimetric and Elastic Data at Room Temperature

θ-value	Substance										
	Al	Cu	Ag	Au	Cd	Sn	Pb	Bi	Pt	Ni	Fe
Elastic	399	329	212	166	168	185	72	111	226	435	467
Calorimetric	396	313	220	186	164	165	86	111	220	441	460

tures. Further, the theory allows a satisfactory correlation of the calorimetric measurements with elastic and other properties of the substance.

2.7. SHORTCOMINGS OF THE DEBYE MODEL

The great popularity of Debye's theory of specific heats should not blind us to its defects. The first hint that all was not well with the theory came from the early observations of Eucken, Grüneisen, and others that if θ was calculated from the low-temperature elastic constants, the agreement with the thermal values became worse instead of better. For instance, in aluminum, θ(elastic) is 399°K at room temperature and 426° at 0°K (Tables 2.IV and 2.V), while θ(thermal) is 396°. Further, θ as deduced from the T^3-law [equation (2.20)] did not always agree with the value needed to fit the whole of the specific-heat curve. This dilemma was resolved only after the development of the lattice theory.

When accurate values of specific heats at low temperatures became available with improved calorimetric techniques, it was found that equation (2.17) for C_v did not fit the experimental results exactly. This is usually demonstrated by calculating the effective values of θ necessary to fit the experimental data with equation (2.17) at each temperature. Of course, if Debye's model is really correct, a constant value of θ should be obtained, but in practice this is not so.[14] Often, as the temperature is lowered the effective value of θ begins to decrease slightly around $\theta/2$, has a minimum, and then rises to attain a constant value below $\theta/50$. Thus, at temperatures well below $\theta/50$ and above $\theta/2$, the theory works well, with a different θ-value in each range. Figure 2.3 shows a recent study of the θ–T dependence in sodium iodide.[16] At one time, such deviations were attributed to experimental errors, impure specimens, and other extraneous causes, but since the theoretical work of Blackman in 1937, to be discussed below, it has been known that these deviations are genuine.

The fundamental deficiency in the Debye model is the inadequate treatment of the effects arising from the discreteness of atomic arrangements in the crystal. The periodicity of the lattice causes the medium to be dispersive; that is, the velocity of propagation of the lattice wave is a function of the frequency. This phonon dispersion was correctly taken into account in the model proposed by Born and Von Kármán in the same year (1912) as Debye's work. However, the lattice model resulted in cumbersome mathematics, and Born and Von Kármán's original calculation did not give as good a fit with experiments as Debye's simpler analysis. Hence, the application of lattice dynamics (which Born continued to develop in connection

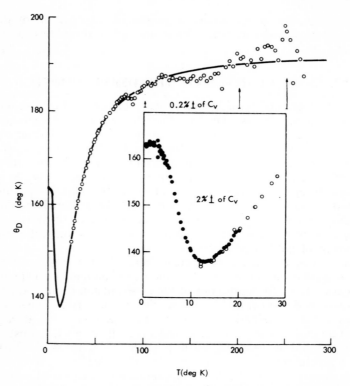

Fig. 2.3. Variation of effective Debye temperature θ with T for sodium iodide.[16]

with other problems in solid state) to the question of specific heats lay dormant until Blackman's analysis showed its fundamental significance.[17]

2.8. THE BORN–VON KÁRMÁN MODEL

A complete enumeration of the vibrational modes of a three-dimensional lattice involves formidable computations, as will become obvious later. In an elementary text, it is not practicable to go into these details, and so only the simplified case of a one-dimensional lattice will be considered. It turns out that a linear monatomic lattice does not exhibit one of the characteristic features of a three-dimensional crystal, namely, the presence of optical modes. Therefore, the simplest illustrative case is that of a linear diatomic lattice.

To visualize the effects caused by the atomic structure of crystals, consider a one-dimensional chain with two kinds of atoms, spaced a apart. Atoms of mass m are placed at even lattice points ... $2na$, $(2n + 2)a$, ..., while masses M are at odd sites ... $(2n - 1)a$, $(2n + 1)a$,... . For simplicity, assume further that each atom interacts only with its two neighbors so that a relative displacement $u_{n+1} - u_n$ causes a force $\beta(u_{n+1} - u_n)$ to act on atom n. Then the equations of motion for the $2n$ and $2n + 1$ particles are

$$m\ddot{u}_{2n} = \beta(u_{2n+1} - u_{2n} + u_{2n-1} - u_{2n})$$

$$M\ddot{u}_{2n+1} = \beta(u_{2n+2} + u_{2n} - 2u_{2n+1})$$

The boundary conditions do not significantly alter the distribution of frequencies,[9] and so the solutions may be taken in the simple form

$$u_{2n} = \xi \exp i(\omega t + 2nqa)$$

$$u_{2n+1} = \eta \exp i[\omega t + (2n + 1)qa] \tag{2.21}$$

Substituting in the equations of motion,

$$-\omega^2 m\xi = \beta\eta(e^{iqa} + e^{-iqa}) - 2\beta\xi$$
$$\tag{2.22}$$
$$-\omega^2 M\eta = \beta\xi(e^{iqa} + e^{-iqa}) - 2\beta\eta$$

The condition that there are nonzero solutions ξ, η describing a wave is that the determinant of the coefficients must vanish:

$$\begin{vmatrix} 2\beta - m\omega^2 & -2\beta\cos qa \\ -2\beta\cos qa & 2\beta - M\omega^2 \end{vmatrix} = 0 \tag{2.23a}$$

or

$$\omega^2 = \beta(M^{-1} + m^{-1}) \pm \beta[(M^{-1} + m^{-1})^2 - 4M^{-1}m^{-1}\sin^2 qa]^{1/2} \tag{2.23b}$$

The two roots correspond to two different branches of the frequency–wave vector relationship, which is shown in Fig. 2.4a. For small q, the roots are (i) $\omega^2 = 2\beta a^2 q^2/(M + m)$ and (ii) $\omega^2 = 2\beta(M^{-1} + m^{-1})$. If the root (i) is used, equation (2.22) gives $\xi \approx \eta$; that is, the atoms move together as in ordinary sound vibrations with velocity $[2\beta a^2/(M + m)]^{1/2}$. This branch is called the *acoustical branch*. If the root (ii) is used, equation (2.22) gives $\xi \approx -(m/M)\eta$; that is, the atoms vibrate against each other. If m and M have opposite charges, such a motion may be excited with electric waves, as, for example, by light waves. For this reason, the branch (ii) is called the *optical branch*. The ω–q curve may be stopped at $q = \pi/2a$,

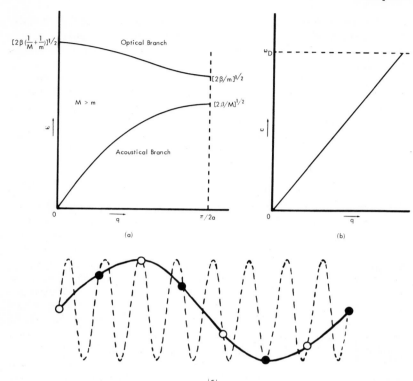

Fig. 2.4. Phonon dispersion: (a) linear diatomic lattic showing dispersion of acoustical and optical branches, (b) elastic continuum, (c) atomic displacements for a wavelength $\frac{7}{8}a$ (broken line) indistinguishable from those for a wavelength $7a$ (full line).

because a continuation beyond this gives no new frequency, and it may be shown[18] from the solutions $u_{2n}, u_{2n+1} \dots$, (see also Fig. 2.4c) that the atomic displacements are indistinguishable from those corresponding to $|q| \leq \pi/2a$. In three dimensions, the lattice constant a varies with direction in the crystal, and all the frequencies are included in a volume of q-space called the *first Brillouin zone*. Elementary discussions of wave propagation in crystals, together with several electrical and mechanical analogies, have been given by Brillouin[18] and Wannier[19].

Compared to the dispersion relation $\omega = cq$ in an elastic continuum (Fig. 2.4b), the lattice case has two special features. Firstly, the diatomic or polyatomic lattice has additional types of vibration in the form of optical modes, and secondly the phase velocity ω/q varies with q even in the acoustical vibrations. In recent years, experiments using neutrons as probes have strikingly confirmed these predictions.[20,21] It may be noted in passing that for a monatomic chain ($M = m$) the determinant (2.23a) has only the acoustical branch as a solution.

Next, it is necessary to find out which values of q are allowed. For this purpose, consider first a chain of $N + 1$ atoms with the atoms 0 and N fixed. Standing waves of the type $U_n = A \sin \omega t \sin nqa$ are the solutions appropriate to this case. The condition that the end atoms are fixed gives $\sin Nqa = 0$ or $q = (\pi/Na)r$, where $r = 1, 2, ..., N - 1$. The condition $r = 0$ is excluded because this gives $u_n = 0$; that is, all the particles are at rest. The number of allowed modes is the same as the number of vibrating atoms. The ω–q relationship consists of $N - 1$ discrete points, but when N is large (of the order of 10^{23}, as in practical cases) it may be taken as a continuous curve. While a finite chain has standing-wave solutions, it is often convenient to work with traveling waves, which are easily introduced by the Born–Von Kármán cyclic boundary condition. On account of the macroscopic homogeneity of a crystal, a segment containing a large number N of atoms may be assumed to have the same microstructure as a nearby piece. In other words, it is assumed that $u_{n+N} = u_n$. This gives $\exp(iNqa) = 1$ or $q = (2\pi/Na)r$, where $r = \pm 1, \pm 2, ..., \pm N/2$. Again, $r = 0$ is omitted because there is no motion in this case. There are N allowed values of q describing progressive waves traveling in either direction. The number of allowed modes is equal to the number of particles in the segment. The q-values are uniformly distributed in the fundamental interval, and when N is large the discrete distribution may be replaced by a continuous distribution. By a similar argument, it may be shown that in three dimensions the allowed values of q are uniformly distributed within the first Brillouin zone and that their number is thrice the number of atoms in the crystal.

Qualitatively, it is easy to see how the dispersion of acoustical and optical phonons affects the distribution of frequencies and the specific heat of a crystal. Suppose the dispersion relations have been found for all the directions in the lattice, each involving, of course, different limiting frequencies. Now, over a solid angle $d\Omega$ (instead of over 4π), equation (2.11) may be written as

$$n(v) \, dv \, d\Omega = V q^2 (dq/d\omega) \, d(2\pi v) \, d\Omega \qquad (2.24)$$

so that $g(v)$ is proportional to $q^2(dq/d\omega)$. In a continuum, this term is $c^{-3}v^2$ [equation (2.11)]. In the lattice case, $n(v)$ starts as v^2 near zero on account of the low-frequency phonons. As the frequency is increased toward the limiting value of the acoustic mode, $dq/d\omega$ and hence $n(v)$ become very large. With further increase of v, there is a gap, followed by another peak due to the limiting value of the optical modes at $q = \pi/2a$, and finally the contribution from the optical modes.

When $n(v)$ is summed over all directions, $g(v)$ has a characteristic presence of two peaks from the various limiting frequencies at $q = \pi/2a$ (Fig. 2.5c). Instead of a gap between the two peaks, there is only a smeared-out shallow minimum, because the limiting frequencies depend upon the direction of wave propagation. The frequencies of the optical modes in Fig. 2.4a do not vary very much, and since their contributions cover a narrow range of v, the second peak in Fig. 2.5c is very much higher than the broad acoustic peak. [In ionic crystals, the optical modes cover a wide range of frequencies, and correspondingly the optical peak is weak in comparison to the first peak (Fig. 2.6a).] Further, $g(v)$ is proportional to v^2 at $v \to 0$, being the result of low-frequency acoustic modes averaged over all directions. These features were pointed out first by Blackman in 1937 in the calculation of $g(v)$ for a simple cubic lattice.

The lattice heat capacity C_g (g from German *Gitter* = *lattice*) given by such a frequency distribution is easily estimated, if it is recalled that at low temperatures only the low-frequency modes with small values of hv will be excited. Near $v = 0$, $g(v)$ varies in the Debye fashion, which means that at very low temperatures θ will be a constant. As the temperature is raised, more modes are excited than given by the Debye model; that is, the specific heat is greater. Therefore, the effective Debye temperature decreases. The presence of the maximum followed by a minimum ensures that the effective θ goes through a minimum and then levels off. Thus, θ varies in a manner very similar to that shown in Fig. 2.3. The lattice theory explains at one stroke why the Debye model is broadly successful and why the effective Debye temperature is slightly temperature-dependent. In Section 2.10, some examples will be given to show how the lattice calculations are successful in quantitatively explaining the observed variation of θ with T.

2.9. CALCULATION OF $g(v)$

In the elementary calculation of phonon-dispersion relations given above, drastic simplifications were made in assuming a one-dimensional lattice with nearest-neighbor interactions. In an actual case, not only is the solid a three-dimensional lattice but also the atomic interactions extend over several neighbors. Thus the computation of $g(v)$ for any lattice involves two main hurdles: knowledge of the interatomic forces and solution of the equations of motion for a large number of wave vectors along a large number of crystal directions. Since the logical necessity of knowing $g(v)$ to calculate C_v and many other properties of solids is hardly in doubt nowadays, much effort has been put into the problem of evaluating $g(v)$.[10,21,22]

Regarding the nature of interatomic forces, we know that Coulomb forces are present between charged ions, but apart from this little else can be said *ab initio*. The practice has been to assume simple models of forces, for example, bond-stretching and bond-bending forces, volume forces for electronic clouds in metals, etc., and to calculate their magnitude from the experimental values of elastic constants and optical frequencies at $q = 0$. The early calculations of $g(v)$ were made in this way with two or three force constants. More recently, inelastic neutron-scattering experiments have given the ω–q relations along several directions in many crystals. By fitting the theoretical dispersion curves with the experimental ones, numerical values of a number of force constants may be obtained. In this manner, a reasonable, though by no means completely satisfactory, amount of information about interatomic forces may be gathered.

Getting enough frequencies to have a good picture of $g(v)$ is purely a question of the labor and tedium involved in such computations. The original sampling method pioneered by Blackman was to take a set of q-values along different directions and calculate the corresponding v. Use was made of the symmetry properties of the lattice. Of late, the exploitation of electronic computers for such work has eased the formidable computational task, and the resulting $g(v)$ is limited in accuracy only by the knowledge of the force constants. A measure of the progress made in the computational problem may be inferred from the fact that in 1964 Brockhouse, Woods, and co-workers, using phonon-dispersion curves of sodium obtained from neutron-scattering experiments, determined $g(v)$ from 35 million points inside the Brillouin zone,[23] whereas in 1940 Kellerman's monumental work on sodium chloride was based on 6000 points. Actual frequencies were calculated for about one-twentieth of the total number of points, and the others were obtained by making use of the symmetry of the crystal. In the early calculations on sodium chloride and diamond lattices, symmetry considerations were not properly applied,[21,24] so that the results, quoted widely in many reviews, are somewhat doubtful.

Since the calculation of $g(v)$ is laborious, several approximate methods have been used in the past. In effect, the Einstein and Debye models may be considered very crude approximations to $g(v)$. A somewhat better approximation, first used by Houston, is to calculate ω–q relations for a few symmetric (say, [100], [111], [110]) directions in a cubic crystal and use interpolation techniques to estimate $g(v)$.

Another method, developed by Thirring, Montroll, and others, is to approximate $g(v)$ from a knowledge of its moments $\int g(v)v^{2n}\,dv$, which can be calculated from the dynamical equations of motion. Although these approximations are sometimes convenient for calculating thermodynamic quantities, they are falling into disfavor with regard to mapping $g(v)$.

Besides these numerical estimates, analytical methods have also had some success. Some one- and two-dimensional lattices are amenable to detailed discussions, and exact expressions for $g(v)$ have been obtained,[21] but so far no realistic three-dimensional lattice has yielded its secrets. However, an important advance was made by Van Hove in 1953. Using topological arguments (for which simple explanations have been attempted [19,21]), he showed that the periodicity of the lattice implies the existence of various kinds of

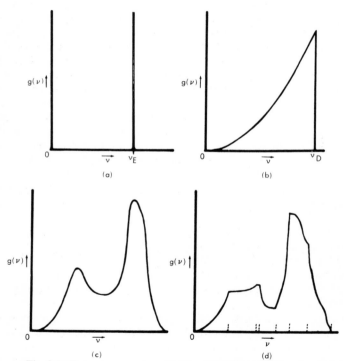

Fig. 2.5. Frequency spectra of lattice vibrations: (a) Einstein model, (b) Debye model, (c) Blackman's approximation of lattice model, (d) schematic exact spectrum with singularities.

singularities in $g(v)$. Thus, in a three-dimensional lattice, infinite discontinuities in the derivative $\partial g/\partial v$ must appear at certain critical points and the curve must have certain well-defined shapes near the singularities. In the more recent calculations of $g(v)$, a knowledge of these critical points has been fruitfully exploited; Fig. 2.5d shows a typical $g(v)$ with the location of the various singularities.

If enough information on the interatomic forces is available and if $g(v)$ is carefully delineated, the lattice theory gives a very good account of the experimental variation of θ with temperature. Often, the theoretical situation is not so fortunate, and several authors have tried somewhat *ad hoc* combinations of Einstein and Debye terms to represent specific-heat variations. Mention was already made of the Nernst–Lindemann equation using two Einstein functions with frequencies v_E and $\frac{1}{2}v_E$. Simon attempted the combination of a Debye term with a Schottky term (Sections 4.9 and 7.1). Raman and coworkers have used a Debye term together with Einstein terms corresponding to optical frequencies, a practice common in representing the specific heats of organic solids. By a suitable choice of the frequencies, any type of θ–T curve may be obtained.[25] All these refinements of the Einstein and Debye models may yield a reasonable variation of θ with T, but they have neither the simplicity of Debye's theory nor the theoretical justification of lattice dynamics. Since the specific heat is the average over the entire $g(v)$, agreement with the observed C_v should not be taken as a criterion for the correctness of a calculation of $g(v)$. It is also clear that any method to find $g(v)$ from the experimental values of C_v is not likely to be accurate. In the past, several attempts at the inversion of specific heats to get $g(v)$ have been made, which amply demonstrated how insensitive C_v is to the details of the frequency spectrum.[10,26] At present, experimental information on phonon spectra is most conveniently obtained from neutron scattering, and to a lesser extent from diffuse X-ray scattering.

2.10. COMPARISON OF LATTICE THEORY WITH EXPERIMENTS

The literature on the theoretical calculation of $g(v)$, both as an exercise in mathematical physics and in relation to specific heats c_g of the lattice, is extensive.[10,21,22] The purpose of the present work is best satisfied by a few examples illustrating the problems involved.

The first example is sodium chloride,[27] which is a simple lattice investigated several times. The Na^+ and Cl^- ions exert Coulomb forces on one another in addition to the short-range repulsive forces arising from the overlap of electron clouds. Dielectric studies reveal

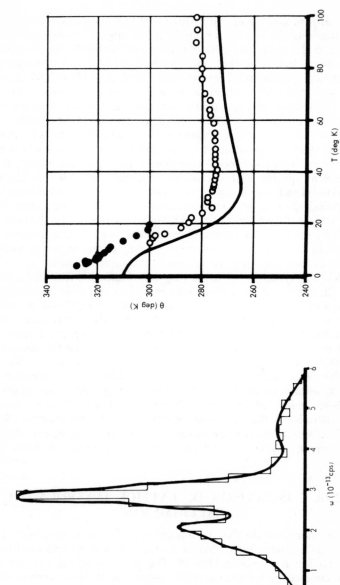

Fig. 2.6. Sodium chloride[27]: (a) frequency distribution (full line drawn through the histograms), (b) Temperature variation of effective θ.

that the effective charge on the ions is about $\pm 0.8e$ rather than $\pm 1e$, on account of the partial shielding of the charges by the electronic clouds. Further, the polarizability of the ions means that small virtual dipoles will be induced during the lattice vibrations. These factors were taken into account using elastic and optical data at $q = 0$, but the distribution was calculated from only about 500 points in the Brillouin zone. A smooth line drawn through the histogram is shown in Fig. 2.6a; such $g(v)$ are typical of many early calculations. The temperature variation of θ shown in Fig. 2.6b follows the experimental results closely. Considering the uncertainties in estimating the interatomic forces and the approximate calculation of $g(v)$, we should hardly expect an exact fit with the experiments. The fact that theory and experiment follow the same trend and differ only in a normalizing factor must be considered satisfactory. It is also to be noticed that the minimum in θ is very shallow and may easily be mistaken for the true T^3-region reached at very much lower temperatures. For this reason, such shallow minima are called *pseudo T^3-regions*.

The second example to be considered is aluminum,[28] for which a model of interatomic forces was fitted to the experimental phonon dispersions along simple directions obtained from diffuse scattering of X-rays at about 300°K. The $g(v)$ was deduced from a total (including those obtained by symmetry) of 150,000 points, and is illustrated in Fig. 2.7a. The singularities were located by Phillips, and the full line shows the theoretical curve, taking into account the infinite changes in slope at, for example, $v = 4.1$, 5.9, 7.8, 8.1, 8.3, 9.0, and 9.4×10^{12} cps. This has transformed $g(v)$ from a dull-looking affair into an interesting curve. Only after such detailed calculations can it be said that for the given force constants the curve of Fig. 2.7b is representative of $g(v)$. The calculated values of θ(curve A) do not at first agree well with the experimental values for the simple reason that no account has been taken of the anharmonic effects present. (For the sake of simplicity, we have preferred to leave the complicated effects of anharmonicity in lattice dynamics to the specialized reviews[29] on the subject.) When they are approximately included (curve B of Fig. 2.7b), the agreement with the experiments is noticeably improved. At 0°K, the θ-values calculated from elastic data must agree with the calorimetric values (Table 2.V); the fact that they do not in Fig. 2.7b shows that the model of force constants used in the calculations is not very accurate, as later studies have also revealed. Nevertheless, there is little doubt that if better force constants are used, the theory will accurately describe the experimental variation of θ with T.

Our final example is sodium,[23] subjected to one of the most detailed studies so far. Information about the interatomic forces was

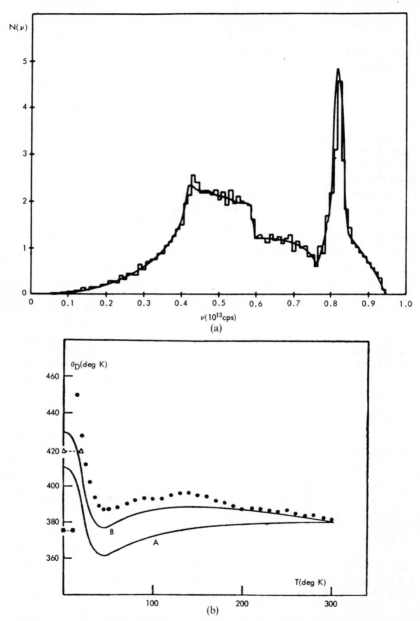

Fig. 2.7. Aluminum[28]: (a) frequency distribution (full line calculated using singularities in phonon spectra), (b) effective θ-values obtained from $g(v)$. Curve A is with no allowance for anharmonicity, and B is with partial allowance for anharmonicity.

derived from the complete phonon-dispersion relations along several directions obtained by inelastic scattering of neutrons. The $g(v)$, given in Fig. 2.8a, was based on 35 million frequencies. Critical points are located at $v = 0.93$, 1.67, 2.56, 2.88, 3.47, 3.58, and 3.82 (units 10^{12} cps). The calculated specific heats are in good agreement with the experimental values. Unfortunately, a martensitic transformation at low temperatures makes an interpretation of the experiments below about 30°K very difficult, and the values given refer to a slightly different crystal structure. Nevertheless, the calculated θ–T curve fits reasonably well with the experimental curve. Sodium melts at 370°K, and even at about 200°K the lattice vibrations are no longer harmonic. The specific heat usually rises above the classical Dulong–Petit value of $3R$, although detailed measurements are not available in many cases. At $T \approx \theta$, anharmonic effects are appreciable, and the consequent increase in specific heats is reflected as a reduction of the effective θ, as in Fig. 2.8b. Theoretically, the change in $g(v)$ caused by the presence of anharmonicity has to be taken into consideration. Moreover, near the melting point, the generation of vacancies makes an additional contribution to the specific heat (Section 8.4).

There are numerous calculations of $g(v)$ and its relation to specific heats and other properties. The net impression is that the lattice theory is logically correct and esthetically satisfying. It correlates thermal, elastic, dielectric, and other properties not only with each other but also with the fundamental interactions among the atoms. In practice, it requires formidable calculations involving several parameters. Where detailed information on the interatomic forces and facilities for computation are available, the experimental variation of θ with T is explained to satisfaction, an example of the saying, "No pains, no gains." If the Debye theory is sufficient as a rule of thumb, the lattice calculation repays the labor involved in it with a significant improvement.

2.11. DEBYE θ IN OTHER PROPERTIES OF SOLIDS

From the above discussion, it is obvious that the Debye characteristic temperature θ has lost its original significance as a measure of the limiting frequency of lattice vibrations and has become an effective parameter describing the thermal behavior of the solid. Many phenomena in solids involve lattice vibrations, and their theories become far too complicated to be of practical use unless they descend to mundane levels by approximating $g(v)$ with a simple Debye function. Thus, the Debye θ is commonly encountered in solid state studies. In view of the approximations made in the theories,

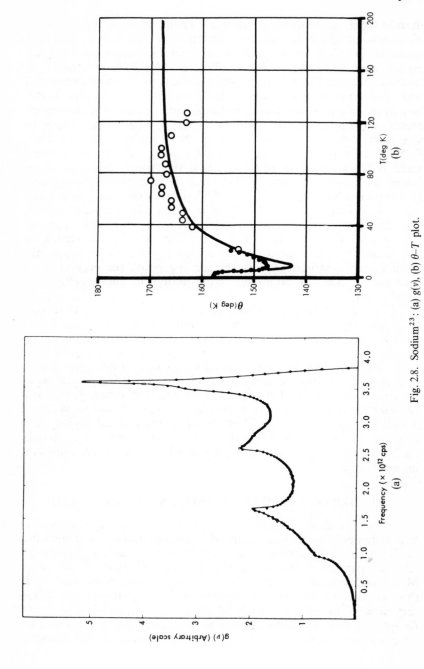

Fig. 2.8. Sodium[23]: (a) $g(v)$, (b) θ–T plot.

there is no reason to expect the numerical values of θ derived from the calorimetric measurements (denoted for clarity by θ_D) to be exactly equal to those obtained from various other properties. All the same, specific heats may be roughly estimated from them if calorimetric data do not exist; conversely, a knowledge of specific heats is of use in other fields of study. In order to illustrate this interrelationship, a brief discussion is given here, leaving the details to suitable reviews.[10,30,31]

2.11.1. θ-Values from Elastic Properties

In Debye's theory, the correlation between thermal and elastic properties is very simple and has been mentioned earlier. In the detailed lattice calculations, $g(v) \propto v^2$ dependence holds good only near $v = 0$ and is the result of averaging low-frequency acoustic phonons over all directions. Near $0°K$, only these waves will be excited to any degree. The propagation of phonons whose wavelength is very much longer than the atomic spacings is not influenced by the details of atomic structure or interatomic forces. Thus, according to lattice theories, θ-values calculated from elastic and thermal measurements should be identical as $T \to 0$. Table 2.V, taken from a careful survey by Alers and Neighbours,[32] shows how closely this relation is obeyed.

At higher temperatures, specific heats depend upon the full $g(v)$, whereas elastic constants measure $g(v)$ only at $v \to 0$. Thus, θ_D is in general different from θ(elastic). This was the anomaly noted earlier in connection with Debye's theory (Section 2.7), and it is now obvious that the difference is not really "anomalous." A calculation of the difference using a quasi-harmonic theory, where the temperature variation of lattice spacings and interatomic forces are included, is obviously very involved. Even at low temperatures, small discrepancies between θ(El.) and θ(thermal) are sometimes observed in glasses, fused quartz, and other glassy materials. They are attributed to nonelastic low-frequency modes present in such amorphous media.[33]

Table 2.V. Comparison[32] of θ_D and θ(El.) at $T \to 0$

	Substance					
	Ag	Cu	Al	NaCl	KBr	LiF
θ(El.)	226.4	344.4	428.2	321.9	172.8	734.1
θ_D	226.2	345.1	426	320	174	737

2.11.2. θ-Values from Compressibility and Melting Point

It was originally noted by Madelung and Einstein that a relation between the compressibility and the characteristic temperature can be derived using simple models of a solid. More recently, Blackman showed that for ionic crystals of NaCl or CsCl structure, the Debye temperature at high temperatures is related to the compressibility $\varkappa$ by means of the relation

$$\theta_\varkappa = \frac{\hbar}{k}\left(\frac{5r_0}{m\varkappa}\right)^{1/2} \tag{2.25}$$

where $2r_0$ is the lattice spacing and m is the reduced mass of the ions. Table 2.VI compares such values of θ(denoted as $\theta_\varkappa$) with the thermal values at high temperatures[10] and a reasonable correlation is found.

Another simple relation, due to Lindemann, connects the characteristic temperature with the melting point T_m of the solid, assuming again a very crude model of the melting process. If M is the mean atomic weight and V the mean atomic volume, then

$$\theta_m = B\left(\frac{T_m}{MV^{2/3}}\right)^{1/2} \tag{2.26}$$

The quantity $B(\approx 115)$ varies slightly with the type of crystal; some values with $B = 115$ are given in Table 2.VI, where approximate agreement is evident.

Table 2.VI. Comparison of $\theta_\varkappa$ and θ_m with High-Temperature θ_D

	Substance						
	LiF	NaCl	KCl	KBr	KI	RbBr	RbI
$\theta_\varkappa$	686	292	233	185	162	136	119
θ_m	1020	294	229	171	119	123	109
θ_D	607–750	275–300	218–235	152–183	115–200	120–135	100–118

The chief merit of these relations is that they give an estimate of the Debye temperature if calorimetric data are completely lacking. Such instances have occurred in the past.

2.11.3. θ-Values from Thermal Expansion

The Einstein and Debye theories give a simple expression for the internal energy of a solid. Grüneisen[34] showed that if the vibrational frequency is taken to depend upon the interatomic distances, a reasonable account of the equation of state is obtained. In particular, the coefficient of thermal expansion β is connected to the heat capacity

C_v and the compressibility $\varkappa$ by

$$\beta = \frac{\gamma \varkappa C_v}{V} \qquad (2.27)$$

with $\gamma = -\partial \ln \nu / \partial \ln V$ called *Grüneisen's constant*. Thus, a plot of β versus T should essentially be of the Debye form $D(T/\theta)$; Table 2.VII shows some values of the characteristic temperature θ_β obtained from such curves. The correlation with θ_D is quite good at high temperatures.

Table 2.VII. Comparison of θ_β with θ_D

	Substance					
	Pt	Cu	Au	Diamond	CaF_2	FeS_2
θ_β	236	325	180	1860	474	645
θ_D	225	310	185	1940	479	620

Recent studies by Barron and others, based on lattice dynamics, have shown that the Grüneisen constant γ does vary with temperature and that different acoustical and optical branches have different γ values. Further, the linear expansion along some directions becomes negative for a few crystals such as Si, ZnS, AgI, and InSb at low temperatures. This can be qualitatively explained by lattice models, but cannot be understood easily from the Debye–Grüneisen equation of state.[35]

2.11.4. θ-Values from Infrared Data

In ionic crystals, there are strong absorption bands in the infrared, associated with the "residual rays." It was one of the early suggestions to use these frequencies to calculate the characteristic temperature, and, indeed, reasonable agreement was found. The situation is somewhat complicated by the fact that the frequency of the reflection maximum is somewhat higher than that of the absorption maximum, the difference being related to the refractive index of the crystal. Thus, the Debye temperature calculated from the reflection maximum (denoted by θ_R) will be larger than θ_A calculated from the absorption maximum. Table 2.VIII[10] shows that θ_R agrees well with the calorimetric θ_D values at high temperatures. The frequency of the absorption maximum is the same as that of the main maximum in the vibrational spectrum, and, since $g(\nu)$ extends beyond the maximum (Fig. 2.6a), it is not surprising that $\theta_A < \theta_D$. The ratio θ_A/θ_R may be calculated from the lattice models, and fair agreement is found for some ionic crystals.

Table 2.VIII. Debye Temperatures from Infrared Data

				Substance			
	LiF	NaCl	KCl	KBr	KI	RbBr	RbI
θ_R	845	276	226	176	153	143	122
θ_A	440	235	203	162	141	126	122
θ_D	607–750	275–300	218–235	152–183	115–200	120–135	100–118

Actual infrared spectra show complicated structure, and some progress has been made in getting information about phonon-dispersion frequencies from the details of infrared and second-order Raman spectra.[36]

2.11.5. θ-Values from Electrical Resistivity

The temperature variation of the electrical resistivity of metals has been studied extensively, and a calculation of θ, denoted here as θ(E.R.), on the basis of Bloch's theory of electrical conductivity was suggested by Grüneisen. He showed that the ratio of the specific resistance σ to its value σ_∞ at high temperatures is of the form

$$\frac{\sigma}{\sigma_\infty} = \frac{20}{x^4} \int_0^x \frac{\xi^4 \, d\xi}{e^\xi - 1} - \frac{4x}{e^x - 1} \qquad \left(x = \frac{\theta}{T} \right) \qquad (2.28)$$

However, as pointed out by Blackman,[10] θ(E.R.) involves only longitudinal phonons in the theory, hence, it should differ considerably from θ_D. In practice, there is a very surprising correlation between θ(E.R.) and θ_D for many metals, as shown by Table 2.IX. At present, there is no satisfactory explanation of the agreement!

Table 2.IX. Correlation of θ (E.R.) with θ_D

				Metal			
	Li	Cu	Ag	Au	Pb	Al	W
θ(E.R.)	363	333	203	175	86	395	333
θ_D	340–430	310–330	212	168–186	82–88	385	305–357

2.11.6. Scattering of X-Rays, γ-Rays, and Neutrons

The vibrations of atoms in a solid affect the reflection of X-rays and other radiations of similar wavelength λ from the crystal lattices. There are two principal effects—a reduction of the intensity of Bragg

Table 2.X. Values of θ (X.R.), θ (El.), and θ_D at 300°K

	Substance					
	Al	Cu	Pb	Fe	Diamond	Si
θ(X.R.)	379	307	80	393	1491	593
θ_D	396	310	93	425	1850	640
θ(El.)	406	331	91	464	2242	647

reflections (by the so-called Debye–Waller factor) and a diffuse scattering of radiation in the non-Bragg directions. The intensity of the Bragg reflection at an angle ϕ from a monatomic solid depends upon the temperature T in the form $I = I_0 \exp(-2M)$, where $M = 8\pi^2 u^2 \sin^2 \phi / \lambda^2$. The mean square amplitude u^2 perpendicular to the reflecting plane may be calculated if a model of the lattice vibration is assumed. For a Debye solid at high temperatures,

$$M = \left(\frac{2kT \sin \phi}{m\lambda}\right)^2 \frac{3h^2}{k^2\theta^2}$$

and thus from the Debye–Waller factor, the characteristic temperature, denoted as θ(X.R.) in Table 2.X, may be calculated. In the lattice case, the term $3h^2/k^2\theta^2$ is replaced by $\int g(v)v^{-2}\,dv/\int g(v)\,dv$, so that θ(X.R.) is in general different from θ_D. Some representative values[30] of θ(X.R.), θ(El.), and θ_D at 300°K are given in Table 2.X. In general, θ(X.R.) is less than θ(El.) or θ_D; this is roughly what is expected from the lattice theory. Herbstein[30] has given a detailed discussion of the thermal effects in X-ray, Mössbauer, and neutron scattering, which may be referred to for further details.

The use of diffuse X-ray reflections and inelastic neutron-scattering in providing information about phonon-dispersion relations has already been mentioned.[20–22,37]

REFERENCES

1. A. Eucken, *Handbuch der experimental Physik*, VIII (I) (1929), chapter 5.
2. A. J. Rutgers, *Physical Chemistry*, Interscience, New York, 1954, chapters 11 and 33.
3. J. C. Slater, *Introduction to Chemical Physics*, McGraw-Hill, New York, 1939, chapters 3 and 4.
4. *Landolt–Börnstein physikalish chemische Tabellen*, Springer-Verlag, Berlin, ed. 5, suppl. 1, p.702 (1927); ed. 6, Vol. 2, Part 4, p.736 (1961).
5. J. Sherman and R. B. Ewell, *J. Phys. Chem.* **46**, 641 (1942). D. R. Stull and F. D. Mayfield, *Ind. Eng. Chem.* **35**, 639 (1943). H. Zeise, *Thermodynamik*, Vol. 3, Hirzel, Leipzig, 1954. W. C. Overton and J. H. Hancock, *Tables of Einstein Functions*, U.S. Naval Res. Lab. Rept. No. 5502 (1960). J. Hilsenrath and G. G. Ziegler, *Tables of Einstein Functions*, Nat. Bur. Std. Monograph No. 49 (1962).

6. J. de Launay, *Solid State Phys.* **2**, 219 (1956).
7. R. F. S. Hearmon, *Introduction to Applied Anisotropic Elasticity*, Oxford University Press, Oxford, 1961.
8. M. J. P. Musgrave, *Rept. Progr. Phys.* **22**, 74 (1959); *Progr. Solid Mech.* **2**, 63 (1961).
9. H. Weyl, *Math. Ann.* **71**, 441 (1911). R. D. Courant, *Math. Ztschr.* **7**, 14 (1920). W. Ledermann, *Proc. Roy. Soc. (London), Ser. A.* **182**, 362 (1944). R. E. Peierls, *Proc. Nat. Inst. Sci. India* **20A**, 121 (1954).
10. M. Blackman, *Handbuch der Physik, VII (I)*, 325 (1955).
11. J. A. Beattie, *J. Math. Phys. (MIT)*, **6**, 1 (1926).
12. G. F. Newell, *J. Chem. Phys.* **23**, 2431 (1955). L. S. Kothari and V. K. Tewary, *J. Chem. Phys.* **38**, 417 (1963). B. J. C. van der Hoeven and P. H. Keesom, *Phys. Rev.* **130**, 1318 (1963).
13. E. Schrödinger, *Handbuch der Physik, X*, 275 (1926).
14. D. Bijl, *Progr. Low Temp. Phys.* **2**, 395 (1957).
15. J. D. Filby and D. L. Martin, *Proc. Roy. Soc. (London), Ser. A* **276**, 187 (1963).
16. W. T. Berg and J. A. Morrison, *Proc. Roy. Soc. (London), Ser. A* **242**, 467 (1957).
17. M. Blackman, *Rept. Progr. Phys.* **8**, 11 (1941).
18. L. Brillouin, *Wave Propagation in Periodic Structures*, Dover, New York, 1954.
19. G. H. Wannier, *Elements of Solid State Theory*, Cambridge University Press, Cambridge, 1959, chapter 3.
20. L. S. Kothari and K. Singwi, *Solid State Phys.* **8**, 109 (1959).
21. A. A. Maradudin, E. W. Montroll, and G. H. Weiss, *Theory of Lattice Dynamics in the Harmonic Approximation* (suppl. 4 to *Solid State Physics*), Academic Press, New York, 1963.
22. W. Cochran, *Rept. Progr. Phys.* **26**, 1 (1963).
23. A. E. Dixon, A. D. B. Woods, and B. N. Brockhouse, *Proc. Phys. Soc. (London)* **81**, 973 (1963). G. Gilat and G. Dolling, *Phys. Letters* **8**, 304 (1964).
24. B. Dayal and S. P. Singh, *Proc. Phys. Soc. (London)* **76**, 777 (1960). B. Dayal and B. B. Tripathi, *Proc. Phys. Soc. (London)* **77**, 303 (1961).
25. G. Leibfried, *Handbuch der Physik, VII (I)*, 104 (1955).
26. R. G. Chambers, *Proc. Phys. Soc. (London)* **78**, 941 (1961).
27. S. O. Lundqvist, V. Lundstrom, E. Tenerz, and I. Waller, *Ark. Fysik* **15**, 193 (1959).
28. C. B. Walker, *Phys. Rev.* **103**, 547 (1956).
29. G. Liebfried and W. Ludwig, *Solid State Phys.* **12**, 275 (1961). T. H. K. Barron and M. L. Klein, *Phys. Rev.* **127**, 1997 (1962). R. A. Cowley, *Advan. Phys.* **12**, 421 (1963).
30. F. H. Herbstein, *Advan. Phys.* **10**, 313 (1961).
31. J. R. Partington, *Advanced Treatise on Physical Chemistry, Vol. 3*, Longmans–Green, London, 1952, section 9N.
32. G. A. Alers and J. R. Neighbours, *Rev. Mod. Phys.* **31**, 675 (1959). J. L. Feldman, *Proc. Phys. Soc. (London)* **84**, 361 (1964).
33. O. L. Anderson, *J. Phys. Chem. Solids* **12**, 41 (1959). P. Flubacher, A. I. Leadbetter, J. A. Morrison, and B. P. Stoicheff, *J. Phys. Chem. Solids* **12**, 53 (1959). H. B. Rosenstock, *J. Phys. Chem. Solids* **23**, 659 (1962).
34. E. Grüneisen, *Handbuch der Physik X*, 1 (1926). J. K. Roberts, and A. R. Miller, *Heat and Thermodynamics*, Blackie, London, 1960, chapter 22.
35. C. Domb in *Proceedings of the Eighth International Conference on Low Temperature Physics* (London, 1962, R. O. Davies, editor), Butterworth, London, 1963, p.385. J. G. Collins and G. K. White, *Progr. Low Temp. Phys.* **4**, 450 (1964).
36. S. S. Mitra, *Solid State Phys.* **13**, 1 (1962). F. A. Johnson and R. Loudon, *Proc. Roy. Soc. (London), Ser. A* **281**, 274 (1964).
37. W. A. Wooster, *Diffuse X-Ray Reflections from Crystals*, Clarendon, Oxford, 1962.

Chapter 3

Electronic Specific Heat

3.1. SPECIFIC HEAT OF METALS

Metals are characterized by their high electrical and thermal conductivities at ordinary temperatures. When the discrete nature of electric charges became clear, by about 1900, it was also realized that freely moving electrons were the charge carriers in metals. Drude, Lorentz, and others applied the methods used in the kinetic theory of gases to explain how these electrons were responsible for the observed high thermal and electrical conductivities.[1]

In spite of the success of the free-electron gas model, the classical theory had a fundamental inconsistency. If the electrons are considered as small particles freely moving through the crystal lattice, the equipartition law attributes to each electron an internal energy $\frac{3}{2}kT$, associated with the three translational degrees of freedom. Therefore, the electrons should contribute $\frac{3}{2}R$ per mole to the specific heat. A monovalent metal such as copper should thus have $C_v \approx 9$ cal/mole·degK, $3R$ from the lattice and $\frac{3}{2}R$ from the conduction electrons. The experimental value of 6 cal/mole·degK is entirely accounted for by the lattice contribution. The same is true for almost all metals at room temperature, as can be seen from the values given in Table 2.I. The model of an electron gas in a metal explained the transport properties reasonably well, but the caloric behavior was in complete disagreement with the equipartition theorem.

It was only in 1928, after Sommerfeld's application of quantum statistics to free electrons in a metal, that the reason for the small electronic specific heat became evident. Even as Bose–Einstein statistics applied to phonons brings about a reduction of lattice heat capacity at low temperatures, the Fermi–Dirac statistics obeyed by electrons makes the electronic specific heat comparatively small at room temperatures. It became clear that the electronic contribution could be observed only at very low temperatures, in the liquid-helium range, and the first experiments to study electronic specific heats in detail were performed by Keesom and coworkers in the early 1930's.

3.2. QUANTUM STATISTICS OF AN ELECTRON GAS

It is a fundamental feature of quantum statistics, as explained in several texts,[1,2] that because of the Pauli exclusion principle and because the various electrons are indistinguishable from one another, Fermi–Dirac statistics should be applied to electronic systems. According to F–D statistics, the probable number N_k of particles in energy state ε_k is

$$N_k = \frac{g_k}{\exp[(\varepsilon_k - \varepsilon_F)/kT] + 1} \tag{3.1}$$

where g_k is the number of levels with energy ε_k and the parameter ε_F (the Fermi energy) is so chosen that the total number of particles is equal to N. The energy levels are often so closely spaced that it is convenient to define the density of states $\mathfrak{N}(\varepsilon)\,d\varepsilon$ as the number of energy states per unit volume between ε and $\varepsilon + d\varepsilon$.

For a F–D system, marked deviations from classical Maxwell–Boltzmann behavior occur when the temperatures are lower than the Fermi temperature $T_F = \varepsilon_F/k$, which in ordinary metals is of the order of $10^5\,°K$. The shape of the F–D function

$$f(\varepsilon) = \frac{1}{1 + \exp[(\varepsilon - \varepsilon_F)/kT]} \tag{3.2}$$

is shown in Fig. 3.1 for various temperatures. As $T \to 0$, $f(\varepsilon)$ equals unity for any energy less than ε_F and then abruptly drops to zero for $\varepsilon > \varepsilon_F$. In other words, all the energy states below ε_F are fully occupied, while all states above ε_F are empty. At a finite temperature T, some of the particles within a distance of approximately kT of ε_F have enough thermal energy to become excited to higher energy states, as shown in Fig. 3.1. However, at $T/T_F \sim 0.01$, the distribution has changed little from the behavior at $T \sim 0$; it is only for $T \sim T_F$ that the familiar Boltzmann tail of the distribution makes its appearance.

The magnitude of the Fermi temperature T_F, which is obviously fundamental to an understanding of the behavior of an electron gas, can be easily calculated as follows. In Chapter 2, it was shown that for free particles in a volume V, the number of allowed energy states between momenta p and $p + dp$ is

$$n(p)\,dp = \frac{4\pi V}{h^3}\, p^2\, dp \tag{2.18}$$

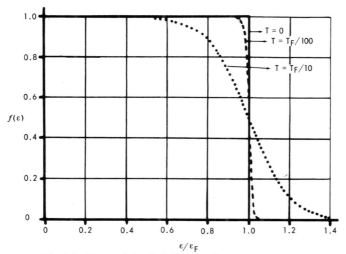

Fig. 3.1. Shape of the F–D function [equation (3.2)] at various temperatures.

If m is the mass of an electron, the number of allowed states can be written in terms of the energy $\varepsilon = p^2/2m$ as

$$V\,\mathfrak{N}(\varepsilon)\,d\varepsilon = 2\pi(2m)^{3/2}\,\frac{V}{h^3}\,\varepsilon^{1/2}\,d\varepsilon \qquad (3.3)$$

At 0°K, all states below ε_F are occupied, and, further, each state can be filled by two electrons of opposite spins. So the total number of states is

$$\frac{N}{2} = \tfrac{4}{3}\pi(2m)^{3/2}\,\frac{V}{h^3}\,\varepsilon_F^{3/2}$$

or

$$\varepsilon_F = \frac{1}{2m}\left(\frac{\tfrac{3}{8}Nh^3}{\pi V}\right)^{2/3} \qquad (3.4)$$

This formula is valid for a gas of free electrons; nevertheless, suppose a value typical of a metal $N/V \approx 10^{23}/\text{cm}^3$ is substituted. Then

$$T_F = \frac{\varepsilon_F}{k} \approx 90{,}000°\text{K}$$

The Fermi energy ε_F of a gas of electrons with metallic densities is two or three orders of magnitude greater than the thermal energy of approximately kT at room temperatures. The electron gas is said to be *highly degenerate* under such conditions.

It is very surprising that in spite of such high energy content the specific heat of the electron gas is quite small. This comes about because the internal energy changes very little at ordinary temperatures. To a first approximation, a fraction ($\sim kT/\varepsilon_F$) of the number of electrons is excited at a temperature T into higher energy states (see Fig. 3.5). Each electron gains an energy of about kT, and so the increase in energy per mole is $\delta E \sim RT(kT/\varepsilon_F)$. The heat capacity is therefore approximately $2R(T/T_F)$ per mole. Since $T_F \approx 10^4$ to $10^5 °\text{K}$, the electronic heat capacity is about $10^{-2}R$ at room temperature. This is only 1 % of the lattice heat capacity at ordinary temperatures. However, at very low temperatures, the lattice heat capacity, falling off as T^3, decreases much faster and becomes comparable to the electronic term, which decreases only linearly with T. These qualitative conclusions are in excellent agreement with experimental results.

3.3. SPECIFIC HEAT OF ELECTRONS IN METALS

The model of a free-electron gas, although forming an elementary introduction to the behavior of electronic systems, is unnecessarily crude when applied to actual metals. The electrons in the inner shells of an atom are tightly bound to the nucleus; only the electrons in the outer unfilled shells have any chance to wander through the metal. Their movement is subject to the three-dimensional periodic potential field associated with the atoms of the lattice. Under these conditions, the energy levels, instead of being a continuous function $p^2/2m$ of the momentum, become grouped into energy bands.[3] In each band, the energy is a continuous function of momentum, but the bands themselves are separated by gaps in which there are no energy levels (Fig. 3.2). Ordinarily, the first band is completely filled (valence band), while the second band is only partially filled (conduction band). Electrons in any unfilled band can move under applied electric fields and thereby transport quantities of electricity or heat. In an ordinary dielectric, the valence band is just full; in the absence of any free carriers, the material behaves as an insulator. In three momentum dimensions, the surfaces of constant energy have complicated shapes because the energy–momentum relationship depends upon the crystallographic directions. The shape of the Fermi surface, i.e., the surface in the momentum space enclosing the occupied states of electrons in a metal, can in some cases be determined from other electronic properties of the metal.[4,5]

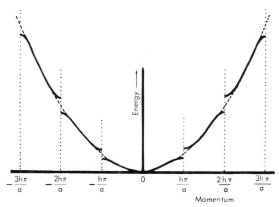

Fig. 3.2. Energy–momentum relation for an electron in a one-dimensional periodic lattice. Dotted line is the parabolic relation for free electrons.

A complete knowledge of the energy levels is luckily not required for calculation of the specific heat of electrons in a metal. The discussions of the previous section show that only electrons within approximately kT of the Fermi surface are excited at room temperature; consequently, knowledge of the number of energy states in the vicinity of the Fermi surface is sufficient to evaluate the electronic specific heat c_e.

Quantitatively, the discussion is fairly straightforward. The energy per mole of the electronic system is

$$E = 2V \int_0^\infty \varepsilon f(\varepsilon)\mathfrak{N}(\varepsilon)\, d\varepsilon = 2V(kT)^2 \int_0^\infty \frac{\mathfrak{N}(kTx)x\, dx}{e^{x-\xi} + 1}$$

where $x = \varepsilon/kT$ and $\xi = \varepsilon_F/kT$. The integral may be split into two ranges, $(0, \xi)$ and (ξ, ∞), so that

$$\frac{E}{2(kT)^2 V} = \int_0^\xi \mathfrak{N}x\, dx - \int_0^\xi \frac{\mathfrak{N}x\, dx}{1 + e^{\xi-x}} + \int_\xi^\infty \frac{\mathfrak{N}x\, dx}{e^{x-\xi} + 1}$$

where the first range has itself been decomposed into two terms. On substituting $u = x - \xi$ in the third term, it becomes the integral 0 to ∞ of $(u + \xi)\mathfrak{N}/(e^u + 1)$. If we set $u = \xi - x$ in the second term, it becomes the integral ξ to 0 of $(\xi - u)\mathfrak{N}/(e^u + 1)$, but extending its range of integration from ∞ to 0 causes a negligible error of only

$e^{-\xi}$. Therefore, to the lowest-order terms,

$$E = 2V \int_0^{\xi} \mathfrak{N}(\varepsilon)\varepsilon \, d\varepsilon + 4V(kT)^2\mathfrak{N}(\varepsilon_F) \int_0^{\infty} \frac{u \, du}{e^u + 1}$$

The first term on the right is the internal energy at 0°K, while the integral 0 to ∞ of $u/(e^u + 1)$ may be transformed into the series

$$\sum_1^{\infty} (-1)^{s+1}s^{-2}$$

which has the value $\pi^2/12$. So the energy per mole is

$$E = E_0 + \tfrac{1}{3}\pi^2 V(kT)^2\mathfrak{N}(\varepsilon_F) \tag{3.5}$$

The molar heat capacity of the electronic system is

$$C_e = \tfrac{2}{3}\pi^2 k^2 V\mathfrak{N}(\varepsilon_F)T = \gamma T \tag{3.6}$$

The electronic specific heat is determined only by the density of states at the Fermi surface $\mathfrak{N}(\varepsilon_F)$, as was expected earlier. To make a numerical estimate of C_e, assume the metallic electrons to be free. From equations (3.3) and (3.4), the molar density of states is

$$V\mathfrak{N}(\varepsilon_F) = \frac{2\pi m}{h^2}\left(\frac{3NV^2}{\pi}\right)^{1/3} \tag{3.7}$$

Consequently,

$$\begin{aligned} C_e &= \frac{4\pi^3 mk^2}{3h^2}\left(\frac{3NV^2}{\pi}\right)^{1/3} T \\ &= 3.26 \times 10^{-5}V^{2/3}n_\alpha^{1/3}T \text{ cal/mole·deg} \tag{3.8} \\ &= 1.36 \times 10^{-4}V^{2/3}n_\alpha^{1/3}T \text{ J/mole·deg} \end{aligned}$$

where n_α is the number of free electrons per atom. For a typical metal, say, copper at room temperature, $V \sim 7$ cm^3/mole, $n_\alpha = 1$, $T \sim 300$°K, and so $C_e \approx 0.04$ cal/mole·deg. This is less than 1% of the lattice heat capacity of 6 cal/mole·deg at the same temperature. Therefore, the electronic specific heat is not normally detected in room-temperature measurements. This explanation was indeed one of the great triumphs of Sommerfeld's application of quantum statistics to the theory of metals.

The above linear variation of electronic specific heat is valid only at low temperatures ($T \ll T_F$). At higher temperatures, the calculations are involved[6]; the full variation is shown in Fig. 3.3. For $T \gg T_F$, the limiting value is $\tfrac{3}{2}R$, which is the classical equipartition value for a gas of structureless mass points (Section 6.2).

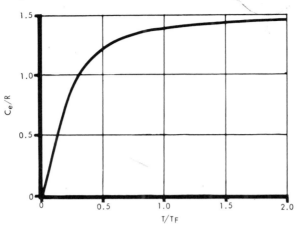

Fig. 3.3. Temperature variation of the heat capacity of an electron gas.

3.4. ELECTRONIC SPECIFIC HEAT AT LOW TEMPERATURES

Although at room temperature the electronic contribution to the heat capacity of a metal is insignificant compared to the lattice contribution, the situation is quite different at low temperatures. C_e decreases linearly with T, whereas C_g, as seen in the previous chapter, is proportional to T^3 at low temperatures. Therefore, at some temperature, the two terms become equal; at still lower temperatures, C_e is larger than C_g (Fig. 3.4). For instance, copper at about 4°K has $C_v \sim 6 \times 10^{-3}$ J/mole·degK, which is equally shared between electronic and lattice contributions. Above about 4°K, the lattice part rapidly dominates the specific heat, while below that temperature the electronic part remains significant. In general, at liquid-helium temperature, both terms are of comparable magnitude and the observed specific heat is of the form

$$C = C_g + C_e = \beta T^3 + \gamma T \qquad (3.9)$$

A plot of C/T against T^2 should therefore be a straight line, and, indeed, a typical example was given in Fig. 1.1b to illustrate how well the relation (3.9) is obeyed, if the T^3-region of the lattice specific heat has been reached. Such a plot permits determination of both β and γ. From equation (2.20) it is evident that $\beta = 12\pi^4 R/5\theta^3$. The value of the Debye temperature at very low temperatures (θ_0) and the coefficient γ of the electronic specific heat for a number of metals are given in Table 3.I. The values refer to materials of the highest-

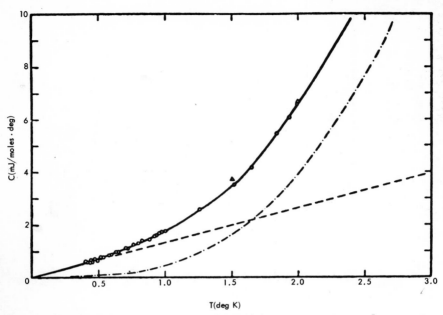

Fig. 3.4. Typical low-temperature heat capacity of a metal, sodium:[7] $-\circ-\circ-\circ-$ observed C_p; $-\cdot-\cdot-\cdot$ lattice term; $----$ electronic term.

available purity. Impurities in the metal affect the specific heat slightly, and in some cases anomalous values have been obtained.[8] Besides the possible changes in $\mathfrak{N}(\varepsilon_F)$ due to the impurities, dilute magnetic contaminations may in some cases give a term linear in T; careful analysis is needed to unravel the various effects (Section 3.6).

The free-electron gas model is obviously oversimplified. Nevertheless, equation (3.8) gives a value of γ of the right order of magnitude. For example, in sodium, there is one electron in the outer unfilled shell, which is almost free to move; according to (3.8), γ should have a value of 11×10^{-4} J/mole·deg^2. Similarly, copper, which also has one outer electron, should have $\gamma = 5.4$ in the same units. The experimental values are Na = 13.7 and Cu = 7.0. A simple way of illustrating the difference between theory and experiment is to introduce an "effective mass" m^* which takes into account the partial binding, namely, the fact that the electrons are not completely free but are only loosely bound to the metallic ions. The electron mass m in equation (3.8) is now replaced by m^*, so that

$$\frac{\gamma_{\text{exp}}}{\gamma_{\text{theor}}} = \frac{m^*}{m} \tag{3.10}$$

Table 3.I. Representative Values of θ_0 (in deg K) and γ (in 10^{-4} J/mole·deg^2)

Metal	θ_0	γ	Metal	θ_0	γ
Ag	225	6.09	Na	158	13.7
Al	426	13.6	Nb	250	88.2
Au	164	7.0	Ni	440	72.8
Ba	110	27.0	Os	500	23.5
Be	1160	2.22	Pb	108	33.6
Ca	229	27.3	Pd	299	99
Cd	209	6.9	Pt	221	66.3
Co	443	47.5	Rb	55	24.1
Cr	585	15.5	Re	450	24.5
Cs	39	32.0	Rh	478	48.9
Cu	348	7.0	Ru	600	33.5
Fe	464	50.2	Sn (white)	195	17.5
Ga	324	6.0	Sr	147	36.5
Hf	261	26.4	Ta	245	58.5
Hg	72	18.6	Th	170	46.8
In	109	18.4	Ti	430	35.5
Ir	420	31.4	Tl	90	15.2
K	91	20.8	U	200	109
Li	369	17.5	V	380	92
Mg	342	13.7	W	405	12.1
Mn	450	180	Zn	310	6.27
Mo	470	21.1	Zr	310	30.3

Thus, m^*/m has a value of about 1.2 for sodium and about 1.3 for copper. For other metals, the appropriate valence of the atom is used to represent n_∞ the number of electrons per atom. In this manner, m^*/m-values have been calculated and tabulated in several reviews.[8–10]

Although the value of m^*/m suggests the degree of departure from the electron gas model, the quantity has only a limited significance. In metals, the bands usually overlap, and the details of the band structure are quite complicated.[4,5] The idea of an effective mass, which can be easily introduced in the case of a single band, is not appropriate under such conditions. Moreover, in cyclotron resonance, the de Haas–van Alphen effect, and other phenomena which reveal the properties of Fermi surfaces more directly, different "effective masses" are introduced, leading to some confusion in comparing the values of m^*/m for any particular substance. The situation corresponds to the confusion concerning the indiscriminate use of the Debye θ to characterize different physical properties, as mentioned in Chapter 2. Therefore, it appears best to express the experimental results in terms of γ, as done in Table 3.I.

Electrons, because of their electric charge, exert Coulomb forces upon one another; these forces are of long range, falling off as $1/r^2$. It would appear that the use of a perfect-gas model is inconsistent with the existence of such long-range interactions. In fact, early approximate calculations showed that the specific heat would be about ten times smaller than the Sommerfeld value and would also have a different temperature dependence, thereby destroying even the qualitative agreement between equation (3.8) and experiments. More recently, the exchange and correlation effects of the Coulomb interaction have been analyzed in detail, using the mathematical techniques developed for handling many-body problems. It turns out that each electron is shielded, as it were, by the nearby polarization cloud of the electron gas. The interaction potential $V(r)$ becomes screened, $V(r) \sim e^2 r^{-1} \exp(-\lambda r)$, so that it becomes a short-range force, which is compatible with the perfect-gas model of the electrons. The collective motion of the electron clouds is then described in terms of what are called *plasma modes*, which have too high a frequency to be involved in specific-heat studies. The details of these calculations are left to suitable reviews.[11]

Another aspect of the electronic specific heats of metals, which cannot be treated here, is the interaction between electrons and phonons. In writing equation (3.9), it is implictly assumed that electronic motions are independent of lattice vibrations, so that the two terms are simply added together. It is, however, obvious that the vibrations of an atom will influence the motion of electrons in its neighborhood; conversely, the presence of the electron cloud will affect the lattice vibrations. For many metals, the effect is very small,[12] but two exceptional situations occur. In some cases, the electron–phonon interaction results in the phenomenon of superconductivity, as originally suggested by Fröhlich in 1950. The properties of super-conductors are so striking that they are discussed separately in Sections 3.8 to 3.10. In a few special cases, electron–phonon inter-actions result in small anomalies, known as *Kohn anomalies*, in the lattice ω–q dispersion relations.[13]

3.5. SPECIFIC HEAT AND BAND STRUCTURE OF METALS

A discussion of the values of γ for all metals is clearly to be left to special reviews on the subject.[8,9,10,14] Only a few typical metals are considered here, in order to illustrate the special factors involved in a study of electronic specific heats.

The alkali metals lithium, sodium, potassium, rubidium, and cesium, have one "free" electron in the outer shells. The inner closed shells are tightly bound to the nucleus, and consequently we may assume that there are N electrons per gram-atom. The number of states in the valence band is N, which can be filled by $2N$ electrons. The first Brillouin zone is thus only half-filled, and the free-electron model may be expected to be useful. This model gives

$$V \mathfrak{N}(\varepsilon)\, d\varepsilon = 2\pi(2m)^{3/2} V h^{-3} \varepsilon^{1/2}\, d\varepsilon$$

as shown in Fig. 3.5. Nevertheless, the observed values of γ are not in good agreement with equation (3.8). Apart from sodium, mentioned earlier, m^*/m has a value[15] of 1.25 (K), 1.26 (Rb), and 1.43 (Cs), showing that even in such simple cases the free-electron model is not adequate. Calculations using details of the band structure, electron–phonon and electron–electron couplings, account reasonably well for the experimental values of m^*/m.

The noble metals, copper, silver, and gold, are also monovalent and have their first Brillouin zones half-empty. The values of m^*/m, 1.36 (Cu), 1.05 (Ag), and 1.16 (Au), differ appreciably from unity, which at this stage is not surprising. The Fermi surface of copper has been investigated by several methods; its shape is shown in Fig. 3.6. In a free-electron gas model, it will be a sphere, whereas in copper it is actually pulled out and touches the zone boundaries along the $\langle 111 \rangle$ directions. Detailed calculations based on such Fermi surfaces do fit in well with the experiments. The specific-heat data are not very useful for finding the shape of the Fermi surface, because the electronic term measures merely an averaged density of states at

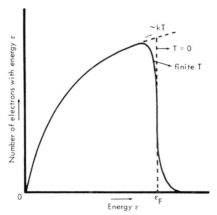

Fig. 3.5. Energy distribution in an electron gas. Full line is the number of electrons at a finite temperature, broken line is that at absolute zero.

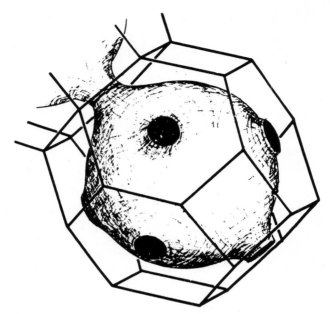

Fig. 3.6. Fermi surface of copper.

the Fermi surface. If the shape of the Fermi surface is known from other studies,[4,5] γ can be used as a final check.

The divalent metals, beryllium, magnesium, calcium, zinc, cadmium, etc., have hexagonal crystal structure. With two "free" electrons per atom, the Brillouin zones should be exactly filled and the substances should be insulators. As a matter of fact, the first and second bands overlap to some extent, which accounts for the electrical conductivity of the metals. The Fermi surface intersects the zone boundary and has a complex shape. The theoretical calculation of $\mathfrak{N}(\varepsilon_F)$ is a matter of considerable labor. The only simple statement that can be made[16] is that $\mathfrak{N}(\varepsilon_F)$ varies rapidly when the axial ratio c/a of the hexagonal lattice is small and is nearly constant when the ratio is large. Beryllium ($c/a = 1.57$, $\gamma = 2.22 \times 10^{-4}$ J/mole·deg^2) and magnesium ($c/a = 1.62$, $\gamma = 13.7$) belong to the first set, while zinc ($c/a = 1.86$, $\gamma = 6.3$) and cadmium ($c/a = 1.89$, $\gamma = 6.3$) are examples of the second case.

The transition metals form another interesting example of the effect of electronic structure, as was first pointed out by Mott. An inspection of the values of γ for the first group of metals (Table 3.II) shows that the electronic specific heats are unusually large. In

Table 3.II. Values of γ for the First Group of Transition Metals

	Metal						
	Ti	V	Cr	Mn	Fe	Co	Ni
$\gamma \times 10^4$ J/mole·deg^2	35.5	92	15.5	180	50.2	47.5	72.8

isolated atoms of these metals, the filled 4s-subshell, containing two electrons, has as usual a lower energy than the partially filled 3d-states (chromium has only one electron in the 4s-level, and the value of γ is also exceptional). When the atoms are brought together to form a metal, the wave functions of the states overlap, which produces a characteristic broadening of the energy levels. The wave functions for the 4s-states are more extended than those of the 3d-states. Consequently, the 4s-band is broader and covers a much wider range than does the 3d-band. This occurs to such an extent that some states in the 4s-band have higher energies in the metal than those of the 3d-band, as schematically represented in Fig. 3.7a. Moreover, the 4s-band contains only two states per atom, or $2N$ states per mole of the metal. It has a large energy spread, and so its density of states is low. The 3d-band contributes $10\,N$ states to the metal; since its energy spread is small, the density of states is large. The resultant density of states as shown in Fig. 3.7b, has a sharp maximum. The Fermi levels lie in this region, and hence C_e is unusually large for

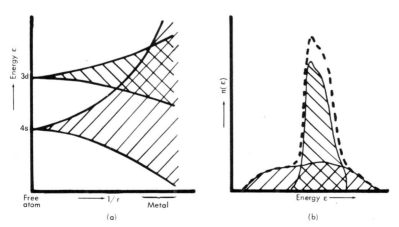

Fig. 3.7. (a) Broadening of 4s- and 3d-bands in a metal due to overlap. (b) Density of states for 4s- and 3d-bands. Dotted line is the resultant density of states.

these metals. For a quantitative analysis, the details of the band structure must be worked out.[14]

The metals of the second and third transition groups also have large values of γ, for similar reasons. Furthermore, the unfilled shells give rise to magnetic interactions among the atoms. The resulting para-, ferro-, and antiferromagnetic behavior produces interesting effects in specific heats which will be discussed in the next chapter. The ions of rare-earth metals also have unfilled shells. But the coupling among the ions is weak, and various magnetic and other transitions occur below room temperature. Rare-earth specific heats are discussed in Chapter 7, Section 6.

3.6. SPECIFIC HEAT OF ALLOYS

When two metals are alloyed, there is in general a change in the lattice structure. A structural change alters not only the lattice specific heat directly, as is clear from Chapter 2, but also the electronic term, through the influence of the lattice structure upon the energy-band scheme. In such general cases, no simple rule can be given. It is only in special circumstances that simple correlations exist. One such instance is that of a binary alloy, for instance, β-brass (CuZn), which exhibits an order–disorder transition, but this is more appropriately taken up in Chapter 7.

In several dilute alloys, especially of elements of near atomic number and similar atomic radii, the elements go into solid solution without any appreciable change of crystal structure. The observed variation of specific heats may then be attributed to variation in $\mathfrak{N}(\varepsilon)$, and some information may be obtained about the shape of the density-of-states curve. The simplest hypothesis, the rigid-band model, is to assume that in the process of alloying, the band structure remains unchanged and only the number of available electrons is altered. The value of $\mathfrak{N}(\varepsilon_F)$ at the new Fermi level determines the electronic specific heat of the alloy [equation (3.6)]; depending upon the slope of the $\mathfrak{N}(\varepsilon)$ curve at the band edge, the γ of the alloy will be larger or smaller than that of the pure metal. In this manner, the electronic specific heat may be correlated with the shape of the energy-band scheme.

As an instance, palladium can be freely alloyed with its neighboring elements silver and rhodium. The γ-values of these alloys[17] are shown in Fig. 3.8a. In the rigid-band model, the addition of silver to palladium gives an extra electron per atom of silver; these extra electrons fill the band to a higher energy level. The alloying with rhodium gives one hole per Rh atom, and so the Fermi level occurs at a lower value of energy. Thus, the density-of-states curve (Fig. 3.8b)

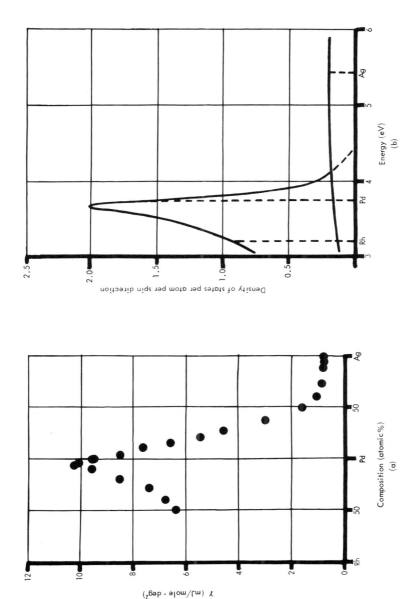

Fig. 3.8. (a) Electronic specific-heat coefficients for palladium–silver and palladium–rhodium alloys. (b) Density of states per atom, rhodium–palladium–silver, for one direction of spin.[17]

may be drawn at once. For reasons set forth in the previous section, the 4d-band in a metal of the second transition group should be sharply peaked, while the 5s-band should be comparatively flat. There is indeed a striking similarity between Figs. 3.7b and 3.8b. Theoretical calculations of the band structures are in good agreement with Fig. 3.8b, but the details of such studies[14,17] cannot be included here.

Dilute alloys of transition elements show several peculiarities which have not yet been clarified.[18] As an example, if small amounts of manganese are added to copper, the specific heat in the liquid-helium range is abnormally increased.[19] The heat capacity is linear in T at very low temperatures and is roughly independent of the manganese concentration c. At higher temperatures, it falls rapidly to the pure-metal value. The temperature at which this decrease occurs is proportional to c, so that the entropy associated with the extra heat capacity ΔC is proportional to the number of manganese ions. Figure 3.9 shows how at low concentrations of manganese, the γ-values are abnormally high and independent of c, while at high concentrations normal behavior is approached. Similar results are obtained in dilute alloys of iron in copper, also. In some alloy systems, the specific heat shows a definite maximum before the $\Delta C \propto T$ region is reached. These deviations are accompanied by corresponding anomalies in other properties such as magnetic susceptibility and electrical conductivity.

The theoretical picture of dilute alloys of transition elements is

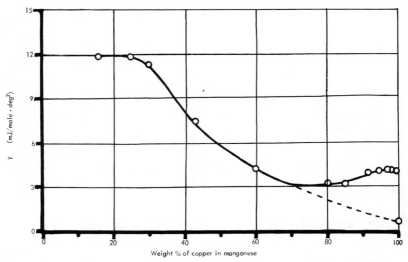

Fig. 3.9. Electronic specific-heat coefficients of copper–manganese alloys.[19] The broken line shows the expected behavior of dilute manganese in copper.

still under debate, although considerable progress has been made by Friedel and others[18] regarding the formation of localized moments. It was Overhauser[20] who suggested an explanation for the observed specific-heat behavior; subsequent developments have been due to Marshall and others.[20] They all involve some form of magnetic ordering and the extra specific heat ΔC arises when a number of spins are located in regions of near-zero magnetic field. The near-zero field regions may arise from the stationary spin–density waves, from the large separation between the magnetic ions, or from the approximate cancellation of the exchange interactions of opposite sign. Although magnetic interactions are taken up in Chapter 4 only, the effects may be calculated in a crude manner as follows. At a temperature T and in a field H, a magnetic dipole μ has an average energy [see equation (4.15)] $-\mu H \tanh(\mu H/kT)$. In an alloy, the local magnetic field varies from site to site, and, if $f(H)$ is the probability of having a field H at the site of μ, the internal energy is

$$E \approx -\tfrac{1}{2}Nc \int_{-\infty}^{\infty} f(H)\mu H \tanh\left(\frac{\mu H}{kT}\right) dH$$

where c is the concentration of manganese ions and Nc their total number. Most of the ions will be rigidly aligned because they are in effective fields much larger than kT/μ at low temperatures. So they do not contribute to the heat capacity. Only the ions situated in near-zero fields $\mu|H| \lesssim kT$ will be able to change their orientations and hence give an excess specific heat ΔC. Thus

$$\Delta C \sim \tfrac{1}{2}Ncf(0) \int_{-\infty}^{\infty} \left(\frac{\mu^2 H^2}{kT^2}\right) \text{sech}^2\left(\frac{\mu H}{kT}\right) dH$$

In a fully aligned perfect lattice, the magnetic field at an ion has a definite value, though thermal fluctuations smear out the field to some extent. In an alloy, the field is completely smeared out and has a wide range of values. Under these conditions, the probability of finding zero field at a site is proportional to $1/\langle H \rangle$, where $\langle H \rangle$ is the mean field at an ion. Since the interactions are mainly dipolar, $\langle H \rangle$ will be proportional to R^{-3} (R is the mean distance between Mn ions) and hence to c, the concentration of Mn ions. Therefore, with suitable constants A, A',

$$\Delta C \approx AT \int_{-\infty}^{\infty} x^2 \, \text{sech}^2 x \, dx = A'T$$

At low temperatures, the specific heat is proportional to T and independent of the manganese concentration; these are the two important experimental observations. Detailed calculations[20] show that at higher temperatures ΔC falls off as T^{-2}; the temperature at which this occurs is proportional to c, which again agrees with the observations. The subject is of current interest, and the overall picture is just emerging.

3.7. SPECIFIC HEAT OF SEMICONDUCTORS

A pure semiconductor differs from a metal in that, at absolute zero, the first Brillouin zone is completely filled by electrons and the next zone is completely empty. There is no overlap between the bands (Fig. 3.10a). The energy gap is small, however, and at ordinary temperatures some electrons are excited from the valence band to the conduction band (Fig. 3.10b.) The material is now electrically conducting and becomes more so when the temperature is raised, unlike pure metals, which become less conducting when T is increased. In practical applications, materials with controlled amounts of suitable impurities (dope) are of tremendous importance. The impurity atoms introduce extra energy levels into what was earlier the forbidden energy gap. The presence of such levels alters the electrical properties profoundly, because electrical conduction can take place without thermal activation of electrons across the energy gap. The special properties of semiconductors are far too numerous to chronicle here; for an introduction, one may refer to the elementary texts mentioned earlier.[3]

In all types of semiconductors, whether pure or slightly doped, the density of excited current carriers decreases rapidly as the temperature is reduced. Therefore, at low temperatures only the lattice specific heat is observed for most semiconductors.[21] Germanium, silicon, and indium antimonide are among the most intensely studied

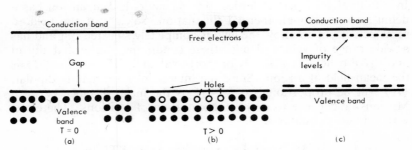

Fig. 3.10. Simplified energy-level diagram of semiconductors. (a) Pure semiconductor at 0°K. The valence band is full, the conduction band is empty, and there is no electrical conduction. (b) At $T > 0$°K, some excitation of electrons across the gap takes place, permitting electrical conduction. (c) Doped semiconductor, with impurity levels depending upon the dope.

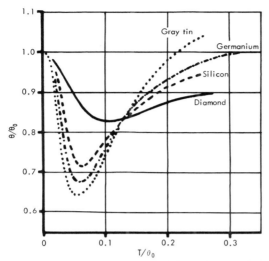

Fig. 3.11. Temperature variation of Debye θ for several diamond-type lattices.

semiconductors. They all have the diamond-type of crystal structure, and the lattice vibrational spectra may be expected to be of a similar form for all of them. This is supported by the fact that the Debye θ has the same type of temperature dependence for these substances, as shown in Fig. 3.11. The true T^3-region is observed below $\theta/100$. At higher temperatures, θ drops considerably and passes through a minimum at about $\theta/20$. The actual θ-values form a regular sequence, as shown in Table 3.III.

In heavily doped silicon and germanium (containing approximately 10^{19} carriers/cm^3), the specific heat of free carriers has been observed.[22] In these specimens, the impurity states overlap the conduction or valence band, so that free carriers are present even without thermal activation. The specific heat at low temperatures is of the form $C = \beta T^3 + \gamma T$ [equation (3.9)], as in a metal. The value of the

Table 3.III. Values of θ for Semiconductors with Diamond-Type Crystal Structure

	Material				
	Diamond	Si	Ge	Sn(grey)	InSb
θ(degK)	2200	636	360	212	200

effective mass m^* calculated from the values of γ agrees well with the effective mass derived from measurements of cyclotron resonance.

While on the subject of semiconductors, it is appropriate to point out that the use of semiconductors (in particular, commercial carbon radio resistors and suitably doped germanium crystals) as thermometers has greatly facilitated calorimetric measurements at low temperatures. Nowadays, almost all workers dealing with the liquid-helium range use such semiconducting thermometers for ease of operation and accuracy of thermometry.

3.8. PHENOMENON OF SUPERCONDUCTIVITY

In 1911, Kamerlingh Onnes discovered superconductivity in mercury. The electrical resistance of the substance, which was gradually decreasing as the temperature was lowered from room temperature (Fig. 3.12a), abruptly became immeasurably small at 4.2°K. Experiments showed that in the superconductive state below T_c the resistance is for all practical purposes equal to zero. Another fundamental property of superconductors, namely, perfect diamagnetism, was discovered by Meissner and Ochsenfeld in 1933. If placed in a small magnetic field, the superconductor completely expels the magnetic flux from its inside (Fig. 3.12b). This perfect diamagnetism as well as the perfect conductivity are destroyed if the magnetic field H is increased beyond a critical value H_c. For many common superconductors, mercury, lead, tin, vanadium, cadmium, tantalum, etc., the dependence of H_c upon temperature is approximately of the form

$$H_c = H_0 \left[1 - \left(\frac{T}{T_c} \right)^2 \right] \tag{3.11}$$

Detailed studies show, however, that the magnetic field penetrates the surface layers to a depth of about 10^{-4} cm. Further, the critical field H_c and the critical temperature T_c depend upon the purity and perfection of the specimen. If a suitable magnetic field is applied to a spherical specimen, some layers of the specimen become normal, while some remain superconductive, resulting in what is known as the intermediate state. Superconductors exhibit other special electrodynamic and transport properties. These matters belong to the special texts on the subject.[23] For the present simple discussion of specific heats, an idealized sharp transition at (H_c, T) may be assumed and demagnetization effects dependent upon the shape of the specimen may be neglected.

In the following chapter it will be shown that in many magnetic problems H behaves in the same way as P in ordinary thermodynamic

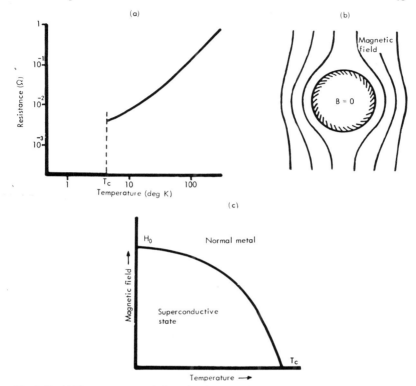

Fig. 3.12. (a) Temperature variation of resistance, showing sudden infinite conductivity at superconducting transition T_c. (b) Meissner effect. Magnetic flux is expelled by a superconductor. (c) $H-T$ phase diagram of a superconductor.

considerations. It is therefore natural to represent the equilibrium between the normal and superconductive states as a curve in the $H-T$ plane (Fig. 3.12c) which separates the two phases. If G_s is the Gibbs' free energy of the superconductive phase at zero field, its value at a field H is $G_s - \frac{1}{2}MH$ (see Chapter 4), where because of perfect diamagnetism the moment induced per unit volume is $M/V = -H/4\pi$. On the equilibrium curve, the free energies of both phases must be equal, and so

$$G_n - G_s = \frac{H_c^2}{8\pi}V \tag{3.12}$$

Since $S = -\partial G/\partial T$, the entropy difference is

$$S_n - S_s = -\frac{H_c V}{4\pi}\frac{\partial H_c}{\partial T} \tag{3.13}$$

The temperature variation of H_c, given by equation (3.11), shows that $\partial H_c/\partial T$ is always negative, and hence $S_s \leqslant S_n$; that is, the super-conductive state is more ordered than the normal state. The entropy difference vanishes at T_c ($H_c = 0$ at $T = T_c$) and at $0°K$ ($\partial H_c/\partial T = 0$ at $T \to 0$). At an intermediate temperature, about $0.3T_c$, $S_n - S_s$ reaches a maximum. $S = 0$ at $T \to 0$, it will be recalled, is in con-sonance with the third law of thermodynamics. $S = 0$ at $T = T_c$ implies that in the transition at zero field, no latent heat is involved. (This is an example of a phase change of the second order to be discussed in Section 8.1.) At intermediate temperatures, the liberated latent heat L is equal to

$$L = -T \frac{H_c V}{4\pi} \frac{\partial H_c}{\partial T} \qquad (3.14)$$

which agrees well with the experiments.

The entropy difference (3.13) shows that there is a difference between the heat capacities of the superconductive and normal phases:

$$C_n - C_s = T\frac{\partial}{\partial T}(S_n - S_s) = -\frac{TV}{4\pi}\left[H_c\frac{\partial^2 H_c}{\partial T^2} + \left(\frac{\partial H_c}{\partial T}\right)^2\right] \quad (3.15)$$

At the transition temperature, there is an abrupt jump in the specific heats

$$(C_n - C_s)_{T_c} = -\frac{T_c V}{4\pi}\left(\frac{\partial H_c}{\partial T}\right)^2 \qquad (3.16)$$

a relation often called *Rutger's relation*. Near T_c, the superconductive phase has a higher specific heat than the normal state, whereas at very low temperatures the normal phase has a higher heat capacity. At a temperature where the magnitude of ΔS is maximum, C_n and C_s are equal.

The above formulas are strictly valid only when the magnetic field destroying the superconductivity is along the axis of a long cylindrical specimen. For other orientations and shapes, an inter-mediate state must be considered. It was shown by Peierls that the specific heat then exhibits two discontinuities, a sharp rise and a sharp fall, marking the beginning and the end of the intermediate state.[24] For the sake of simplicity, these calculations are not worked out here.

3.9. SPECIFIC HEAT OF SUPERCONDUCTORS

The measurements of specific heat made immediately after the discovery of superconductivity showed no striking difference between C_n and C_s. With improvements in thermometry, Keesom and Van

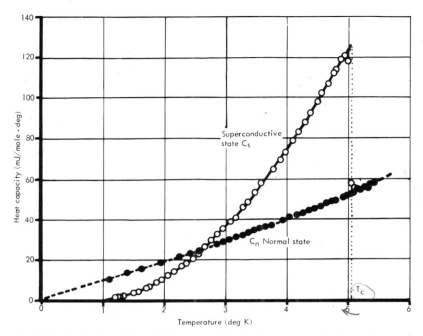

Fig. 3.13. Typical variation of heat capacities in the superconductive and normal states (vanadium[25]).

den Ende discovered the discontinuity [equation (3.16)] in the specific heat of tin at the superconducting transition. A typical variation of specific heat, shown in Fig. 3.13, brings out the characteristic features: C_n is greater than C_s at very low temperatures, C_s overtakes C_n as the transition is approached, and a sharp discontinuity occurs at T_c.

If the H_c–T threshold curve is known completely, equation (3.15) enables $C_n - C_s$ to be calculated. In general, the calculation involves a double differentiation of the H_c–T curve and is therefore not very accurate. At T_c, however, only the first derivative is needed, and a test of the thermodynamic relation (3.16) is possible. The measured values of $(C_s - C_n)_{T_c}$ in the carefully studied cases of indium, tin, and tantalum are In = 9.75, Sn = 10.6, Ta = 41.5 mJ/mole·deg, while the values calculated from the threshold curves are In = 9.62, Sn = 10.56, Ta = 41.6, showing excellent agreement. In some cases, especially with alloys, discrepancies arising from a different cause are found (Section 3.10). In most cases, the experimental confirmation of the thermodynamic relations is good.

Besides the simple relation given in Section 3.8, a somewhat more involved relation connecting the coefficients of thermal expansion and the compressibility of the two phases may be derived by taking the higher derivatives of equation (3.12) with respect to p and T (see *Ehrenfest relations* in Section 8.1). There are many experimental difficulties in confirming these relations, but, on the whole, reasonable agreement is found.[23]

Thermodynamics by itself does not give any further information on the variation of C_s, C_n with T. In general, the observed specific heat may be separated into lattice and electronic contributions $C_n = C_{gn} + C_{en}, C_s = C_{gs} + C_{es}$. In the normal state, equation (3.9) shows that $C_{gn} = \beta T^3, C_{en} = \gamma T$ at low temperatures. Now, in the superconducting transition, no structural changes are observed in the lattice, and the elastic properties are changed only minutely. Therefore, it is reasonable to assume that the lattice part of C_s and C_n are equal, so that

$$C_n - C_s = C_{en} - C_{es} \tag{3.17}$$

By such an analysis, C_{es} may be calculated; in many cases, it is approximately proportional to T^3. This variation is indeed compatible with equations (3.11) and (3.15). From them, it follows that

$$C_n - C_s = C_{en} - C_{es} = \frac{H_0^2 V}{2\pi T_c^2} T \left[1 - 3 \left(\frac{T}{T_c} \right)^2 \right] \tag{3.18}$$

and therefore

$$\gamma = \frac{H_0^2 V}{2\pi T_c^2} \tag{3.19}$$

$$C_{es} = \left(\frac{3 H_0^2 V}{2\pi T_c^4} \right) T^3 \tag{3.20}$$

$$(C_s - C_n)_{T_c} = 2\gamma T_c \tag{3.21}$$

These relations [equations (3.18 to 3.21)] suggest several methods of finding γ, the coefficient of electronic specific heat in the normal state, from the magnetic threshold curves. Actual computations[26] show that γ calculated in this manner from magnetic measurements agrees well with the calorimetric determinations. Such a comparison depends upon the assumed T^3-variation of C_{es} or the equivalent parabolic variation of H_c. Without invoking this, but assuming that C_{es} contains no term linear in T, it follows from equation (3.17) that

$$\lim_{T \to 0} \frac{C_n - C_s}{T} = \gamma \tag{3.22}$$

The advantage of this procedure in not assuming the parabolic temperature dependence of H_c is to some extent countered by the need for making magnetic measurements down to very low temperatures. Where this has been done, the relation (3.22) is found to be obeyed very well.

While all these results show the internal consistency in the application of thermodynamic relations to superconductors, they do not throw much light on the microscopic mechanism of superconductivity. Very accurate measurements of C_{es} made since 1954 have revealed that at low temperatures it varies as

$$C_{es} \approx a e^{-b/T} \tag{3.23}$$

A typical result based on one of the early measurements is shown in Fig. 3.14. Departures from a T^3-law occur at very low temperatures, and thus probably escaped notice in the experiments made earlier. Similar small deviations of the H_c–T curve from the parabolic law were also observed. By analogy to the studies of Einstein's model of lattice vibrations (Section 2.4), the Schottky peak in paramagnetic salts (Section 4.9), and the roton specific heat in liquid helium II (Section 5.4), it may be inferred that such an exponential variation

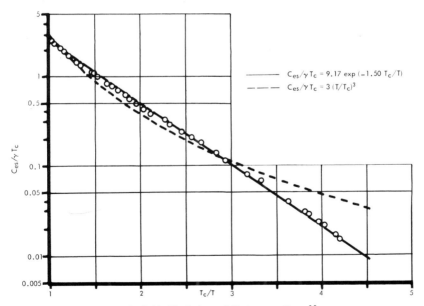

Fig. 3.14. Variation of C_{es} in vanadium.[25]

of the specific heat is characteristic of the presence of an energy gap separating the normal and superconducting electrons.

In 1950, it was also found that the transition temperature T_c depended on the isotopic mass M of the atom, $T_c \sim \alpha M^{-1/2}$, which suggested that the interaction of the electrons with the lattice was somehow responsible for superconductivity. These ideas culminated in a satisfactory theory of simple superconductors by Bardeen, Cooper, and Schrieffer in 1957.

3.10. RECENT STUDIES

It is hardly possible here to do justice to the theoretical concepts underlying the Bardeen–Cooper–Schrieffer (BCS) theory, which has successfully correlated several effects discovered earlier and predicted new phenomena as well. The task is ameliorated by the existence of several texts.[27] The theory shows that owing to the presence of virtual phonons, there is a tendency for the electrons to be correlated in pairs, called *Cooper pairs*. It requires an energy of approximately kT_c to break up this correlation, and the presence of such pairs allows a dissipationless flow of electric current. We shall content ourselves with a brief exposition of how the specific-heat studies fit into the theory.

The fact that an exponential variation of C_{es} [equation (3.23)] indicates the presence of an energy gap is easily visualized from Section 4.9, where it is proved that if two energy levels are separated by a gap ε, the specific heat at low temperatures has a dominant term of the form $\exp(-\varepsilon/kT)$. The detailed calculations of the BCS theory yield

$$\frac{C_{es}}{\gamma T_c} = 8.5 \exp \frac{-1.44 T_c}{T} \qquad \text{for } 2.5 < \frac{T_c}{T} < 6 \qquad (3.24)$$

$$= 26 \exp \frac{-1.62 T_c}{T} \qquad \text{for } \quad 7 < \frac{T_c}{T} < 12$$

where the gap $2\varepsilon_0$ is related to T_c by means of the relation

$$2\varepsilon_0 = 3.52 kT_c \qquad (3.25)$$

The form of the specific-heat curves resemble equation (3.24) closely, and some values of $2\varepsilon_0/kT_c$ determined by fitting this equation are given in Table 3.IV. For widely different metals, the values do cluster around the idealized 3.52 of the BCS model, which incidentally assumes the metal to be isotropic.

Another simple prediction of the theory is that

$$C_{es}(T_c) = 2.43 \gamma T_c \qquad (3.26)$$

Table 3.IV. Values of $2\varepsilon_0/kT_c$ Obtained from $C_{es}-T$ Curves

	Metal				
	In	Ta	Tl	Sn	V
$\dfrac{2\varepsilon_0}{kT_c}$	3.9	3.6	3.2	3.6	3.6

analogous to equation (3.21). A few values shown in Table 3.V show that many metals do not deviate much from this equation. Considering the simplicity of the model chosen for analysis and the wide variety of phenomena explained by it, the BCS theory must surely be considered as a significant advance toward the elucidation of a very complicated physical phenomenon.

Earlier, it was mentioned that the thermodynamic relations (3.12) to (3.16) are not very well satisfied for many alloys. Recent studies have shown that superconductors must be broadly divided into two categories. The superconductors of the first kind exhibit complete Meissner diamagnetism and seem to obey the thermodynamic relations derived for them. The BCS model explains their behavior reasonably well. Superconductors of the second kind do not exhibit the full Meissner effect. As shown in Fig. 3.15b, the magnetic field begins to penetrate the specimen at a lower critical field H_{c1}, but the last traces of superconductivity are destroyed only at a much higher field H_{c2}. Thus, type II superconductors show even in longitudinal magnetic fields the characteristics similar to the intermediate state of an ordinary type I superconductor. Following some earlier suggestions by Ginzburg and Landau, Abrikosov showed that the mixed state between H_{c1} and H_{c2} of a type II superconductor may be considered as a bundle of normal filaments in a superconductive medium. The filaments, or fluxoids, which are the magnetic analogs of hydrodynamic vortices, have special quantum properties and may also be pinned down by dislocations and other defects in the solid. Therefore,

Table 3.V. Values of C_{es} at T_c

	Metal					
	Hg	Sn	Al	Ta	Zn	Tl
$\dfrac{C_{es}(T_c)}{\gamma T_c}$	3.18	2.60	2.60	2.58	2.25	2.15

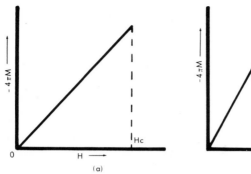
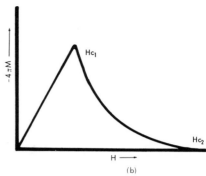

Fig. 3.15. (a) Expulsion of flux in a superconductor of the first kind up to a critical field H_c. (b) Incomplete Meissner effect in a superconductor of the second kind. Flux penetration begins at H_{c1} and is complete at H_{c2}.

the model allows the irreversibility of magnetization observed in type II superconductors. Further, the magnetization measurements do not have the same simple relationship to the measurement of electrical resistivity, as in type I superconductors. Many alloys are type II superconductors, and obviously the simple relations derived in Section 3.8 have to be generalized suitably.[28] Indeed, careful measurements on ideal type II superconductors, clearly exhibiting the specific-heat singularities at the transitions, are only now available.[29] The theory of Ginzburg and Landau, developed by Abrikosov and Gor'kov, explains many features of the behavior of type II superconductors, which are gaining technical importance in the generation of high magnetic fields. These matters are taken up at length in some recent reviews of the field.[27,30]

REFERENCES

1. J. L. Olsen, *Electron Transport in Metals*, Interscience, New York, 1962.
2. M. Born, *Atomic Physics*, Blackie, London, 1962, chapter 8. D. ter Haar, *Elements of Statistical Mechanics*, Rinehart, New York, 1954, chapter 4.
3. C. Kittel, *Solid State Physics*, Wiley, New York, 1956, chapters 11 and 13. A. J. Dekker, *Solid State Physics*, Prentice-Hall, New York, 1957, chapters 10 and 13. L. V. Azaroff and J. J. Brophy, *Electronic Processes in Materials*, McGraw-Hill, New York, 1963, chapters 7, 8, and 10.
4. J. M. Ziman, *Contemp. Phys.* **3**, 241, 321, 401 (1962); **4**, 1, 81 (1963).
5. W. A. Harrison and M. B. Webb (editors), *The Fermi Surface*, Wiley, New York, 1960.
6. E. C. Stoner, *Phil. Mag.* **21**, 145 (1936).
7. R. E. Gaumer and C. V. Heer, *Phys. Rev.* **118**, 955 (1960).
8. D. H. Parkinson, *Rept. Progr. Phys.* **21**, 226 (1958).
9. J. G. Daunt, *Progr. Low Temp. Phys.* **1**, 202 (1955).

10. P. H. Keesom and N. Pearlman, *Handbuch der Physik*, *XIV(I)*, 282 (1956).

11. D. Pines, *Solid State Phys.* **1**, 367 (1955). S. Raimes, *Rept. Progr. Phys.* **20**, 1 (1957).

12. G. V. Chester, *Advan. Phys.* **10**, 357 (1961).

13. P. L. Taylor, *Phys. Rev.* **131**, 1995 (1963). S. K. Koenig, *Phys. Rev.* **135**, A 1693 (1964).

14. N. F. Mott, *Rept. Progr. Phys.* **25**, 218 (1962); *Advan. Phys.* **13**, 325 (1964).

15. W. H. Lien and N. E. Phillips, *Phys. Rev.* **133**, A1370 (1964).

16. W. Hume-Rothery, *Electrons, Atoms, Metals, and Alloys*, Iliffe, London, 1955, chapter 29.

17. F. E. Hoare, in: *Electronic Structure and Alloy Chemistry of Transition Elements*, P. A. Beck (ed.), Interscience, New York, 1963, p. 29.

18. G. J. van den Berg, *Progr. Low Temp. Phys.* **4**, 194 (1964).

19. J. E. Zimmerman and F. E. Hoare, *J. Phys. Chem. Solids* **17**, 52 (1960). J. E. Zimmerman and H. Sato, *J. Phys. Chem. Solids* **21**, 71 (1961). J. P. Franck, F. D. Manchester, and D. L. Martin, *Proc. Roy. Soc. (London)*, *Ser. A* **263**, 494 (1961).

20. A. W. Overhauser, *J. Phys. Chem. Solids* **13**, 71 (1960). W. Marshall, *Phys. Rev.* **118**, 1519 (1960). K. P. Gupta, C. H. Cheng, and P. A. Beck, *J. Phys. Chem. Solids* **25**, 73 (1963).

21. V. A. Johnson and K. Lark-Horovitz, *Progr. Low Temp. Phys.* **2**, 187 (1957).

22. P. H. Keesom and G. Seidel, *Phys. Rev.* **113**, 33 (1959).

23. D. Shoenberg, *Superconductivity*, Cambridge University Press, Cambridge, 1952. E. A. Lynton, *Superconductivity*, Methuen, London, 1962.

24. D. C. Rorer, H. Meyer, and R. C. Richardson, *Z. Naturforsch.* **18a**, 130 (1963).

25. W. S. Corak, B. B. Goodman, C. B. Satterthwaite, and A. Wexler, *Phys. Rev.* **102**, 656 (1956).

26. J. Eisenstein, *Rev. Mod. Phys.* **26**, 277 (1954). B. Serin, *Progr. Low Temp. Phys.* **1**, 138 (1955).

27. J. Bardeen and J. R. Schrieffer, *Progr. Low Temp. Phys.* **3**, 170 (1961). J. M. Blatt, *Theory of Superconductivity*, Academic, New York, 1964. G. Rikayzen, *Theory of Superconductivity*, Interscience, New York, 1965. J. R. Schrieffer, *Theory of Superconductivity*, Benjamin, New York, 1965.

28. R. R. Hake (in press).

29. T. McConville and B. Serin, *Phys. Rev. Letters* **13**, 365 (1964). B. B. Goodman, *Phys. Letters* **12**, 6 (1964).

30. Proceedings of the IBM Conference on Superconductivity, *IBM J. Res. Dev.* **6**, 1–125 (1962). Proceedings of the Colgate Conference on Superconductivity, *Rev. Mod. Phys.* **36**, 1–331 (1964).

Magnetic Contribution to Specific Heats

4.1. THERMODYNAMICS OF MAGNETIC MATERIALS

The behavior of magnetic materials at low temperatures is of widespread interest, be it in demagnetization techniques to produce very low temperatures or in the use of superconducting magnets. Therefore, it is worthwhile to consider the specific heats of magnetic materials separately. It is well known that the magnetic energy depends upon the operative magnetic field H, and so it is first necessary to inquire how the specific heat is defined for a system capable of magnetization.

For a simple fluid, the basic thermodynamic relation used in Chapter 1 was

$$T \, dS = dE + dW = dE + P \, dV \tag{4.1}$$

If the fluid is magnetizable, a term $\mathbf{M} \cdot d\mathbf{H}$ must be added to dW as the work done in changing the magnetic field. For simplicity, the scalar product $\mathbf{M} \cdot d\mathbf{H}$ may be replaced by $M \, dH$ where M, the magnetic moment of the substance, is interpreted as the component of $\mathbf{M}$ in the direction of $\mathbf{H}$. Then

$$T \, dS = dE + P \, dV + M \, dH = dE' + P \, dV - H \, dM$$

where $E' = E + MH$. It is somewhat arbitrary whether E or E' is considered as the internal energy of the substance. This depends on whether the energy MH arising from the simultaneous presence of the field and the body is included in the energy content of the field or of the body. In several cases, it is advantageous and logical[1] to use E' as the internal energy. Further, in the problems of interest here, the mechanical work $P \, dV$ may be neglected in comparison with the magnetic part $- H \, dM$. So the fundamental relation may be written as

$$T \, dS = dE' - H \, dM \tag{4.2}$$

A comparison of equations (4.1) and (4.2) shows immediately that all the relations derived in Chapter 1 may be taken over to the magnetic case simply by replacing P and V by H and $-M$, respectively. The principal magnetic heat capacities, C_H at constant field and C_M at constant magnetization, are

$$C_H = \left(\frac{dQ}{dT}\right)_H = T\left(\frac{\partial S}{\partial T}\right)_H \qquad C_M = \left(\frac{dQ}{dT}\right)_M = T\left(\frac{\partial S}{\partial T}\right)_M \qquad (4.3)$$

The equations (1.12) and (1.14) between C_p and C_v are transformed into

$$C_H - C_M = -T\left(\frac{\partial H}{\partial T}\right)_M\left(\frac{\partial M}{\partial T}\right)_H = \frac{T(\partial M/\partial T)_H^2}{(\partial M/\partial H)_T} \qquad (4.4)$$

while the relation (1.16) giving the ratio of isothermal to adiabatic compressibility becomes

$$\frac{(\partial M/\partial H)_T}{(\partial M/\partial H)_S} = \frac{C_H}{C_M} \qquad (4.5)$$

In general, $(\partial M/\partial H)$ depends upon the shape of the body. For a long rod set parallel to H, the field H_i inside the body is the same as the outside field H, whereas for other orientations and shapes, appropriate coefficients of demagnetization have to be introduced. Assuming this to be done, the differential molar susceptibility χ may be introduced by the relation

$$\frac{\partial M}{\partial H} = \chi \qquad (4.6)$$

where M refers to the moment per mole.

The correspondence $C_p \leftrightarrow C_H$ and $C_v \leftrightarrow C_M$ suggests that C_M is the quantity of greater theoretical interest. This is true to some extent because in an "ideal" paramagnetic material, which obeys the relation $M = f(H/T)$, C_M is independent of the external field. A simple way of showing this is to write the magnetic analogs of equation (1.17), namely,

$$\left(\frac{\partial C_M}{\partial M}\right)_T = -T\left(\frac{\partial^2 H}{\partial T^2}\right)_M \qquad \left(\frac{\partial C_H}{\partial H}\right)_T = T\left(\frac{\partial^2 M}{\partial T^2}\right)_H \qquad (4.7)$$

For an "ideal" paramagnet, $M = f(H/T)$ or $H = Tf^{-1}(M)$. Therefore, $(\partial C_M/\partial M)_T = 0$, whereas C_H depends upon H.

These relations concerning the magnetic contributions to the heat capacity and hence to the entropy of a substance are of importance in the process of adiabatic demagnetization. A full discussion of the question may be found in the many reviews on the subject.[2]

4.2. TYPES OF MAGNETIC BEHAVIOR[3]

The molecules of most materials have no permanent magnetic moments. Under such conditions, an applied field H induces a magnetic moment in the electronic system of the molecules which is in a direction opposite to that of H; this behavior is said to be *diamagnetic*. Diamagnetism is independent of temperature, and so it is of little interest in specific-heat studies. Some molecules, oxygen, for example, have elementary magnetic moments μ; at high temperatures, they are ordinarily oriented at random. On applying a magnetic field, there is a preferential orientation of the moments along H, resulting in a magnetization parallel to H (paramagnetic behavior). At low temperatures, an ordered arrangement of the elementary magnets is possible. This ordering process was attributed phenomenologically to internal magnetic fields by Weiss in 1907, but in 1928 Heisenberg showed that it is due to the quantum-mechanical exchange interaction between neighboring electrons. An ordered state with parallel spins and therefore parallel magnetic moments (Fig. 4.1b) produces a large spontaneous magnetization even in the absence of H. In this ferromagnetic state, M becomes a nonlinear function of H and hysteresis effects are also present.

The exchange interaction is able to overcome the thermal randomization of the spins at a sufficiently low temperature. The Curie temperature T_c, below which the spins become ordered, is as high as 1080°K for iron and less than 1°K for some alums. However, the ordered state need not always be ferromagnetic, as was shown by Néel. In some cases, the adjacent spins may be aligned antiparallel (Fig. 4.1c). In this antiferromagnetic state there is no net spontaneous magnetization, but hysteresis is present and the susceptibility shows a sharp maximum at the transition temperature (Néel point). In a few cases, alternate magnetic moments are unequal and become arranged with adjacent spins antiparallel (Fig. 4.1d). This ferrimagnetic state is macroscopically similar to a ferromagnetic state, but the substances—ferrites and garnets find important practical

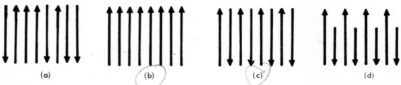

Fig. 4.1. Schematic order–disorder state in a lattice of elementary magnets: (a) paramagnetism—disordered spins; (b) ferromagnetism—parallel spins; (c) antiferromagnetism—adjacent spins antiparallel; (d) ferrimagnetism—adjacent unequal spins antiparallel.

applications—are poor conductors of electricity. Other types of ordering in which the spins are arranged along spirals are also possible (Section 7.6), and simple surveys of para-,[4] ferro-,[5] antiferro-,[6] and ferrimagnetic[7] states are available.

It is clear that, if the atoms or molecules of a substance possess permanent magnetic moments, the magnetic state depends very much upon the temperature, which means that interesting effects may be expected in the specific heats. In discussing them, it is convenient to start from the ordered state at low temperatures and then to pass on to the behavior as the temperature is raised.

4.3. SPIN WAVES—MAGNONS

The ideal ordered state described above exists only in the absence of thermal agitation. Taking first the case of ferromagnets, the spins at the lattice sites are aligned at $0°K$ along, say, Z so that the angular momentum $\hbar s$ is along Z. At a finite temperature, the spins at some sites j may be excited to higher energy states, i.e., point in other directions. Such distributions may be Fourier-analyzed into a set of waves. A spin wave may then be described as a sinusoidal disturbance of the spin system. The usefulness of describing a ferromagnet at finite temperatures as a superposition of spin waves was pointed out by Bloch in 1930. It permits a correlation of the various magnetic and other properties. A full description of the subject[8] is outside the scope of the present work, and only a qualitative derivation[9] of the spin wave spectrum in a ferromagnet can be given here. Unfortunately, this conceals some of the difficulties involved in the concept of spin waves, which are treated at length elsewhere.[8]

For simplicity, consider a linear ferromagnetic chain with a small field H_0 along $-Z$. Then the spins will all be pointing up with angular momenta $\hbar s_i$ about Z. Further, $s_i = \mu_i/g\beta = \mu_i/\hbar\gamma$ where $\beta = he/4\pi mc$ is the Bohr magneton, $\gamma = ge/2mc$ is the magneto-mechanical ratio, and g is the Landé factor equal to approximately 2 in ferromagnets. Classically, at $0°K$ all the spins will precess in phase about Z at the Larmor frequency $\omega_0 = \gamma H_0$. If now a spin wave is excited, the situation will be as shown in Fig. 4.2a. The spins are no longer in phase, and the phase angle between successive spins is equal to qa, where a is the lattice constant and $2\pi/q$ is the wavelength.

In an effective field H_{eff}, each spin, because of its magnetic moment, will experience a torque $\mu_i \times H_{eff} = \gamma\hbar s_i \times H_{eff}$. This torque is equal to the time rate of change of angular momentum

$$\frac{d(\hbar s_i)}{dt} = \gamma\hbar s_i \times H_{eff}$$

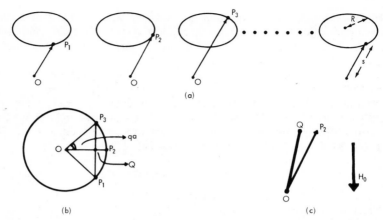

Fig. 4.2. Classical picture of a spin wave q in a linear ferromagnetic chain.

The effective field is calculated from the Hamiltonian [compare equation (4.18)]

$$\mathscr{H}_i = -g\beta \mathbf{s}_i \cdot \left(\mathbf{H}_0 + \frac{2J}{g\beta}\sum_j \mathbf{s}_j\right) = -g\beta \mathbf{s}_i \cdot \mathbf{H}_{\mathrm{eff}}$$

where the sum Σ_j is over the two near neighbors and J is the quantum-mechanical exchange constant. Using this value of $\mathbf{H}_{\mathrm{eff}}$,

$$\frac{d(\hbar \mathbf{s}_i)}{dt} = \gamma \hbar \mathbf{s}_i \times \left(\mathbf{H}_0 + \frac{2J}{g\beta}\sum_j \mathbf{s}_j\right) \tag{4.8}$$

If R is the amplitude of precession, $\mathbf{s}_i \times \mathbf{H}_0 = sH_0 \sin(s, H_0) = RH_0$. Figures 4.2 (a and b) shows that the resultant of OP_1 and OP_3 is $2\,OQ$ where $P_2Q = \frac{1}{2}Rq^2a^2$, and from Fig. 4.2c $\phi = \angle P_2OQ = \frac{1}{2}Rq^2a^2s^{-1}$. Therefore, the right-hand side of equation (4.8) is equal to $\gamma\hbar[RH_0 + (2J/g\beta)sRq^2a^2]$. The left-hand side is $\hbar\omega'R$, where ω' is the angular velocity of precession, and so

$$\omega' = \gamma H_0 + \frac{2J}{g\beta}sq^2a^2$$

The Larmor frequency of the spin system is γH_0, and the frequency of the spin wave itself is

$$\omega = \frac{2J}{\hbar}sa^2q^2 \tag{4.9}$$

In a three-dimensional crystal, the same dispersion law $\omega \propto q^2$, first found by Bloch, is obeyed, and the general ferromagnetic spin wave frequency may be taken as

$$\omega_q = \alpha_f \frac{2Jsa^2}{\hbar} q^2 \tag{4.10}$$

The constant α_f depends upon the details of the crystal structure and has been calculated in several practical cases.[8] The same $\omega \propto q^2$ is also obeyed by the spin waves in a ferrimagnet. However, in anti-ferromagnets, special considerations come into play in defining the normal modes of disturbances. It was first shown by Hulthén that the spin-wave spectrum is given as

$$\omega_q = \alpha_a \frac{2J'sa^2}{\hbar} q \tag{4.11}$$

where J' is the magnitude of the exchange constant. The antiferro-magnetic spectrum is linear in q, unlike the quadratic dependence in ferro- and ferrimagnets. To establish equation (4.11) would require a longer discussion than is warranted here, and so it suffices to mention the references to elementary[9] and rigorous[8] derivations.

It is interesting to compare the spin waves with the lattice waves analyzed in Chapter 2. At low frequencies, the normal modes of a lattice have a dispersion relation $\omega \propto q$, whereas the allowed modes in the spin system may be either $\omega \propto q^2$ as in ferromagnets or $\omega \propto q$ as in antiferromagnets. A set of mass points connected by elastic springs will form a model for lattice vibrations. A model for spin waves will be a set of arrows, each connected to its two neighbors by torsional springs. The angular displacement of a spin out of the line with its neighbors gives rise to a torque proportional to the excess displacement and tending to restore equilibrium. The analogy with lattice waves is actually very deep. The spin waves may be quantized into magnons, which play the same role in magnetic phenomena as phonons do in lattice dynamics. Magnons and phonons obey Bose–Einstein statistics. These similarities have been very fruitful in the study of magnetic systems.

4.4. SPIN WAVE SPECIFIC HEATS

The fact that magnons obey Bose statistics allows easy calculation of the low-temperature thermal properties of magnetic materials. It was seen in Chapter 2 that at a temperature T the mean energy of a Bose oscillator of angular frequency ω is $\hbar\omega/[\exp(\hbar\omega/kT) - 1]$ [equation (2.8a)] and that the number of energy states between momenta p and $p + dp$ is $(4\pi V/h^3)p^2\,dp$ [equation (2.18)]. Using the dispersion relations (4.10) and (4.11), the specific-heat contributions at low temperatures can be easily derived.

Taking first ferro- and ferrimagnets, where $\omega \propto q^2$,

$$E = 4\pi V \int_0^{} \frac{(2\alpha_f J s a^2 q^2) q^2 \, dq}{\exp(2\alpha_f J s a^2 q^2 / kT) - 1}$$

$$= 4\pi V (2\alpha_f J s a^2) \left(\frac{kT}{2\alpha_f J s a^2}\right)^{5/2} \int_0^{} \frac{x^4 \, dx}{e^{x^2} - 1} \tag{4.12}$$

The upper limit of integration over q cannot be specified without detailed analysis, but at low temperatures the upper limit for x may be taken as infinity without serious error and the integral may be evaluated suitably. The specific heat now follows as

$$C_M = \frac{dE}{dT} = c_f N k \left(\frac{kT}{2Js}\right)^{3/2} \tag{4.13}$$

where the constant c_f has been calculated for several crystal structures.[8] For example, $c_f \sim 0.113$ in a simple cubic arrangement of spins. Equation (4.13) is an important result, that at low temperatures the ferromagnetic contribution to specific heats is proportional to $T^{3/2}$. A similar $T^{3/2}$-variation is obeyed by the saturation magnetization of ferromagnets, for which the $T^{3/2}$ behavior had been observed for a long time. In specific heats, the measurement of spin wave contributions has been only recently successful.

In metals (Chapter 3), the conduction electrons give a specific heat proportional to T, the phonons give a T^3-term, and, if the above magnetic term is added, the low-temperature specific heat will be of the form

$$C_v = \gamma T + \beta T^3 + \delta T^{3/2}$$

The temperature variation of the heat capacity will be dominated by the term with the lowest power of T, namely, the electronic term. With a few exceptions discovered recently, most ferromagnets are metallic; therefore, a clear resolution of the magnetic $T^{3/2}$-term is a matter of considerable experimental difficulty. Not surprisingly, the spin wave effects were not easily observed in the specific heats of ferromagnets, although the magnetic measurements had borne out the theoretical predictions. The situation is quite different in ferrimagnets. They are electrical insulators, and in the absence of free electrons the specific heat is of the form

$$C_v = \beta T^3 + \delta T^{3/2}$$

At low temperatures, the spin wave is dominant, and a plot of $CT^{-3/2}$ against $T^{3/2}$ should be a straight line. The first such experiments

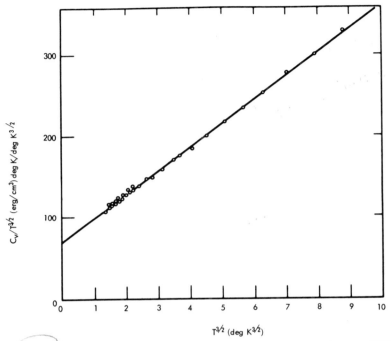

Fig. 4.3. Low-temperature specific heat of YIG showing the spin wave $T^{3/2}$-contribution.[10]

were made on magnetite Fe_3O_4 by Kouvel in 1956; since then, similar measurements have been made on several garnets, ferrites, and very recently on some ferromagnetic insulators. Figure 4.3 shows a typical result for yttrium iron garnet (YIG), with clear evidence for the $T^{3/2}$-term.[10] The exchange constant J may also be obtained from various other experiments, such as magnetic resonance and neutron scattering. The agreement among the values of J is fair, when the large corrections for demagnetizing effects and anisotropy are taken into account.

Going now to the case of antiferromagnets, the dispersion relation $\omega = \alpha_a(2J'sa^2/\hbar)q$ means that

$$E = 4\pi V \int_0 \frac{2\alpha_a J' sa^2 q^3 \, dq}{\exp(2\alpha_a J' sa^2 q/kT) - 1}$$

$$= 4\pi V (2\alpha_a J' sa^2) \left(\frac{kT}{2\alpha_a J' sa^2}\right)^4 \int_0 \frac{x^3 \, dx}{e^x - 1}$$

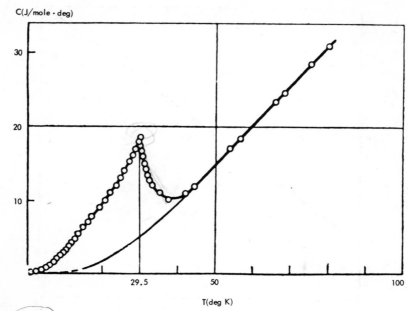

C(J/mole · deg)

T(deg K)

Fig. 4.4. Heat capacity of MnCO$_3$ (circles and thick lines) and CaCO$_3$ (thin lines) showing antiferromagnetic contribution.[11]

At low temperatures, the upper limit for x may again be taken as infinity, and the specific heat becomes

$$C_M = c_a Nk \left(\frac{kT}{2J's}\right)^3 \qquad (4.14)$$

The constant c_a has been calculated for several types of lattices. The T^3 spin wave specific heat in antiferromagnets is strikingly different from the $T^{3/2}$-dependence in ferromagnets. The temperature dependence is of the same form as the lattice contribution in the Debye T^3-region. This makes an experimental separation of the spin wave and lattice specific heats almost impossible in metals and very difficult in nonmetallic antiferromagnets. In the carbonates of manganese and cobalt, the antiferromagnetic T^3-contribution is about ten to twenty times larger than the lattice term, as may be seen in Fig. 4.4, where the specific heat of MnCO$_3$ is compared with that of CaCO$_3$, which has no magnetic contribution.[11] The experimental values agree very well with those calculated from magnetic measurements.

It must be added that the spin wave specific-heat relations (4.13) and (4.14) hold good at moderate temperatures only. At very low temperatures, some of the approximations made above are not valid and the specific heat may decrease exponentially. At high temperatures, interactions among magnons give rise to other terms, as shown in detail by Dyson, and the simple spin wave picture is no longer very useful. For the sake of simplicity, these details[8] are left out here.

4.5. THE WEISS MODEL FOR MAGNETIC ORDERING

As mentioned earlier, the ordered ferro-, ferri-, or antiferromagnetic states go over into the paramagnetic state at sufficiently high temperatures. The change in the magnetic properties is accompanied by a sharp peak in the specific-heat curve at T_c. Figure 4.5 shows the typical example of nickel. The magnetic contribution C_M is obtained by subtracting the lattice and electronic terms from the total C_v. The behavior near T_c is typical of a general class of cooperative transitions, which will be discussed at length in Chapter 7.

Historically, it was Weiss who in 1907 gave a simple explanation of ferromagnetism. A few years earlier, Langevin had shown that the

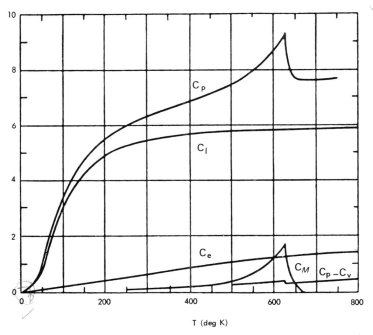

Fig. 4.5. Heat capacity of nickel (in cal/g-atom·deg) showing the magnetic contribution C_M besides lattice and electronic terms.

competition between the magnetic field **H** tending to align the elementary magnets μ and the thermal agitation causing a random arrangement results in a net magnetization of the form

$$M = N\mu \tanh\left(\frac{\mu H}{kT}\right) \tag{4.15}$$

Langevin's theory explained many aspects of paramagnetic behavior—in particular, Curie's law, that the susceptibility varies as $1/T$, arises because for ordinary fields and temperatures $\mu H/kT \ll 1$. Weiss suggested that because of the magnetization of the other parts of a solid there is an internal magnetic field αM (α a constant) and that the effective field acting on the elementary dipoles is

$$H_{\text{eff}} = H_{\text{ext}} + \alpha M$$

Substitution of H_{eff} in place of H in equation (4.15) shows that even in the absence of an external field H_{ext} there is a spontaneous magnetization given by the implicit equation

$$M_s = N\mu \tanh\left(\frac{M_s T_c}{N\mu T}\right) \tag{4.16}$$

where $T_c = \alpha N\mu^2/k$. This is the ferromagnetic state. Weiss's theory also explained hysteresis and other features of M–H_{ext} curves. For many metals, equation (4.16) satisfactorily describes the variation of M_s with T, except very near the transition temperature T_c. The moment μ comes out to be equal to the Bohr magneton $he/4\pi mc$, showing that ferromagnetism is due to the magnetic moment of electrons. [As a matter of fact, equation (4.15) is the quantum-mechanical expression for particles of spin $\frac{1}{2}\hbar$.]

The energy of magnetization in the absence of H_{ext} is

$$E_M = -\int_0^M H_{\text{int}} \, dM = -\tfrac{1}{2}\alpha M^2$$

and so the magnetic contribution to specific heat is

$$C_M = -\tfrac{1}{2}\alpha \frac{dM^2}{dT} \tag{4.17}$$

The magnetic specific heat given by the Weiss model is shown in Fig. 4.6. C_M steadily increases from zero at $T = 0$ to a maximum $\frac{3}{2}R$ at $T = T_c$. This maximum is followed by a discontinuous drop to $C_M = 0$ in the paramagnetic state $T > T_c$. No latent heat is liberated at T_c, and the transition in the Weiss model is a phase change of the second order (see Section 8.1).

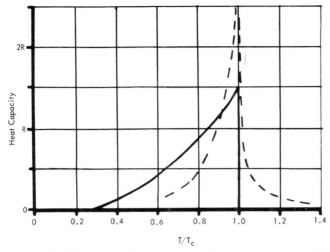

Fig. 4.6. Schematic variation of magnetic heat capacity near T_c in the Weiss model (full line) and in statistical theories (broken lines).

The experimental values of C_M, as seen in Figs. 4.4 and 4.5, follow the general trend in being small at low temperatures and beginning to rise as T_c is approached. Near T_c, there is not even qualitative agreement with the above theory. C_M often rises to a value much higher than the predicted maximum; furthermore, the specific-heat curve has a "tail" above the transition. C_M decreases sharply, no doubt, but instead of falling abruptly to zero it lingers on for a considerable range of temperatures before becoming immeasurably small.

The phenomenological theory may be suitably modified to give a small "tail" to the specific-heat curve,[12] but the agreement is not very much improved. It is generally believed that an explanation of the behavior of ferro- and antiferromagnets near T_c belongs to the realm of proper statistical theories.

4.6. THE HEISENBERG AND ISING MODELS

Very soon after the development of quantum mechanics, Heisenberg (in 1928) gave an explanation of the origin of Weiss's internal magnetic fields, whose large magnitudes of around 10^5 Oe remained puzzling. On account of the Pauli exclusion principle, two electrons with spins s_1, s_2 have an interaction energy of the form $-2Js_1 \cdot s_2$, where the exchange integral J is a function of distance. For large separations of the electrons, J is very small, but for spacings of the

order of a few Ångstroms the exchange energy becomes large enough
to be comparable to chemical binding energies. Thus, if the energy
were written in terms of the electronic magnetic moments μ, it would
be of the same form and magnitude as the internal magnetic energy
in the Weiss model, even though it is basically electrostatic in origin.
If J were positive, a parallel (ferromagnetic) alignment of spins would
be favored, while a negative J results in antiparallel alignment.

The statistical theory of magnetic systems thus involves the
calculation of the partition function $\Sigma \exp(-E_r/kT)$ of the system.
With the general form of the exchange interaction, the calculations are
so prohibitively complicated that it is normal to make two stages of
approximations. The Heisenberg model assumes that, since J falls
off rapidly with increasing distance, it is enough to take the interactions
as extending only to the nearest neighbors. Thus the energy of the
system in this model is

$$E(\text{Heisenberg}) = -2J \sum_{i,j} \mathbf{s}_i \cdot \mathbf{s}_j - \mu \mathbf{H} \cdot \sum_i \mathbf{s}_i \qquad (4.18)$$

where Σ is over all pairs of direct neighbors. This model has been
quite successful in explaining, for example, the spin waves at low
temperatures (Section 4.3). However, even this approximation involves formidable difficulties, so that in many statistical problems a
further simplification is commonly used, though the model was introduced slightly earlier by Ising. In the Ising model, the scalar product
$\mathbf{s}_i \cdot \mathbf{s}_j$ is replaced by $s_{iz} s_{jz}$ on the basis that if Z is the direction of
alignment, the expectation value of $\mathbf{s}$ in X, Y directions is zero. Then

$$E(\text{Ising}) = -2J \sum_{i,j} s_{iz} s_{jz} - \mu H \sum_i s_{iz} \qquad (4.19)$$

where Σ is again over pairs of adjacent neighbors.

The Ising model is a scalar problem in that it deprives magnetism
of its intimate connection with the angular momentum of electrons.
Further, it does not admit a spin wave picture at low temperatures.
Hence, it may be considered a poor model for magnetic studies.
However, near or above T_c, the statistical enumeration of the states,
which is correctly taken into account, assumes dominant importance
in the thermodynamic and other properties of the system. Therefore,
a large amount of theoretical work has been done on the behavior of
the simple Ising model near T_c, where its deficiencies are unimportant.
There are two reasons for the great interest in the field: In the first
place, the Ising and Heisenberg models furnish instructive theoretical
schemes not only for magnetic transitions but also for other cooperative transformations, which will be discussed in Chapter 7. The Ising
model is the simplest one which appears to reproduce many of the

features observed experimentally. Secondly, the general problem for a three-dimensional solid has remained so far an unsolved challenge. The exact solution for a two-dimensional Ising model was given by Onsager in 1944, but even this is a remarkable *tour de force* to be savored only by professional theoreticians.[13]

It is now superfluous to add that the solutions of the Heisenberg and Ising models, even in their approximate form, are far too sophisticated to be reproduced here. As regards the specific heat, which is the prime concern in this text, the two-dimensional Ising lattice exhibits a logarithmic singularity:

$$C_M \approx A \log (T - T_c) \ldots \qquad T > T_c$$
$$\approx B \log (T_c - T) \ldots \qquad T < T_c \qquad (4.20)$$

where the constants A, B have been calculated for several lattices. In a three-dimensional case, such exact relations are not yet available, and various approximate calculations have been made. The nature of the singularity, whether an inverse power of $|T - T_c|$ or logarithmic in $|T - T_c|$, cannot be described with certainty, although for a diamond-type Ising lattice the approximations have been carried sufficiently far to suggest a logarithmic infinity in specific heat below the ferro-magnetic transition.[14] To be fair, it must be mentioned that a logarithmic singularity at the cooperative transition had been revealed by calorimetric measurements performed somewhat earlier (Figs. 4.9 and 5.5). Above T_c the experiments can be fitted to a logarithmic term in some cases and to a power law singularity in others.[14a]

It is also possible to estimate the ferromagnetic transition temperature T_c, as well as the magnetic part of the entropy S and internal energy E that are removed at the transition. For a fcc lattice, the values are

$$2kT_c/zJ \qquad 0.68 \qquad 0.82$$

$$(S_\infty - S_c)/k \qquad 0.27 \qquad 0.10 \qquad (4.21)$$

$$(E_\infty - E_c)/kT_c \qquad 0.44 \qquad 0.15$$

Here z is the number of nearest neighbors and J is the exchange constant. The values are for spin $\frac{1}{2}$, and the first column refers to the Heisenberg model and the second to the Ising model. The entropy values show that the Heisenberg model has a larger tail on the high-temperature side than the Ising model. For bcc or other types of lattices, the constants in (4.21) are slightly different. Similar small variations arise for spins greater than $\frac{1}{2}$. In particular, the specific heat on the high-temperature side rises more rapidly for larger spins. Antiferromagnetic transitions may be studied similarly, but calculations are scanty. A schematic variation of the specific heat near T_c is shown in Fig. 4.6.

In contrast to these approximate values, which depend upon the model chosen for calculations, a very general result may be given for the total magnetic entropy S_M. It is well known that a particle with spin sh has $2s + 1$ quantized orientations. In a field H, the levels have slightly different energies, but in the absence of H the energies are all equal and there is a $2s + 1$ degeneracy in the state of the system. The entropy corresponding to this is $k \ln(2s + 1)$ per particle, which is the entropy that comes into play here. The rule

$$S_M = R \ln(2s + 1) \text{ per mole} \tag{4.22}$$

has been verified in many cases.[15] Only a small part of this entropy is removed as the substance is cooled to T_c from a high temperature. This percentage is slightly larger in a Heisenberg model with its larger tail above T_c. Most of the ordering takes place below the transition.

4.7. SPECIFIC HEATS NEAR THE TRANSITION TEMPERATURE

It is only recently that careful experimental studies have been made to check the various predictions of the statistical theories; on the whole, reasonable agreement is found.[16] As an example of ferromagnets, the complete magnetic and calorimetric studies[17] on copper ammonium and copper potassium chlorides, $Cu(NH_4)_2Cl_4 \cdot 2H_2O(T_c = 0.70°K)$ and $CuK_2Cl_4 \cdot 2H_2O(T_c = 0.88°K)$, may be considered. Below about $0.5T_c$, the specific heat follows the variation given by this spin wave theory (Section 4.3). For the ammonium salt, the exchange constant J/k given by the spin wave variation is about $0.28°K$, compared to the values of approximately $0.30°K$ calculated from the Curie–Weiss constant and approximately $0.29°K$ derived from the behavior of the specific heat in the paramagnetic state $T > T_c$. Near T_c, the statistical theory suggests that the specific heat is a function of T/T_c only; Fig. 4.7 shows how closely this is verified. (The lattice contribution is negligible at these low temperatures.) The entropy calculated from the full line has a value of 5.8 J/mole·degK, whereas the theoretical value for $s = \frac{1}{2}$ of Cu^{2+} ion is $R \ln 2 = 5.76$ J/mole·degK. Further, the authors obtain $2kT_c/zJ = 0.75$, $(S_\infty - S_c)/k = 0.22$, $(E_\infty - E_c)/kT_c = 0.38$. These values are in between the numbers given in (4.21), although the Heisenberg model gives a good explanation of the other properties of the substance. A part of the discrepancy may be due to the bcc structure of these salts,

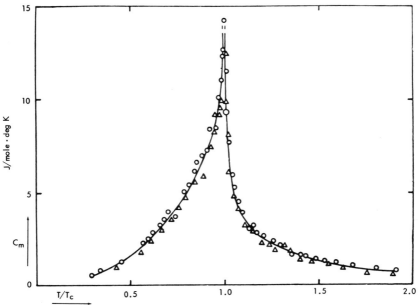

Fig. 4.7. Heat capacity of $CuK_2Cl_4\cdot 2H_2O$ ($T_c = 0.882°K$, circles) and $Cu(NH_4)_2Cl_4\cdot 2H_2O$ ($T_c = 0.704°K$, triangles) plotted as a function of T/T_c.[16]

whereas equation (4.21) refers to a fcc lattice. Support for this view is given by the fact that a Heisenberg model for a bcc lattice gives $2kT_c/zJ = 0.72$, in much better agreement with the experiments.

Antiferromagnetic transitions are exemplified by the study[18] of nickel and cobalt chlorides, $NiCl_2\cdot 6H_2O$($T_N = 5.34°K$), $CoCl_2\cdot 6H_2O$ ($T_N = 2.29°K$). The specific heat of the nickel salt is shown in Fig. 4.8, while that of the cobalt salt is similar except for the change in the Néel temperature. The lattice term, which is nearly the same in both salts, was found from the T^3-behavior of the lattice specific heat and the T^{-2}-variation of the paramagnetic specific heat at $T \gg T_N$ (compare Section 4.9). The magnetic specific heat is obtained by subtracting the lattice contribution from the total specific heat. Because of the influence of the crystalline electric field upon the electronic levels of the transition metal ions, one should expect $s = \frac{1}{2}$ for the cobaltous ion and $s = 1$ for the nickelous ion. The magnetic entropy was equal to 9.13 J/mole·degK for the nickel salt, which is within 1% of $R \ln 3$. That of cobaltous chloride was 5.80 J/mole·degK $\sim R \ln 2$. The exchange constant $|J|/k$ has a value of approximately 1.6°K for $CoCl_2\cdot 6H_2O$ if calculated from the total ordering energy and about 1.5°K if calculated from the Néel temperature. Of more interest is

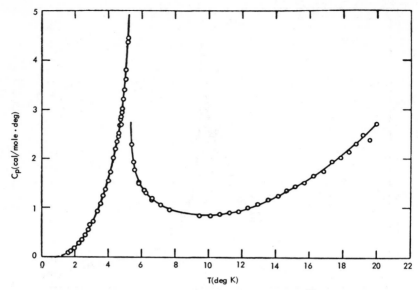

Fig. 4.8. Heat capacity of $NiCl_2 \cdot 6H_2O$.[18]

the behavior of C_M found near T_N (Fig. 4.9). The data appear to suggest that the specific heat becomes logarithmically infinite at the Néel temperature. This singularity and the similar behavior found in liquid ^4He (Fig. 5.6) are of special interest because Onsager's solution for a two-dimensional cooperative transition shows a logarithmic infinity, while no firm predictions are as yet available for a three-dimensional case.

4.8. PARAMAGNETIC RELAXATION

Specific-heat studies in paramagnetic salts are important in two respects. In the first place, the attainment of temperatures much lower than 1°K by adiabatic demagnetization techniques involves a thorough knowledge of the magnetic entropy which can be extracted from the system. Secondly, paramagnetic salts furnish an interesting class of specific-heat anomalies, namely, the Schottky peak. Before these matters are taken up in detail, it is convenient to discuss a special method of measuring specific heats which is very useful when they are not easily separated from the lattice contributions.

The method is based on paramagnetic relaxation,[3,4] discovered by Gorter. If a magnetic field is applied to a paramagnetic salt, the internal energy of the system is changed. It is found that the time taken for the transfer of the heat of magnetization from the dipoles to the crystal lattice (spin–lattice relaxation time) is much longer than the time needed for the establishment of thermal equilibrium among the dipoles themselves (spin–spin relaxation time). On suddenly changing H, the dipoles very quickly (in about 10^{-10} sec) follow the field, but the magnetic energy is given to the lattice only in a leisurely (of the order of 10^{-6} sec) fashion. Therefore, for any variation of H over a time long compared to the spin–spin relaxation time but short compared to the spin–lattice relaxation time, the dipoles are in equilibrium among themselves but do not exchange heat with the lattice. A measurement of the variation of M under such conditions gives the adiabatic susceptibility χ_S. The normal DC measurement yields the isothermal susceptibility χ_T. Equations (4.4) to (4.6) now show that

$$\frac{\chi_T}{\chi_S} = 1 + \frac{T(\partial M/\partial T)_H^2}{\chi_T C_M} \quad \text{or} \quad C_M = T\left(\frac{\partial M}{\partial T}\right)_H^2 \frac{\chi_S}{(\chi_T - \chi_S)\chi_T} \quad (4.23)$$

As pointed out first by Casimir, du Pre, and de Haas in 1938–1939, the lattice temperature is not changed during the measurement, and so the lattice specific heat does not enter the calculation.

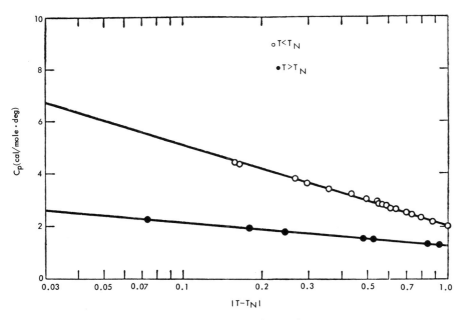

Fig. 4.9. Plot of C_M versus $\log |T - T_N|$ for NiCl$_2$·6H$_2$O.

By this technique it is possible to measure magnetic contributions to specific heats at liquid-nitrogen temperatures, where they may amount to only 10^{-6} of the total heat capacity of the salt. Since the spin–lattice relaxation time is about 10^{-6} sec at these temperatures, the adiabatic susceptibility must be determined at radio frequencies. At liquid-helium temperatures the spin–lattice relaxation time is usually of the order of 10^{-3} sec and audiofrequency measurements suffice. The details of the experimental techniques are thoroughly discussed by Benzie and Cooke.[19] At very low temperatures ($\ll 1°K$), the heating produced in AC measurements is considerable, and direct calorimetry is preferred. At these temperatures, the lattice specific heat is so small that the entire specific heat measured calorimetrically may be taken as arising from magnetic effects. At higher temperatures, the paramagnetic relaxation technique is very useful, because the lattice and magnetic terms are nearly comparable and not easily separated out.

At very low temperatures, since the spin system can exist for an appreciable time without interacting with the lattice, it is advantageous in magnetic studies to attribute a separate (spin) temperature and specific heat to the spin system. Discussions of such nonequilibrium concepts can be found in the treatises on magnetic resonance and are not appropriate here.

4.9. SCHOTTKY EFFECT

It is well known that a particle with spin $s\hbar$ has $2s + 1$ possible orientations of the spin; in a magnetic field, the particle has a number of discrete energy levels. This spacing of the quantized energy levels is reflected in the specific heat in an interesting way. Consider for a moment a system with two levels, Δ apart. At $T \ll \Delta/k$, the upper level will scarcely be populated, whereas at $T \gg \Delta/k$ both levels will be nearly equally populated. Only at temperatures comparable to Δ/k will transitions from one level to another take place in appreciable amounts. This rapid change in the internal energy corresponds to a large specific heat which becomes zero at both high and low temperatures. Thus there is the intriguing possibility of a hump in C_v, which will in general be superimposed on the lattice and other contributions.

A general problem of this kind was considered by Schottky in 1922. Suppose there is a system in which the particles can exist in a group of m levels, separated from the ground state by energies $\varepsilon_1, \varepsilon_2, ..., \varepsilon_m$ and with degeneracies $g_1, g_2, ..., g_m$. Using the Boltzmann factor $\exp(-\varepsilon/kT)$, the probability of a particle occupying the rth level is

$$\frac{g_r \exp(-\varepsilon_r/kT)}{\sum_n g_r \exp(-\varepsilon_r/kT)}$$

With N independent particles in the system, the mean energy at a temperature T is

$$E = \frac{N \sum_{r=0}^{m} \varepsilon_r g_r \exp(-\varepsilon_r/kT)}{\sum_{r=0}^{m} g_r \exp(-\varepsilon_r/kT)} \tag{4.24}$$

The specific heat is obtained by calculating dE/dT. The simple case of two levels illustrates all the features of such calculations. For a two-level system, equation (4.24) becomes

$$E = \frac{N g_1 \varepsilon_1 \exp(-\varepsilon_1/kT)}{g_0 + g_1 \exp(-\varepsilon_1/kT)}$$

and the Schottky specific heat is

$$
\begin{aligned}
C_{\text{Sch}} &= \frac{N \varepsilon_1^2}{kT^2} \frac{g_0}{g_1} \frac{\exp(\varepsilon_1/kT)}{[1 + (g_0/g_1)\exp(\varepsilon_1/kT)]^2} \\
&= R\left(\frac{\delta}{T}\right)^2 \frac{g_0}{g_1} \frac{\exp(\delta/T)}{[1 + (g_0/g_1)\exp(\delta/T)]^2}
\end{aligned}
\tag{4.25}
$$

where $\delta = \varepsilon_1/k$ is the energy separation measured in degK. C_{Sch} is plotted in Fig. 4.10 for a few values of g_1/g_0.

The qualitative remarks made earlier about the behavior at low and high temperatures may now be made quantitative. From equation (4.25) it is easy to see that

$$C_{\text{Sch}} = R\left(\frac{g_1}{g_0}\right)\left(\frac{\delta}{T}\right)^2 \exp\left(-\frac{\delta}{T}\right) \qquad T \ll \delta \tag{4.26}$$

$$= R g_0 g_1 (g_0 + g_1)^{-2} \left(\frac{\delta}{T}\right)^2 \qquad T \gg \delta \tag{4.27}$$

The specific heat attains a maximum value at an intermediate temperature T_m given by

$$\left(\frac{g_0}{g_1}\right) \exp\left(\frac{\delta}{T_m}\right) = \frac{(\delta/T_m) + 2}{(\delta/T_m) - 2} \tag{4.28}$$

and the maximum itself is equal to

$$C_{\text{Sch}}(\text{max}) = \frac{R}{4} \frac{T_m}{\delta}\left[\left(\frac{\delta}{T_m}\right)^2 - 4\right] \tag{4.29}$$

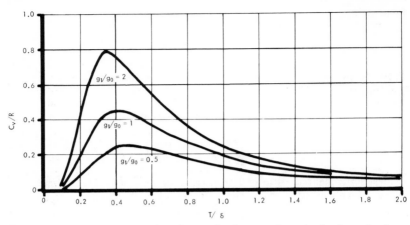

Fig. 4.10. Schottky heat capacity of a two-level system for several values of g_1/g_0.

Thus if $g_0/g_1 = 1$, the maximum occurs at $T_m = 0.42\delta$ and has a value $C_{Sch}(max) = 3.6$ J/mole·deg. Table 4.I gives T_m/δ and $C_{Sch}(max)$ for several values of g_1/g_0. When these values are compared with the typical lattice and electronic contributions of 10^{-2} J/mole·deg at $4°K$, it is evident that a Schottky peak occurring at liquid-helium temperatures will dominate the variation of specific heat (see Fig. 4.11).

If C_{Sch} is isolated from the observed total specific heat, by the methods to be discussed below, there are several ways of finding δ and g_1/g_0. The position and magnitude of the peak, the behavior at high temperatures ($C_{Sch} \cdot T^2 = $ constant) or at low temperatures ($\log(C_{Sch} \cdot T^2)$ linear in $1/T$) may all be used. This, of course, assumes that there are only two energy levels to be considered. If more levels are involved, the full equation (4.24) has to be used, or, alternatively,

$$C_{Sch} = T\frac{d^2(RT\ln z)}{dT^2} = RT^{-2}\frac{d^2\ln z}{d(1/T)^2}$$

TABLE 4.I

g_1/g_0	C_{Sch} (max) J/mole·deg	T_m/δ	Total entropy
0.5	2.00	0.448	$R\ln\frac{3}{2}$
1.0	3.64	0.417	$R\ln 2$
1.5	5.06	0.394	$R\ln\frac{5}{2}$
2.0	6.31	0.377	$R\ln 3$
5.0	12.0	0.320	$R\ln 6$

where

$$z = \sum g_r \exp\left(-\frac{\varepsilon_r}{kT}\right)$$

Apart from the behavior $C_{Sch} \propto T^{-2}$ at high temperatures, no simple results can be given. In such cases it is necessary to start with some schemes of energy levels derived either theoretically or from susceptibility, paramagnetic resonance, and other data. The specific-heat curve then serves as a check on the correctness of the assumed model.

The entropy associated with the Schottky peak may be obtained by integrating $C_{Sch} \cdot T^{-1}$; the values for the two-level case are given in Table 4.I. These results may also be obtained by enumerating the possible configurations of the system, as was done with equation (4.21). For example, if there are m levels of equal degeneracy, the extra entropy is $R \ln m$ per mole. In the two-level case, $S = R \ln [1 + (g_1/g_0)]$. Usually, a comparison of the theoretical and experimental values of the excess entropy serves to verify the correctness of separating out C_{Sch} from the observed total specific heat.

The problem of getting C_{Sch} from the observed specific heat by subtracting the lattice and other contributions is one of considerable difficulty. If the Schottky peak occurs at low temperatures, the lattice term may be taken as βT^3. At temperatures well above the peak, $C_{Sch} \propto T^{-2}$, and the total specific heat will be of the form $C = \beta T^3 + BT^{-2}$. Thus a plot of CT^2 versus T^5 should be a straight line, which permits the desired resolution to be carried out. The magnetic contribution in Fig. 4.9 was obtained from Fig. 4.8 in this manner. For this separation to work, the lattice term must be proportional to T^3 and the two terms must be of similar magnitude. If this restriction cannot be satisfied, it is usual to take for $C_{lattice}$ the specific heat of a salt of similar composition and same crystal structure, but which does not have an anomaly. The case of $MnCO_3$ and $CaCO_3$ (Fig. 4.4) is an example of this type of analysis. In some cases, the magnetic contribution may be evaluated separately from measurements of paramagnetic relaxation or adiabatic demagnetization from different magnetic fields. In general, the Schottky term, if present at liquid-helium temperatures, is so large a fraction of the observed specific heat that small errors in evaluating the lattice corrections are not serious.

4.10. SPECIFIC HEAT OF PARAMAGNETIC SALTS

Paramagnetic salts, in which the magnetic dipoles have energy levels with spacings of approximately 1 to 10°K, form the natural examples of simple systems exhibiting a variety of Schottky peaks. That such a close relationship should exist may be inferred in the following way. For the magnetic moment of a paramagnet, Langevin's theory gives an expression of the form

$$M = N\mu \tanh (\mu H/kT) \tag{4.15}$$

In a field H, the energy of the magnetic moment of the body is MH; this corresponds to a specific heat

$$C_M = (N \mu^2 H^2/kT^2) \operatorname{sech}^2 (\mu H/kT) \tag{4.30}$$

If the energy difference between two levels $2\mu H$ of a particle is put equal to ε_1, this is nothing but equation (4.25) with $g_0 = g_1$. Figure 4.10 with $kT/2\mu H$ instead of T/δ and $g_1/g_0 = 1$ will represent equation 4.30 equally well. In a paramagnetic gas, the position of the specific-heat maximum may be shifted at will by applying a magnetic field. For the fields normally used, this is practicable only at low temperatures.[20] The entropy of the spin system can be increased merely by demagnetizing a magnetically saturated specimen. If the process is done adiabatically, a compensating decrease of temperature is enforced to keep the entropy constant. This forms the basis of the adiabatic demagnetization technique to reach temperatures below 1°K and to measure the magnetic specific heats in that region.[2]

A similar electrocaloric effect is also possible, in which excitations occur between the different levels of electric dipoles.[20a]

In a solid, the magnetic ions have energy levels about 1°K apart even in the absence of external fields. These closely spaced levels arise in several ways. In any solid, there are crystalline electric fields which remove the spin degeneracy of some atomic energy levels through the familiar Stark effect. There are magnetic dipole and exchange interactions among neighboring ions, which also split the energy levels, though Stark-splitting accounts for the major share in the level splitting. Besides these causes attributed to the electronic spin, nuclear effects may also arise from the energy levels of the nuclear dipoles and quadrupoles. The specific-heat studies, being integrated measurements, give no clue to the origin of the energy splittings. This must come from other theoretical and experimental studies, especially those on magnetic susceptibility and paramagnetic resonance. The resonance studies are particularly fruitful in directly giving the separation and degeneracy of the various levels. A good account of the interrelations among the various measurements is given by Rosenberg.[21]

A prerequisite for applying the simple Schottky theory is that the various ions should be independent of one another. Since the magnetic interactions do not fall off very rapidly with increasing distance, the ions will not respond independently, except as a first approximation, to the applied magnetic fields. An approximate correction for the lack of statistical independence may be applied, but it is more usual to dilute the specimen with isomorphous diamagnetic salts so that the various ions are far removed from one another. In some salts, such as alums and Tutton salts, the water molecules in the crystal provide the necessary dilution, but where nature does not perform the decoupling well enough, artificial measures have to be employed. Even when a complete picture of the energy levels is available, small discrepancies between the calculated and theoretical specific heats are often present. They are usually attributed to the lack of statistical independence caused by coupling among the ions themselves and among the ions and the lattice phonons.[22]

An example of the good agreement between theory and experiment is the Schottky effect in $\alpha - NiSO_4 \cdot 6H_2O$.[23] The Ni^{2+} ion can have in general three energy levels on account of the removal of spin degeneracy by the crystalline electric and magnetic fields, although approximate calculations suggested two levels with $g_1 = 2$ and $g_0 = 1$. The experimental curve does resemble Fig. 4.10, with

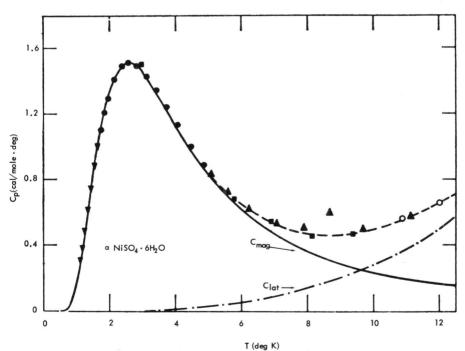

Fig. 4.11. Heat capacity of α-$NiSO_4 \cdot 6H_2O$.[23] Full line is the calculated magnetic term. Dot-dashed line is the lattice heat capacity.

$g_1/g_0 = 2$ as regards C_{Sch} (max). Detailed comparisons showed three levels with spacings 6.44 and 7.26°K above the lowest spin state. The agreement with the experimental values, after taking into account the lattice contribution (which is about 7% of the total C_v at 6°K and about 1% at 4°K), is seen to be very good. The total entropy of the magnetic system is $R \ln 3$. With this knowledge of the energy levels, other properties, such as susceptibility and magnetization, have been calculated in reasonable agreement with the observed values.

An illustration of the great utility of calorimetric data in supplementing the information from paramagnetic resonance and susceptibility measurements is furnished by the case of ferric methylammonium sulfate $Fe(NH_3CH_3)(SO_4)_2 \cdot 12H_2O$.[24] Paramagnetic resonance studies by Bleaney and coworkers showed that Fe^{3+} ion has three doublet states. The middle $S_z = \pm\frac{3}{2}$ level is separated from the other two by energies of 1.05 and 0.58°K, but it was not known which of the levels $\pm\frac{1}{2}$, $\pm\frac{5}{2}$ was the lowest spin level. Therefore two schemes, shown in Fig. 4.12, are possible, and the corresponding C_{Sch} are compared with the experimental specific heats. There is no doubt that scheme 2, with $S_z = \pm\frac{1}{2}$ as the lowest level, is the correct one. The addition of

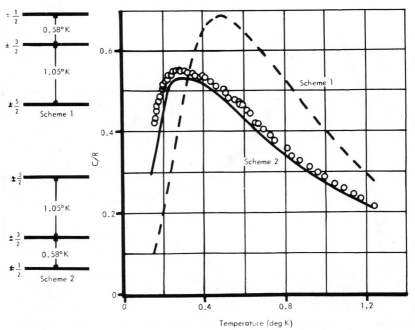

Fig. 4.12. Heat capacity of $Fe(NH_3CH_3)(SO_4)_2 \cdot 12H_2O$ compared with two possible level schemes. Obviously, scheme 2 with $\pm\frac{1}{2}$ level lowest gives a better fit.

the magnetic dipolar contribution removes the small discrepancy found in Fig. 4.12. In this salt, measurements of susceptibility could not throw much light on the energy level schemes, and the calorimetric data gave an elegant solution to the problem.

Although the spin disorder in the paramagnetic state, which gives a T^{-2} specific heat at high temperatures, should eventually be removed at 0°K, it is not easy to say whether the removal will involve a Schottky peak or a cooperative singularity. In general, with dilute systems, the spin disorder is removed with a Schottky peak. If the exchange interactions are strong, a cooperative transition to the ferromagnetic, antiferromagnetic, or other states occurs before a Schottky peak can be observed.

4.11. NUCLEAR SCHOTTKY EFFECTS

Schottky effects are widely observed in the electron paramagnetism of crystalline salts or of some gases such as nitric oxide and oxygen. In the solid state, Schottky peaks may arise from a different source. If the atomic nucleus has a magnetic moment μ_N, it may have a set of energy levels in an effective field H_{eff}, arising from orbital and conduction electrons. The splitting is similar to the hyperfine structure (hfs) observed in spectroscopy. Moreover, if the nucleus has a quadrupole moment, its interaction with the field gradients produced by neighboring atoms will cause small level splittings. The change in population of these levels is readily observed as a Schottky effect in the specific heats.

The hfs effect was first observed in ferromagnetic materials, where the presence of internal fields of the order of $10^5 Oe$ obviously suggests that the nuclear levels will be appreciably split. Since then, such effects have been observed in antiferromagnets and more prominently in many ferromagnetic rare-earth metals. In holmium, the peak occurs at a reasonable temperature of 0.3°K, and so the complete anomaly has been mapped out.[25] The levels of a nucleus of spin I may be written as

$$\varepsilon_i/k \approx ai$$

where $i = -I, -I + 1, ..., I$ and a is the hfs coupling constant. For holmium, $I = \frac{7}{2}$ and there are eight levels. From paramagnetic-resonance studies, Bleaney had calculated $a \approx 0.31$°K. The specific-heat studies give $a \approx 0.32$°K, in excellent agreement with paramagnetic-resonance data. Actually, in holmium there is a small quadrupole contribution which is taken into account in the theoretical curve of Fig. 4.13. The excellent fit with the experiments needs no further description.

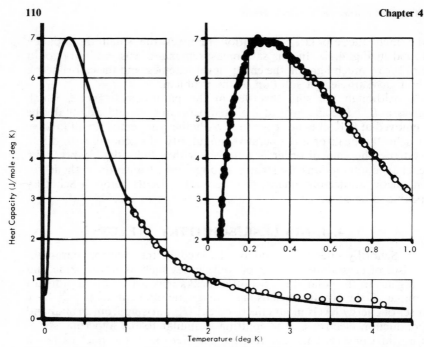

Fig. 4.13. Heat capacity of holmium metal.[25] Full line is theoretical Schottky curve.

If a nucleus with a quadrupole moment is situated in a non-spherical or noncubic electronic environment, the quadrupole inter-action with the electric field gradient gives a set of energy levels

$$\varepsilon_i/k \approx P'[i^2 - \tfrac{1}{3}I(I + 1)]$$

Here P' is the quadrupole coupling constant, which may be related to the quadrupole moment and the field gradient. The T^{-2} high-temperature Schottky term arising from such splittings has been observed in substances such as rhenium, mercury, indium, and gallium.[26]

Because of the smallness of the nuclear moments compared to the electronic moments, the nuclear anomalies occur in the region of 10^{-2}K, whereas the electronic peaks are present at 1 to 10°K. On the other hand, the nuclear effects may arise even in diamagnetic materials.

REFERENCES

1. E. A. Guggenheim, *Thermodynamics*, North Holland, Amsterdam, 1957, chapter 12. A. B. Pippard, *Elements of Classical Thermodynamics*, Cambridge University Press, Cambridge, 1957, pp. 23 and 63.

2. C. G. B. Garrett, *Magnetic Cooling*, Harvard University Press, Cambridge, 1954.
D. de Klerk and M. J. Steenland, *Progr. Low Temp. Phys.* **I**, 273 (1955).
D. de Klerk, *Handbuch der Physik*, *XV*(2), 38 (1956).
E. Ambler and R. P. Hudson, *Rept. Progr. Phys.* **18**, 251 (1955).
W. A. Little, *Progr. Cryogenics* **4**, 99 (1964).

3. A. J. Dekker, *Solid State Physics*, Prentice-Hall, New York, 1957, chapters 18 and 19.
J. B. Goodenough, *Magnetism and the Chemical Bond*, Interscience, New York, 1963, chapter 2.

4. J. H. van den Handel, *Advan. Electron. Electron Phys.* **6**, 463 (1954).

5. E. C. Stoner, *Rept. Progr. Phys.* **11**, 43 (1948); **13**, 83 (1950).

6. A. B. Lidiard, *Rept. Progr. Phys.* **17**, 201 (1954). T. Nagamiya, K. Yosida and R. Kubo, *Advan. Phys.* **4**, 1 (1955).

7. W. P. Wolf, *Rept. Progr. Phys.* **24**, 212 (1961). R. K. Wangsness, *Progr. Cryogenics* **4**, 73 (1964).

8. J. van Kronendonk and J. H. van Vleck, *Rev. Mod. Phys.* **30**, 1 (1958). A. I. Akhiezer, V. G. Bar'yakhtar, and M. I. Kagano, *Soviet Phys. Uspekhi* **3**, 567, 661 (1960).

9. F. Keffer, H. Kaplan, and Y. Yafet, *Am. J. Phys.* **21**, 250 (1953).

10. D. T. Edmonds and R. G. Petersen, *Phys. Rev. Letters* **2**, 499 (1959).

11. A. S. Borovik-Romanov and I. N. Kalinkina, *Soviet Phys. JETP* **14**, 1205 (1962). I. N. Kalinkina, *Soviet Phys. JETP* **16**, 1432 (1963).

12. K. P. Belov, *Magnetic Transitions*, Consultants Bureau, New York, 1959.

13. G. H. Wannier, *Elements of Solid State Theory*, Cambridge University Press, Cambridge, 1959, chapter 4. H. Eyring, D. Henderson, B. J. Stover, and E. M. Eyring, *Statistical Mechanics and Dynamics*, Wiley, New York, 1964, chapter 10.

14. J. W. Essam and M. F. Sykes, *Physica* **29**, 378 (1963).

14a. A. R. Miedema, R. F. Wielinga, and W. J. Huiskamp, *Phys. Letters* **17**, 87 (1965). D. T. Teaney, *Phys. Rev. Letters* **14**, 898 (1965).

15. J. A. Hofmann, A. Paskin, K. J. Tauer, and R. J. Weiss, *J. Phys. Chem. Solids* **1**, 45 (1956).

16. C. Domb and A. R. Miedema, *Progr. Low Temp. Phys.* **4**, 296 (1964).

17. A. R. Miedema, H. van Kempen, and W. J. Huiskamp, *Physica* **29**, 1266 (1963).

18. W. K. Robinson and S. A. Friedberg, *Phys. Rev.* **117**, 402 (1960). J. S. Skalyo and S. A. Friedberg, *Phys. Rev. Letters* **13**, 133 (1964).

19. R. J. Benzie and A. H. Cooke, *Proc. Phys. Soc. (London)*, *Ser. A* **63**, 213 (1950).

20. W. F. Giauque, D. N. Lyon, E. W. Hornung, and T. E. Hopkins, *J. Chem. Phys.* **37**, 1446 (1962).

20a. I. Shepherd and G. Feher, *Phys. Rev. Letters* **15**, 194 (1965).

21. H. M. Rosenberg, *Low Temperature Solid State Physics*, Oxford University Press, Oxford, 1963, chapters 1 and 9.

22. J. H. van Vleck, *J. Chem. Phys.* **5**, 320 (1937). M. H. Hebb and E. M. Purcell, *J. Chem. Phys.* **5**, 338 (1937). V. F. Sears, *Proc. Phys. Soc. (London)* **84**, 951 (1964). J. W. Tucker, *Proc. Phys. Soc. (London)* **85**, 559 (1965).

23. J. W. Stout and W. B. Hadley, *J. Chem. Phys.* **40**, 55 (1964).

24. A. H. Cooke, H. Meyer, and W. P. Wolf, *Proc. Roy. Soc. (London)*, *Ser. A* **237**, 404 (1956).

25. O. V. Lounasmaa, *Phys. Rev.* **128**, 1136 (1962). H. van Kempen, A. R. Miedema, and W. J. Huiskamp, *Physica* **30**, 229 (1964).

26. P. H. Keesom and C. A. Bryant, *Phys. Rev. Letters* **2**, 260 (1959). H. R. O'Neal, N. M. Senozan, and N. E. Phillips, *Proceedings of the Eighth International Conference on Low Temperature Physics* (London, 1962, R. O. Davies, ed.), Butterworth, London, 1963. N. E. Phillips, M. H. Lambert, and W. R. Gardner, *Rev. Mod. Phys.* **36**, 131 (1964). J. C. Ho and N. E. Phillips, *Phys. Letters* **10**, 34 (1964).

Chapter 5

Heat Capacity of Liquids

5.1. NATURE OF THE LIQUID STATE

Among the three states of aggregation, solids ⇌ liquids ⇌ gases, less is known about the liquid state than about the other two. To some extent this is not surprising, because the limiting cases of solids and gases are sufficiently clear-cut and simple to allow schematic models to represent their behavior. In gases, the molecules are far apart and have no spatial correlation. In solids, the atoms are arranged in lattice sites. Such situations can be analyzed to a first approximation on the basis of idealized models, perfect gases, or perfect lattices, and these elementary calculations may then be refined, if necessary. The difficulty in developing an adequate theory of the liquid state is that such convenient starting points are not available. Near the freezing point, liquids exhibit many of the characteristics of solids, whereas near the boiling point the behavior of liquids is to some extent similar to that of gases.[1] In liquids, the atomic arrangement in the immediate vicinity of any atom is partially ordered (short-range order), but at great distances the arrangement is completely random (long-range disorder). The absence of long-range order distinguishes a liquid from a solid, while the presence of short-range order differentiates between a liquid and a gas.

The phenomena that occur in a liquid may be described as follows. After melting, the system is no longer crystalline, but each atom still retains much the same relationship to its nearest neighbors as it did in a solid. The thermal energy of vibration of each atom is changed only slightly. In the liquid, rotational motion is possible; furthermore, the atoms can jump from one position to another. The fluidity of a liquid arises because such a jumping process can relax an applied shear stress in a very short time, of the order of 10^{-10} sec; as a matter of fact, at frequencies higher than about 10^{10} cps, liquids do behave like solids in supporting shear waves. As the liquid is

112

warmed, the molecules acquire more freedom of motion and the distance up to which there is short-range order is progressively reduced. This continues until the boiling point is reached, when the molecules are liberated from the liquid lattice at the expense of considerable latent heat.

5.2. SPECIFIC HEAT OF ORDINARY LIQUIDS AND LIQUID MIXTURES

On the basis of the above ideas, one would expect the specific heat to show a small increase on melting, and thereafter in the liquid state it should show a gradual increase until the boiling point is reached. Many liquids do behave in this way. Table 5.I shows the measured specific heat under saturated vapor pressure C_s for some common cryogenic liquids. The gradual increase in C_s up to the boiling point of the liquid is in conformity with the expected behavior.

The specific heat at saturated vapor pressure C_s is the quantity of practical relevance in liquids, since it is more easily measured than C_p or C_v. In Section 8.2 it will be proved that if β is the coefficient of volume expansion, then

$$C_s = C_p - TV\beta\left(\frac{\partial P}{\partial T}\right)_{svp} \tag{5.1}$$

The term $TV\beta(\partial P/\partial T)_{sat}$ increases as the liquid is warmed so that $(C_p - C_s)/C_s$ is about 1% near the melting point and about 25% near the boiling point. Thus in Table 5.I the increase in C_p as the liquid is warmed is somewhat larger than the rise in C_s. The behavior of C_v is not so simple. The difference between C_p and C_v

$$C_p - C_v = \frac{TV\beta^2}{k_T} \tag{5.2}$$

where k_T is the isothermal compressibility [equation (1.14)], and the ratio C_p/C_v both increase with rise in temperature. C_p/C_v may become

Table 5.I. Heat Capacity of Some Cryogenic Liquids (in cal/mole·deg)

Substance	T (degK)	C_p(solid)	C_s(liquid)	T (degK)	C_s(liquid)	C_p(gas)
N_2	63.2	5.7	6.7	77.3	6.9	6.8
O_2	54.4	5.6	6.4	90.2	6.5	6.9
A	83.8	4.2	5.0	87.3	5.1	5.0

as high as 1.5 in some cases. The specific heat at constant volume, as calculated from the measured values of C_s, β, and k_T, increases with temperature near the melting point, reaches a shallow maximum, and then decreases as the boiling point is approached.[2] In the gaseous state, there are no mean positions for the atoms to vibrate, and only free translation and rotation are possible. Under such conditions, C_v becomes about $\frac{5}{2} R$ for gases such as nitrogen and oxygen and $\frac{3}{2} R$ for gases such as argon, as will be seen in the next chapter.

There are some exceptions to the above general behavior. Water, for instance, is an exception to many of the above statements. This most common of all liquids is in many ways the most exceptional one as well.

Although the behavior of liquids is understood qualitatively, there is no satisfactory theory to explain the details. Several approximate models have been proposed with varying degrees of success. Space does not permit an elaboration of these attempts to calculate the properties of liquids.[1,2] Only in the case of quantum liquids, ^{4}He and ^{3}He, has any reasonable theory accounted for the mass of available observations. Since these two unique liquids are almost ubiquitous in cryogenic laboratories, they are treated separately in detail.

Curiously, the special properties of liquid mixtures are somewhat better understood. When two liquids are mixed, the specific heat, density, and other properties of the mixture are slightly different from what may be expected from a mere addition of the contribution due to the parent liquids. Simple thermodynamic and statistical considerations permit correlation of the various excess quantities with one another. There is a considerable physicochemical literature on this subject, and it appears best to consult some of the introductory texts.[2,3]

5.3. LIQUID ^{4}He AT LOW TEMPERATURES

The helium isotope of mass 4 exhibits several bizarre properties in the condensed state. The atoms obey Bose–Einstein statistics, and the liquid becomes a degenerate Bose system below 2.17°K. Helium-four exists as a liquid even at 0°K and becomes a solid only under a pressure of about 25 atm or more. Below 2.17°K, it flows through narrow channels with practically zero viscosity; it can sustain undamped temperature waves; sometimes it creeps in the form of thin films even against gravitational potential; in fact, its unusual behavior has formed a fascinating field of study in its own merit. Rather than do injustice to the subject by trying to summarize the field,[4] we must content ourselves with an account of the caloric properties.

A fundamental step toward an understanding of the behavior of liquid ^{4}He was taken by Landau in 1941. The zero-point energy of the atoms is so large that the substance remains a liquid even at 0°K. In such a quantum region, one cannot identify any single particle and follow its motion. Instead, we should look at the collective behavior of the system as a whole and enumerate the quantum states. This amounts to the formulation of a theory assuming solid-like behavior rather than gas-like, on the grounds that the determining feature of the entire situation is the interaction among all the atoms.

As seen in Chapter 2, the simplest type of thermal excitation possible in a condensed system is a sound wave or a phonon. In a solid, it can be either longitudinal or transverse, but a liquid can support only longitudinal oscillations. The energy $\varepsilon = \hbar\omega$ and the momentum $p = \hbar q$ of a phonon are related by

$$\varepsilon = cp \tag{5.3a}$$

where c is the velocity of sound. A molecule in a liquid is capable of much more complicated motions than mere back-and-forth oscillations. Rotational or vortex motions are simple examples of the more general motions. On the basis of some plausible arguments, Landau assumed for such motions (called *rotons*) the energy-momentum dispersion relation of the form

$$\varepsilon = \Delta + \frac{(p - p_0)^2}{2\mu} \tag{5.3b}$$

This equation has turned out to be so useful in interpreting the behavior of liquid helium that the uncertain foundations on which it was based were rather glossed over for a long time. Recent theoretical work by Feynman and several others has shown that in a Bose system the dispersion relation has the phonon form (5.3a) at low momenta and the roton form (5.3b) at high momenta, so that the complete spectrum has the form shown in Fig. 5.1. Neutron-scattering experiments carried out since 1958 have strikingly confirmed the details of Landau's energy–momentum relationship.[5]

At thermal equilibrium, the excitations in the liquid are distributed mainly in the regions of energy minima, that is, near $\varepsilon = 0$ and $\varepsilon = \varepsilon(p_0) = \Delta$. Thus it is convenient to speak of long-wave excitations (phonons, $p \sim 0$) and short-wave excitations (rotons, $p \sim p_0$) separately, even though the spectrum of Fig. 5.1 is continuous. The thermodynamic properties may then be calculated as phonon and roton contributions. In the following section, this is carried out in a simple manner.

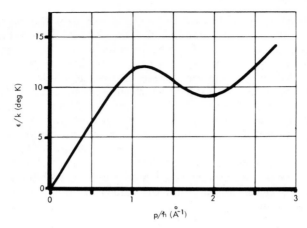

Fig. 5.1. Energy–momentum spectrum in liquid ^{4}He.

The specific heat of liquid ^{4}He has been measured by several investigators,[6] and is shown in Fig. 5.2. This plot immediately exhibits the interesting features of the specific-heat variation. At very low temperatures $(T < 0.6°K)$,, the specific heat is given by $c_s = (0.0205 \pm 0.0004)T^3$ J/g · deg. The T^3-proportionality is reminiscent of the low-temperature behavior of the lattice specific heat and indeed arises from the same reasons, as will be explained in the following section. Above 0.6°K, the specific heat rises faster, somewhat as T^6 or exp $(-10/T)$, culminating in a high narrow peak at the transition temperature 2.17°K. The specific heat drops sharply above this temperature and reaches a value of about $3J/g$ · deg, which is typical of an ordinary liquid at low temperatures. Much above 2.17°K, liquid ^{4}He behaves like an ordinary liquid. It is the curious transition at 2.17°K and the exotic properties below the transition that are responsible for the great interest in the subject.

5.4. PHONON AND ROTON SPECIFIC HEATS

An instructive way of calculating the specific-heat contributions from phonons and rotons is to evaluate first the number of thermal excitations. The number of energy states per mole between momenta p and $p + dp$ is $(4\pi V/h^3)p^2 \, dp$ [equation (2.18)] and the number of Bose excitations in this range is $(4\pi V/h^3)p^2 \, dp/[\exp(\varepsilon/kT) - 1]$. Therefore, the total number of excitations N and the total energy

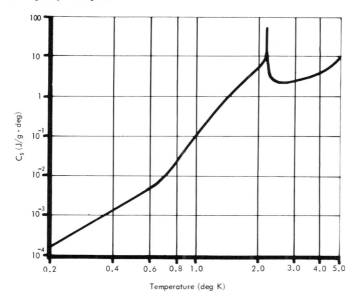

Fig. 5.2. Specific heat of liquid ^{4}He under its saturated vapor pressure.[6]

E per mole are

$$N = \frac{4\pi V}{h^3} \int \frac{p^2 \, dp}{\exp(\varepsilon/kT) - 1} \tag{5.4a}$$

$$E = \frac{4\pi V}{h^3} \int \frac{\varepsilon p^2 \, dp}{\exp(\varepsilon/kT) - 1} \tag{5.4b}$$

Consider first the case of phonons $\varepsilon = cp$. The situation is the same as that occurring in the Debye theory of lattice heat capacity except that only longitudinal phonons are possible in the liquid state. The Debye temperature in the helium problem, obtained as usual by terminating $g(v)$ at v_D, is

$$\theta = \frac{hc}{2\pi k}\left(\frac{18\pi^2 \rho}{m_{He}}\right)^{1/3} \tag{5.5}$$

and has a value of about 30°K. Therefore, regions up to 2°K may be considered as the Debye T^3-region. In this low-temperature region no serious error is made in extending to infinity the integration in equation (5.4) over p/kT, and hence per mole

$$N_{phon} = \frac{4\pi V}{h^3}\left(\frac{kT}{c}\right)^3 \int_0^\infty \frac{x^2\,dx}{e^x - 1} = \frac{4\pi V}{h^3}\left(\frac{kT}{c}\right)^3 \times 2.404 \qquad (5.6)$$

$$E_{phon} = \frac{4\pi Vc}{h^3}\left(\frac{kT}{c}\right)^4 \int_0^\infty \frac{x^3\,dx}{e^x - 1} = \frac{4\pi Vc}{h^3}\left(\frac{kT}{c}\right)^4 \times \frac{\pi^4}{15} \qquad (5.7)$$

The corresponding specific heat per gram is

$$c_{phon} = \frac{16\pi^5 k^4}{15 h^3 c^3 \rho} T^3 \qquad (5.8)$$

For rotons, $\varepsilon = \Delta + (p - p_0)^2/2\mu$. In practice, Δ/k is found to have a value of about $10°K$; therefore, nothing is lost by using the simpler Maxwell–Boltzmann statistics, so that

$$N_{rot} = \frac{4\pi V}{h^3}\int p^2\,dp \exp\left\{\frac{-[\Delta + (p - p_0)^2/2\mu]}{kT}\right\}$$

Further, the parameter p_0 in the helium problem is found to be much greater than μkT, so that in the integration over dp the quantity p^2 may be replaced by p_0^2. Moreover, because of the rapid reduction of the exponential factor for large values of $p - p_0$, the integration may be performed over $p - p_0$ from $-\infty$ to ∞. Thus per mole

$$N_{rot} = \frac{4\pi V}{h^3}p_0^2 e^{-\Delta/kT}\int_{-\infty}^\infty e^{-x^2/2\mu kT}dx = \frac{4\pi V p_0^2}{h^3}(2\pi\mu kT)^{1/2}\, e^{-\Delta/kT} \quad (5.9)$$

A similar calculation gives the specific heat per gram as

$$c_{rot} = \frac{4\pi}{\rho h^3}\left(\frac{2\pi\mu}{kT^3}\right)^{1/2} p_0^2\Delta^2\left[1 + \frac{kT}{\Delta} + \tfrac{3}{4}\left(\frac{kT}{\Delta}\right)^2\right]e^{-\Delta/kT} \qquad (5.10)$$

The temperature dependence of the roton part of the thermodynamic quantities is basically of the form $\exp(-\Delta/kT)$. This is a consequence of the finite energy gap Δ and the need for the Boltzmann-type excitation across the gap [compare equations (2.10) and (4.26)]. The number of phonons is proportional to T^3, and a numerical estimate shows that below $0.6°K$, practically all the excitations are of the phonon type. Around $0.7°K$, the number of rotons overtakes the number of phonons; at temperatures above about $1°K$, most of the excitations are of the roton type. Figures 5.2 and 5.3 show how the specific heat follows the gradual transition in the nature of the thermal excitations.

The phonon-type behavior at low temperatures is similar to the Debye T^3-region discussed in Chapter 2. As a matter of fact, if only

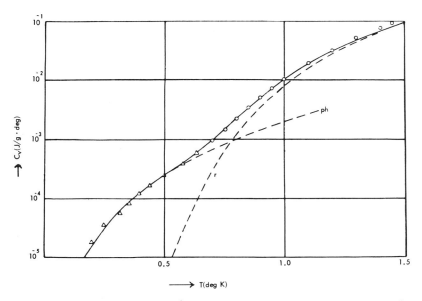

Fig. 5.3. Specific heat of liquid ^{4}He showing phonon and roton contributions.[7]

longitudinal phonons are present, equations (2.13) and (2.20) become

$$\theta = \frac{hc}{k}\left(\frac{9N}{4\pi V}\right)^{1/3}$$

$$C_v = \tfrac{16}{15}\frac{\pi^5 k^4 V}{c^3 h^3}T^3$$

and they are similar to equations (5.5) and (5.8). The velocity of sound in liquid ^{4}He at low temperatures is 239 ± 2 M/sec. Equation (5.8) now gives $c_{\text{phon}} = (0.0204 \pm 0.0005)T^3$ J/g · deg, which is to be compared with the experimental value $c_v = (0.0205 \pm 0.0004)T^3$ mentioned earlier. The excellent agreement provides strong support for the above picture of thermal excitations in liquid ^{4}He at low temperatures.

Above $0.6°$K, the roton contribution becomes significant; up to about $1.6°$K, the specific heat can be accurately fitted by the addition of phonon and roton contributions. In 1947, Landau calculated the values of Δ, p_0, and μ from such an analysis of specific-heat data (which at that time were not known with any great accuracy). A similar analysis was performed by Kramers and coworkers in 1956,

Table 5.II. Comparison of the Values of Δ, p_0, and μ

	$\dfrac{\Delta}{k}(\deg K)$	$\dfrac{p_0}{\hbar}(\text{Å}^{-1})$	$\dfrac{\mu}{m_{^4He}}$
Calorimetry			
Landau (1947)	9.6	2.0	0.77
Kramers (1956)	8.8 ± 0.1	1.96 ± 0.05	0.23 ± 0.1
Neutron scattering			
1.1°K	8.65 ± 0.04	1.92 ± 0.01	0.16 ± 0.01

using carefully determined values of specific heats. In Table 5.II the numerical values of Δ, p_0, and μ are compared with the results of neutron-scattering experiments in which the energy–momentum dispersion relation[5] was studied directly. The close agreement between the values must be taken as a striking vindication of Landau's calculation of the properties of liquid ^{4}He on the basis of the special ε–p relation (5.3).

Above 1.6°K, the number of rotons becomes so large that it is no longer possible to neglect the interactions among the excitations. (The analogy in the case of solids is the anharmonicity of lattice vibrations.) The neutron-scattering experiments show that the parameter Δ changes slightly because of the interactions among the rotons. Taking into account the small temperature dependence of the parameters and also using the full ε–p curve, the Los Alamos group of workers[8] has calculated the specific heats and find excellent agreement over the whole temperature range up to 2°K.

Finally, it must be added that the above picture of a gas of phonon and roton excitations accounts satisfactorily for a number of other properties of liquid ^{4}He. A full account is given in the works cited earlier.[4,5]

5.5. TRANSITION IN LIQUID ^{4}He

It was the specific-heat measurement by Keesom and coworkers in 1932 that gave a definite indication of the special phase change in liquid helium at 2.17°K. There is a sharp peak at 2.17°K, and the shape of the curve (Fig. 5.2) resembles the Greek letter lambda (λ). Phase transitions in which there is a similar sharp λ-peak in the specific heat are now commonly called *lambda-transitions*; they are the result of cooperative effects in the system. A few other λ-anomalies will be discussed in Chapter 7, while the thermodynamics of such phase changes is taken up in Chapter 8.

The characteristic feature of the λ-transitions in liquids and solids is the appearance of a sharp peak in the specific heat (and hence calorimetric measurements are frequently used to detect such transitions). It is obviously of interest to know whether the peak is a sharp maximum or really an infinite singularity with $\int C\, dT$ still remaining finite. The question assumes fundamental importance in the theoretical understanding of such transitions. On the one hand, approximate statistical calculations on reasonable models of substances predict a finite maximum at the transition T_λ, the peak being rounded off in a temperature interval of about 10^{-3}°K near T_λ in some calculations and there being a jump in the specific heat in other theories. On the other hand, exact calculations on highly simplified models predict that the specific heat has a logarithmic or other infinity, i.e., of the form $C \approx$ constant $\times \log|T_\lambda - T|$ near T_λ (see Section 4.6). No reliable guidance could be obtained from experiments on solids, owing to the difficulty of keeping the temperature constant throughout the specimen to within about 10^{-6}°K. Fairbank, Buckingham, and Kellers[9] realized that a temperature resolution of about 10^{-6}°K was possible in liquid helium. It was also pointed out in the *Introduction* that thermal equilibrium occurs very quickly, in a few seconds at temperatures below around 4°K. These workers placed the liquid in intimate contact with copper fins and succeeded in measuring the specific heat to within a microdegree of the λ-point.

In order to exhibit the nature of the specific heat very near $T_\lambda = 2.17$°K, the results are shown on successively expanded temperature scales in Fig. 5.4. The very large amount of expansion of each successive curve is vividly demonstrated by the fact that the width of the small vertical line directly above the origin indicates the fraction of the curve which is shown enlarged in the next curve on the right. The specific-heat curve maintains the same geometrical shape on all the expanded scales, and clearly there is no indication of any rounded maximum within 10^{-4}°K of T_λ, as suggested by some approximate theories. There was also no hysteresis between the values measured with increasing and decreasing temperatures.

The same data are plotted on a logarithmic scale in Fig. 5.5. On both sides of the λ-point the data fall in two parallel straight lines over a factor of 10^4 in $|T - T_\lambda|$. The observations (in J/g·degK) near the λ-point are well fitted by the equation

$$c = 4.55 - 3.00 \log_{10}|T - T_\lambda| - 5.20\delta \qquad (5.11)$$

where $\delta = 0$ for $T < T_\lambda$ and $\delta = 1$ for $T > T_\lambda$. The inclusion of a logarithmic term permits a simple representation of the specific heat

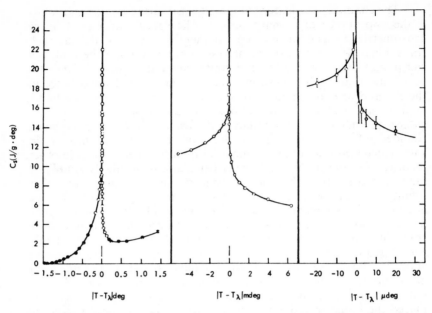

Fig. 5.4. Specific heat of liquid ⁴He near the λ-point.[9] The solid lines represent
equations (5.11) and (5.12). The width of the small line above the origin indicates the
fraction of the curve which is expanded in the next figure on the right.

in joules per gram of liquid helium up to about 3.5°K:

$$c = c_D(T) + [130 - 90.9 \log |T - T_\lambda|] \exp\left(\frac{-7.40}{T}\right) \qquad T < T_\lambda$$

$$= c_D(T) + [23.5 - 16.4 \log |T - T_\lambda|] \exp\left(\frac{-3.70}{T}\right) \qquad T > T_\lambda$$

(5.12)

where $c_D(T)$ represents the Debye function, evaluated at each temperature with the appropriate value of density and velocity of sound.

Besides the specific heat, the thermal expansion coefficient also
shows a logarithmic infinity as the λ-point is approached, although
measurements have been performed up to $|T - T_\lambda| \approx 10^{-4}°K$ only.
It will be seen in Section 8.1 that the behaviors of the two quantities
are interconnected and that

$$\left(\frac{T_\lambda}{T}\right) C_p = T_\lambda \left(\frac{\partial S}{\partial T}\right)_\lambda - \frac{T_\lambda}{\rho_\lambda} \left(\frac{\rho_\lambda}{\rho}\right) \left(\frac{\partial P}{\partial T}\right)_\lambda \beta$$

(5.13)

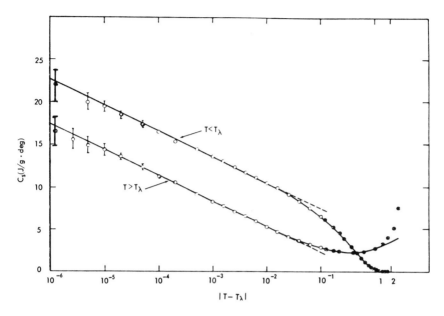

Fig. 5.5. Specific heat of liquid helium versus $\log |T - T_\lambda|$.[9] Solid lines represent equations (5.11) and (5.12).

Figure 5.6 shows a parametric plot of the specific heat and the expansion coefficient.[9] The straight line is the asymptotic value given by equation (5.13) with the experimental values of the various other quantities. The tendency of the observations to attain the limiting value is clear. Thus we must conclude that both the expansion coefficient and the specific heat are consistent with an infinite logarithmic singularity at T_λ.

At present, there is no complete theory of cooperative transitions. In special cases, as with magnetic transitions treated in Section 4.6, much progress has been made in expressing the thermodynamic quantities in powers of $|T - T_\lambda|$. The outstanding observation of a logarithmic singularity in C_p and β is an experimental property which must be explained by any proper statistical theory.

5.6. SPECIFIC HEAT OF LIQUID ^{3}He

The ordinary liquid helium used in bulk is the isotope of mass 4. The isotope ^{3}He is present to about 1 part in 10^7 in natural helium. However, since 1948, small quantities of ^{3}He, produced by nuclear

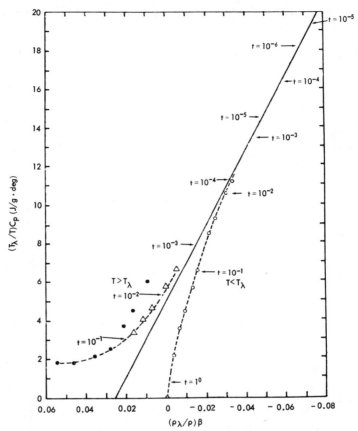

Fig. 5.6. Cylindrical approximation near T_λ.[9] Parametric plot of $(T_\lambda/T)C_p$ versus $(\rho_\lambda/\rho)\beta$. Full line is the calculated asymptotic value.

reactions, have been available for research, and its use in cooling cryostats to approximately 0.3°K was mentioned in Chapter 1. Helium-three exists as a liquid even at 0°K and becomes a solid only under a pressure of about 30 atm or more. It obeys Fermi–Dirac statistics, and the properties of liquid ^{3}He are quite different from those of ^{4}He. The experimental and theoretical evidence unequivocally points out that liquid ^{3}He must be considered a Fermi system, whereas the superfluid properties of liquid ^{4}He arise from the Bose–Einstein condensation.[5] Since ^{3}He offers the possibility of studying a simple Fermi liquid, it has of late become the subject of an active field of study.[10,11]

The equations derived in Chapter 3 for an ideal Fermi–Dirac gas were initially considered as a convenient framework for describing the properties of liquid ^{3}He. For a F–D gas, the degeneracy temperature is

$$T_F = \frac{1}{2mk}\left(\frac{3}{8}\frac{Nh^3}{\pi V}\right)^{2/3} \tag{5.14}$$

which for the density of liquid ^{3}He has a value of about 5°K. Early measurements of nuclear susceptibility showed that χT was constant down to about 1.5°K, and the deviations at lower temperatures could be fitted to a perfect-gas model with a degeneracy temperature of about 0.5°K, nearly ten times smaller than the expected value. In a simple-minded way, this could be explained by saying that the effective mass m^* is about ten times the mass of the ^{3}He atom. The measurements[12] of specific heat above 0.5°K destroyed this naïve

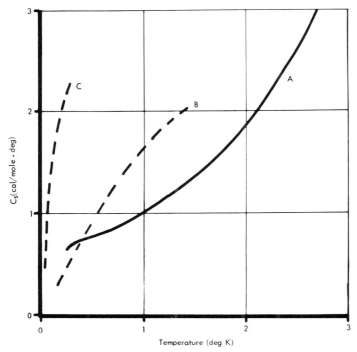

Fig. 5.7. Heat capacity of liquid ^{3}He under its saturated vapor pressure (curve A).[12] Curve B is the specific heat of F–D gas with $T_F = 5.0$°K and curve C is that with $T_F = 0.5$°K.

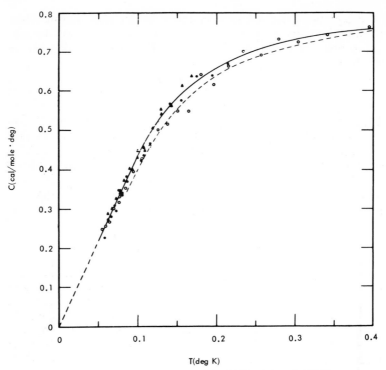

T(deg K)

Fig. 5.8. Heat capacity of liquid ^{3}He below 0.4°K.[14]

picture. The specific heat does not resemble, even qualitatively, the behavior of an ideal F–D gas with any value of m^*. Figure 5.7 compares the specific heats of a F–D gas having $T_F = 5.0$ or 0.5°K with the experimental results. (Strictly, C_v should be compared instead of C_{sat}, but this does not improve matters. In fact, the deviations of C_v are equally serious.[13])

Below 0.2°K, the specific heat of the liquid does vary proportionally with T, as may be expected from the F–D gas relationship:

$$C_v = \frac{4\pi^3 mk^2}{3h^2}\left(\frac{3NV^2}{\pi}\right)^{1/3} T \qquad (5.15)$$

Any satisfaction at such simple behavior is, however, short-lived.

The F–D theory also shows that if γ_0 is the magnetic moment per atom, the molar susceptibility χ should tend to the value

$$\frac{\chi}{V} = \frac{4\pi m \gamma_0}{h^2}\left(\frac{3N}{\pi V}\right)^{1/3} \tag{5.16}$$

This functional relationship is obeyed very well, but quantitatively the agreement is very poor. The $m^*/m_{^3He}$ calculated from the specific-data has a value of about 2, that from susceptibility is about 10, from compressibility data about 0.3, and so on. In other words, even though the F–D gas formulas give the correct temperature dependence at very low temperatures ($\ll 0.3°K$), the observations are not consistent with the quantitative interrelationships among the various formulas.

5.7. LIQUID ^{3}He AS A FERMI LIQUID

A solution to this dilemma at very low temperatures was suggested in 1956 by Landau; since then, the microscopic foundations of such theories have been intensely studied by Brueckner and others.[5,11] According to Landau's theory of a Fermi liquid, the presence of strong interactions among the atoms renders a description of the behavior of single particles meaningless and the statistical behavior is determined by the elementary excitations of the whole system. These excitations or quasiparticles obey Fermi–Dirac statistics and may be taken as an effective description of an atom together with its polarization field caused by the correlated interactions. At low temperatures, the system may be visualized as made up of N quasiparticles of effective mass m^*, but in calculating any physical property the fundamental quantity to be considered is the interaction function. Thus, in calculating the magnetic susceptibility, we must consider the dependence of the interaction function upon the nuclear orientations. In compressibility, the volume dependence of the interactions is involved. The specific heat is determined by the density of states at the Fermi level, and so on.

Detailed calculations show that the specific heat is given by equation (5.15) with m^* instead of m. Therefore, from the experimental data, we can conclude that $m^*/m_{^3He} \approx 2$. The expression for susceptibility involves besides m^* the constants of the spin-dependent part of the interaction function. Thus a calculation of m^* using (5.16) will not give the same effective mass as that calculated from specific-heat data. In this manner, the Fermi-liquid theory gives different interrelationships among the various properties of liquid ^{3}He, although the temperature dependence is in many cases the same as that given by the F–D gas calculations. The details of the theory are unfortunately very complicated, and the mathematical techniques used in these many-body problems are not commonly known. Hence, it seems best to suggest suitable reviews[5,15] for those interested rather than give a garbled version of the theory here. On the whole, the Fermi-liquid theory of the behavior of liquid ^{3}He below 0.2°K appears to be in reasonable accord with the experiments.

The situation at higher temperatures ($T > 0.5°$K) is not very satisfactory. As seen from Fig. 5.7, the curve bears no resemblance to the variation expected for a F–D gas. A heuristic approach[13] has been to assume that the alignment of the nuclear spins gives a spin contribution (similar to the Schottky term discussed in Section 4.9) with a peak around 0.3°K and that at high temperatures there are contributions from excitations not dependent upon the quantum statistics of the atoms. Such calculations have had quite some success in explaining thermal and magnetic properties. However, the concept of splitting the entropy into such contributions has been questioned by others as having no fundamental justification. Further, nothing is said about the origin of the assumed high-temperature contribution, which is independent of the statistics.[11] On account of these factors, the calculations are not here discussed in any detail.

The electrons in a metal form another example of an interacting Fermi system, which has already been considered in Chapter 3. Several authors have conjectured that a phenomenon analogous to superconductivity of the electronic system (Sections 3.8 to 3.10) should occur in liquid ^{3}He, also. The transition temperature cannot be calculated precisely, but is estimated to be approximately $10^{-3}°$K, if not lower. One of the characteristics of the transition, which has been reviewed by Sessler[5,10], for example, is that the specific heat should exhibit an anomaly (Fig. 5.9) similar to the anomaly at the superconducting transition (Fig. 3.11). As mentioned earlier, phase transitions are best detected by specific-heat measurements, and so calorimetric measurements are being made to as low a temperature as possible. At the time of writing, Peshkov[16] has reported a small bump at 0.0055°K. Above $8 \times 10^{-3}°$K, the specific heat increases linearly with T (Fig. 5.8), the value being given by $C_{\text{sat}} \approx 20T$ J/mole·deg. The evidence is not quite conclusive,[17] but Peshkov's observations will constitute the discovery of an eagerly sought phase transition in liquid ^{3}He—of course, by specific-heat studies!

One question which cannot be answered here is why although sound waves can be propagated through liquid ^{3}He as through any

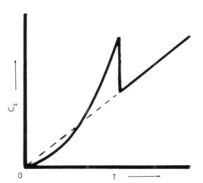

Fig. 5.9. Predicted specific heat of the superphase of liquid ^{3}He.

other system, phonon terms are not included in the specific heat of liquid ^{3}He. The answer lies deeply involved in quantum statistics.[18] Phonon-type thermal excitations obey Bose–Einstein statistics, whereas the system of ^{3}He atoms obeys Fermi–Dirac statistics.

5.8. MIXTURES OF ^{4}He AND ^{3}He

Liquid ^{4}He and ^{3}He are completely miscible, except at low temperatures, where phase separation occurs for a range of concentrations. It has already been mentioned that the properties of mixtures are of considerable interest in chemical thermodynamics.[2,3] In the helium case, since the two pure liquids exhibit peculiar properties of their own, a study of the mixtures has special significance in quantum statistics.[19]

Although considerations of space prohibit a detailed account of the various studies,[10,20] one interesting result is worth mentioning. Taconis, Beenakker, and de Bruyn Ouboter[5] have found that for dilute mixtures of ^{3}He in liquid ^{4}He, the specific heat at low temperatures ($<1°K$) is nearly constant and equal to $\frac{3}{2}Rx$ per mole of the mixture where x is the mole fraction of ^{3}He. This may be explained simply on the basis of an idea put forward by Pomeranchuk that in dilute solutions the ^{3}He atoms do not interact with the superfluid ^{4}He, and so form a gas of excitations. At low concentrations, the ^{3}He atoms may be taken as nondegenerate and so will have a perfect-gas specific heat $C_v = \frac{3}{2}R$ per mole (as will be explained in Chapter 6). Therefore, the excess specific heat of the solution will be $\frac{3}{2}Rx$ per mole of the mixture. Other properties, such as the velocity of sound, confirm this simple picture of the role of ^{3}He atoms.

5.9. SUPERCOOLED LIQUIDS—GLASSES

When a liquid is cooled ordinarily, it solidifies into a crystalline state at its normal freezing point; however, some substances can be supercooled. A classic example is glycerine, which can be easily cooled below its normal freezing point of about 290°K. With some care in avoiding nucleation, the supercooled liquid can be taken right down to approximately 0°K without any crystallization. At about $T_g \sim 180°$K, the behavior of glycerine changes from a liquid-like fluidity above T_g to a solid-like rigidity below T_g. The free energy of this solid is greater than that of the crystalline solid, but it represents a metastable thermodynamic state which can exist indefinitely under certain conditions. This highly supercooled liquid state is typical of most glasses; hence it is called the *glassy state*. The situation is thermodynamically the same with allotropes such as diamond, a metastable form of carbon.

The specific heat of glycerol has been measured by several workers and is summarized in the review on the glassy state by Davies and Jones.[21] The heat capacity of the crystalline state [curve (a) in Fig. 5.10] is due to the vibrations of the molecules in the lattice, as analyzed in Chapter 2. The specific heat of the supercooled liquid [curve (b)] is considerably greater because of the additional complex motions possible in the liquid state. However, over a narrow interval of temperature around $T_g \sim 180°$K, the specific heat falls rapidly to a value just above that of the crystalline solid. Only a small difference persists at lower temperatures. Similar marked decrease around T_g is shown in the thermal-expansion coefficient, electrical conductivity, and other properties. It is an important characteristic of supercooled liquids that the viscosity increases by several orders of magnitude as the temperature is lowered through the transition region. In glycerine, it increases from about 10^6 poise at 190°K to about 10^{13} poise at 170°K. Thus at about 170°K, the stress applied to maintain a strain relaxes to $1/e$ of its initial value in hours, compared to 10^{-3} sec at about 190°K, so that for practical purposes the substance behaves like a solid. Above T_g, the molecules have all the mobility characteristic of liquids, but below T_g they cannot change their configurations in any reasonable amount of time; the only other modes of motion are the lattice vibrations about their mean positions, as in a solid. This is the reason why the specific heat decreases sharply in the transition region.

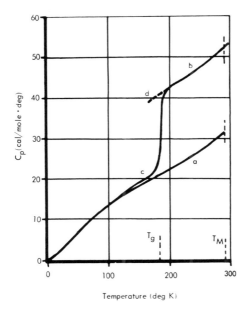

Fig. 5.10. Measured heat capacity of glycerine:
(a) crystalline solid, (b) supercooled liquid,
(c) glassy state, (d) very slowly cooled liquid.

However, the glassy state is not a crystalline state. The viscosity increases so rapidly as the substance is cooled through T_g that the spatial disorder of the liquid has been abruptly "frozen-in." X-ray diffraction studies[22] confirm the molecular disorder in the glassy state. An interesting check is the calculation of the entropy difference between the supercooled glass and the crystalline state (Fig. 5.11). At the melting point, the entropy difference, obtained from the latent heat, is about 15 cal/mole·deg, but below T_g a difference of about 5 units persists right down to 0°K. This is a measure of the configurational entropy of glass which is "frozen-in" at T_g. The persistence of such an entropy difference at 0°K is not really a contradiction of the third law of thermodynamics,[23] because the glassy state is not one of stable internal equilibrium. Suitable nucleation can precipitate a crystallization of the whole system (devitrification of glass). Figure 5.11 shows that above T_g the difference in entropy between the supercooled liquid and the crystal decreases rapidly with lowering temperature. At T_g, however, the liquid

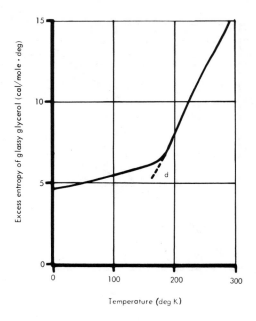

Fig. 5.11. Excess entropy of the glassy solid
over the crystalline state (full line). Curve d
shows the excess entropy if the liquid is cooled
very slowly at T_g.

becomes so viscous that configurational changes to lower the entropy
do not take place in short periods of time. Oblad and Newton showed
experimentally that if glycerine is kept undisturbed for a long time
before the measurement is made at any temperature, the specific-heat
curve appears as a smooth extension of the behavior above T_g [broken
curves (d) in Figs. 5.10 and 5.11]. This shows clearly that if sufficient
time (a whole week of undisturbed waiting just a few degrees below
T_g) is allowed, molecular rearrangements do take place. Because of
the experimental difficulties, measurements could be made to only a
few degrees below T_g. Nevertheless, an inspection of Fig. 5.11 shows
that the entropy difference will undoubtedly extrapolate to zero at
$0°K$. If a liquid can exist in internal equilibrium, such as liquid ^4He
and ^3He, its entropy will vanish at absolute zero.

The entropy difference between crystalline and glassy states is
similar to the problem of entropy differences between the various

allotropes of some solids. Materials such as sulfur, tin, and carbon exist in different crystalline states with different specific heats. An investigation of the entropy differences among them was originally used by Nernst and coworkers to check the validity of the third law of thermodynamics. With crystalline solids, it is, of course, possible to calculate the vibrational specific heats from suitable theoretical models.[24]

Numerical values of the specific heat of glasses are of importance in practice, and Stevels[22] has collected the data for a variety of glasses. Some cases of cryogenic interest are mentioned in Table 8.I.

REFERENCES

1. J. Frenkel, *Kinetic Theory of Liquids,* Dover, New York, 1954.
2. J. S. Rowlinson, *Liquids and Liquid Mixtures*, Butterworth, London, 1959.
3. E. A. Guggenheim, *Mixtures*, Clarendon, Oxford, 1952.
4. K. Mendelssohn, *Handbuch der Physik*, XV (2), 370 (1956). J. Wilks, *Rept. Progr. Phys.* **20**, 38 (1957). K. R. Atkins, *Liquid Helium*, Cambridge University Press, Cambridge, 1957.
5. *Liquid Helium, Proceedings of the International Summer School "Enrico Fermi,"* (Varenna, 1961, G. Careri, ed.), Academic, New York, 1963. J. Wilks, *Liquid Helium*, Clarendon, Oxford, 1966.
6. H. C. Kramers, J. Wasscher, and C. J. Gorter, *Physica* **18**, 329 (1952). R. W. Hill and O. V. Lounasmaa, *Phil. Mag.* **2**, 143 (1957). J. Wiebes, C. G. Niels-Hakkenberg, and H. C. Kramers, *Physica* **23**, 625 (1957).
7. H. C. Kramers, *Progr. Low Temp. Phys.* **2**, 59 (1957).
8. P. J. Bendt, R. D. Cowan, and J. L. Yarnell, *Phys. Rev.* **113**, 1386 (1959).
9. M. J. Buckingham and W. M. Fairbank, *Progr. Low Temp. Phys.* **3**, 80 (1961).
10. J. C. Daunt (ed.), *Helium Three*, Ohio State University Press, Columbus, 1960.
11. E. R. Grilly and E. F. Hammel, *Progr. Low Temp. Phys.* **3**, 113 (1961). N. Bernades and D. F. Brewer, *Rev. Mod. Phys.* **34**, 190 (1962). D. F. Brewer, *Progr. Cryogenics* **4**, 25 (1964).
12. G. de Vries and J. G. Daunt, *Phys. Rev.* **92**, 1572 (1953); **93**, 631 (1954). T. R. Roberts and S. G. Sydoriak, *Phys. Rev.* **93**, 1418 (1954). D. W. Osborne, B. M. Abraham, and B. Weinstock, *Phys. Rev.* **94**, 202 (1954).
13. L. Goldstein, *Phys. Rev.* **112**, 1465 (1958).
14. D. F. Brewer, J. G. Daunt, and A. K. Sreedhar, *Phys. Rev.* **115**, 836 (1959). M. Strongin, G. O. Zimmerman, and H. A. Fairbank, *Phys. Rev. Letters*, **6**, 404 (1961). A. C. Anderson, G. F. Salinger, W. A. Steyert, and J. C. Wheatley, *Phys. Rev. Letters* **7**, 295 (1961).
15. A. A. Abrikosov and I. M. Khalatnikov, *Rept. Progr. Phys.* **22**, 329 (1959).
16. V. P. Peshkov, *Soviet Phys. JETP* **19**, 1023 (1964).
17. E. S. R. Gopal, *J. Sci. Indus. Res.* **23**, 496 (1964). W. R. Abel, A. C. Anderson, W. C. Black, and J. C. Wheatley, *Phys. Rev. Letters* **14**, 129 (1965).
18. K. Huang, *Statistical Mechanics,* Wiley, New York, 1963, pp.262, 384.
19. I. Prigogine, A. Bellemans, and V. Mathot, *Molecular Theory of Solutions,* North Holland, Amsterdam, 1957, chapters 18 and 19.
20. J. J. M. Beenakker and K. W. Taconis, *Progr. Low Temp. Phys.* **1**, 108 (1955). K. W. Taconis and R. de Bruyn Ouboter, *Progr. Low Temp. Phys.* **4**, 38 (1964).

21. R. O. Davies and G. O. Jones, *Advan. Phys.* **2**, 370 (1953).
22. J. M. Stevels, *Handbuch der Physik, XIII,* 510 (1962).
23. J. Wilks, *Third Law of Thermodynamics,* Oxford University Press, Oxford, 1961, chapter 5.
24. F. Seitz, *Modern Theory of Solids,* McGraw-Hill, New York, 1940, chapter 14.

Chapter 6

Specific Heats of Gases

6.1. C_p AND C_v OF A GAS

The heat capacity of a gas depends strongly upon the conditions under which heating is done, whether at constant pressure or at constant volume. Indeed, it was pointed out in Chapter 1 that the ratio C_p/C_v is as high as 1.67 for a monatomic gas. It is possible to measure directly both C_p and C_v in gases and vapors, and a representative list[1] of the values at 300°K is given in Table 6.I. The specific heats refer to the "ideal" state of a gas at zero pressure and are calculated from the values at higher pressures by using a knowledge of the equation of state [see equation (1.17)]. Typically, at a pressure of 1 atm, C_p and C_v are higher than the "ideal" values by less than 1% in the so-called permanent gases and by about 1 to 2% in organic vapors.

The specific heat per gram is different for different gases. For heavy gases, the value of C_v is small, and for light gases, C_v is large.

Table 6.I. Molar Heat Capacities (in cal/mole·deg) at 300°K and $P = 0$ atm

	Gas								
	He	A	H_2	N_2	O_2	CO	NO	HCl	Cl_2
C_p	4.97	4.97	6.85	6.94	7.02	6.96	7.08	6.97	8.02
C_v	2.98	2.98	4.86	4.96	5.03	4.97	5.10	4.98	6.02
$C_p - C_v$	1.99	1.99	1.99	1.98	1.99	1.99	1.98	1.99	2.00
	CO_2	N_2O	SO_2	H_2S	NH_3	CH_4	C_2H_2	C_2H_4	C_2H_6
C_p	8.77	9.25	9.20	8.15	8.49	8.48	10.35	10.15	12.25
C_v	6.78	7.27	7.20	6.15	6.50	6.49	8.35	8.15	10.25
$C_p - C_v$	1.99	1.98	2.00	2.00	1.99	1.99	2.00	2.00	2.00

The consideration of molar heat capacities provides a great simplification: C_v turns out to be about 3 cal/mole·deg for monatomic gases (such as helium and argon) and about 5 cal/mole·deg for diatomic gases (such as H_2, N_2, O_2, CO, NO, HCl). $C_p - C_v$ is approximately equal in all cases to 2 cal/mole·deg. When it is recalled that the gas constant R has a value 1.987 in the same units, the difference between C_p and C_v is nothing other than equation (1.13):

$$C_p - C_v = R$$

a relation first used by Mayer in 1842. Since the natural unit for the molar heat capacity is R, the striking feature of Table 6.I, demanding an immediate explanation, is that $C_v \sim \frac{3}{2}R$ for monatomic gases and $C_v \sim \frac{5}{2}R$ for diatomic gases.

6.2. CLASSICAL THEORY OF C_v OF GASES

Boltzmann's equipartition theorem is able to provide an explanation for the simple coefficients $\frac{3}{2}$ and $\frac{5}{2}$. This theorem, as explained in Section 2.2, connects the internal energy of a system with its number of degrees of freedom (that is, the number of squared terms in the Hamiltonian function, which is the same as the number of independent coordinates required to describe the motion of the system). Each degree of freedom contributes $\frac{1}{2}RT$ to the internal energy of a mole of the substance at thermal equilibrium. A mass point is a good model of the atoms in a monatomic gas. It has three translational degrees of freedom (Hamiltonian $(p_x^2 + p_y^2 + p_z^2)/2m$ where the p are the momenta of the molecules). Therefore, the internal energy is $E = 3 \times \frac{1}{2}RT$ and $C_v = \partial E/\partial T = \frac{3}{2}R$, as is found to be the case. The molecules of a diatomic gas may be represented by a pair of masses rigidly connected together, i.e., a rigid dumbell. Then, besides having the three translatory motions, the molecules can rotate about any pair of directions perpendicular to its axis. There are altogether five degrees of freedom; consequently, $E = \frac{5}{2}RT$ and $C_v = \frac{5}{2}R$. Thus the specific heats of permanent gases are readily understood in classical statistics.

A closer study of Table 6.I reveals, however, that this agreement between the equipartition law and the observed values is only limited. A linear triatomic molecule, such as CO_2 or N_2O, should behave like a diatomic molecule, because it can rotate only about the directions perpendicular to its axis. Therefore, C_v should be $\frac{5}{2}R$, whereas the actual values for CO_2 and N_2O exceed $\frac{5}{2}R$ quite significantly. A general polyatomic molecule which can rotate about all three principal axes should have $C_v = \frac{6}{2}R$, which is also not the case. Even a diatomic molecule such as chlorine exceeds its equipartition value of $C_v = \frac{5}{2}R$.

The discrepancy is partly due to the fact that the molecules can have internal vibrations. Each mode of vibration has two square terms in the Hamiltonian, one for kinetic and one for potential energy, and so counts as two degrees of freedom. A diatomic molecule has one vibrational frequency, and a general polyatomic molecule has $3n - 6$ vibrational modes. If the vibrational contributions are added, $C_v = \frac{7}{2}R \sim 7$ cal/mole·deg for diatomic gases and $C_v = 3(n - 1)R$ for polyatomic gases. (If the molecules of a polyatomic gas are linear, there are only $3n - 5$ vibrations, and C_v is correspondingly less.) The specific heats in Table 6.I are all less than this value. The vibrational heat capacity of polyatomic gases (and of chlorine) falls short of this equipartition value. Experiments made at higher temperatures (Table 6.II) revealed that at 2000°C H_2O, CO_2, and SO_2 attain their equipartition value of $3(n - 1)R \sim 12$ cal/mole·deg, while N_2, O_2, HCl, CO, and H_2 are obviously moving toward their value of approximately 7 cal/mole·deg. (Chlorine exceeds the equipartition value because of anharmonicity and dissociation[1,2], both of which are not considered in this elementary account.)

Measurements at low temperatures revealed another shortcoming of the classical theory. Eucken, as early as 1905, noticed that the heat capacity of hydrogen at liquid-nitrogen temperatures was significantly lower than the room-temperature value. Table 6.III shows that C_v has become equal to about $\frac{3}{2}R$ below about 60°K. C_p decreases by the same amount (recall $C_p - C_v = R$), and the ratio C_p/C_v goes from 1.40 at room temperature to 1.67 at 50°K. The values below 60°K are typical of a monatomic gas, for which only translational degrees of freedom are possible.

The equipartition law provides no reasonable explanation for the observation that at low temperatures the vibrational and rotational degrees of freedom remain "frozen in" and begin to "thaw out" as the temperature is raised. The clarification came from the application

Table 6.II. C_v at High Temperatures (in cal/mole·deg)

Temperature (deg C)	Gas					
	A	N_2, O_2, HCl, CO	H_2	Cl_2	H_2O	CO_2, SO_2
0	2.98	4.98	4.90	5.90	5.93	6.90
500	2.98	5.35	5.29	6.30	6.95	9.43
2000	2.99	6.22	6.10	7.4	11.9	11.5

Table 6.III. Heat Capacities of Hydrogen (in cal/mole·deg)

	Temperature (deg K)					
	300	200	100	80	60	40
C_v	4.86	4.49	3.42	3.18	3.05	3.00
C_p/C_v	1.41	1.45	1.56	1.62	1.66	1.67

of quantum concepts to the problem. Inspired by Einstein's fundamental resolution of the temperature variation of vibrational specific heat in 1907, Nernst suggested in 1911 the quantization of rotational and vibrational levels in gases. Hydrogen remained somewhat anomalous until Dennison suggested an explanation in 1927, following the earlier calculation of Hund. The advances made in quantum mechanics and spectroscopy after 1925 brought the theoretical calculation of thermodynamic properties of simple gases over wide ranges of temperatures to such a high degree of precision that it surpassed the accuracy of the experimental measurements.

6.3. QUANTUM THEORY OF C_v OF GASES

It is qualitatively easy to see why the rotational and vibrational degrees of freedom are not fully excited at low temperatures. For the common molecules, the vibrational frequencies are in the range of about 10^{14}/sec, and the associated energy levels have a spacing equivalent to $hv/k \sim 1000°K$. So, at room temperature ($\sim 300°K$), only a few molecules have enough energy to excite the vibrational modes. The rotational frequencies are about 100 times smaller, so that at any temperature above $10°K$ the rotational modes are fully excited. The rotational energy levels in hydrogen are rather high because of the low moment of inertia of the molecule; therefore, hydrogen begins to contribute the rotational specific heat only above $60°K$. The translation of these ideas into quantitative results is, of course, a standard problem in statistical mechanics.[3,4] The present discussion is limited to some simple cases, which are nevertheless sufficient to illustrate the principles involved.

The simplest case to consider is a monatomic gas, schematically taken as a set of mass points with no interatomic forces. Let a large number of such atoms, each of mass m, be enclosed in a vessel of sides L_1, L_2, L_3 in which they obey the Schrödinger equation

$$\nabla^2\psi + \frac{8\pi^2 mE}{h^2}\psi = 0$$

for free particles of energy E. The wave functions should vanish at the walls, but because the number of particles N is very large in any physical system, the boundary conditions do not affect the final result (see also Section 2.5). It is therefore mathematically convenient to impose a periodic boundary condition, as in lattice dynamics,

$$\psi(x,y,z) = \psi(x \pm L_1,y,z) = \ldots = \psi(x,y,z \pm L_3)$$

so that the solutions can be taken as progressive waves instead of standing waves. The wave functions satisfying these conditions are

$$\psi = A \exp[2\pi i(p_1 x + p_2 y + p_3 z)]$$

where $p_i = hn_i/L_i$ and n_i are positive or negative integers. The energy of a molecule is $\varepsilon = (p_1^2 + p_2^2 + p_3^2)/2m$. The energy of the system is the sum of the energies of the particles, and so the final partition function of the system will involve the product of N terms each equal to

$$z = \sum_{n_i = -\infty}^{\infty} \exp\left[\frac{-(p_1^2 + p_2^2 + p_3^2)}{2mkT}\right] \tag{6.1}$$

A simple calculation shows that the energy levels are approximately $h^2/2mkL^2 \approx 10^{-15}{}^\circ\text{K}$ apart, so that the summation over n_i may be replaced by an integration over p_i:

$$z = \frac{V}{h^3}\iiint \exp\left[\frac{-(p_1^2 + p_2^2 + p_3^2)}{2mkT}\right] dp_1\, dp_2\, dp_3$$

Here $V = L_1 L_2 L_3$ is the volume of the system. The integral from $-\infty$ to ∞ of e^{-x^2} is well known to be $\pi^{1/2}$, and so

$$z = V\left(\frac{2\pi mkT}{h^2}\right)^{3/2} \tag{6.2}$$

The partition function of the system Z would have been just the product of N such terms but for the fact that all the particles are indistinguishable. This means that

$$Z = \frac{1}{N!}(z)^N \tag{6.3}$$

because the $N!$ ways of permuting the particles are indistinguishable from one another and must hence be counted as only one way. Therefore,

$$A = -kT \ln Z = -NkT \ln\left[V\left(\frac{2\pi mkT}{h^2}\right)^{3/2}\right] + NkT \ln N - NkT \tag{6.4}$$

where Stirling's approximation $\ln N! \approx N \ln N - N$ is used. It is now a simple matter to calculate

$$E = -kT^2\left(\frac{\partial \ln Z}{\partial T}\right)_v = \tfrac{3}{2}RT \qquad C_v = \tfrac{3}{2}R \qquad (6.5)$$

The specific heat at constant volume is approximately 3 cal/mole·deg, as was borne out in Table 6.I. This value was also explained by the equipartition law, but the present calculations give the absolute value of the entropy at a pressure $P = NkT/V$ as

$$S = -\left(\frac{\partial A}{\partial T}\right)_v = R\left\{\tfrac{5}{2} + \ln\left[\frac{(kT)^{5/2}}{P}g\left(\frac{2\pi m}{h^2}\right)^{3/2}\right]\right\} \qquad (6.6)$$

(Here a weight factor g, equal to 1 for structureless particles and equal to 2 for vapors of sodium, potassium, and thallium, which have doubly degenerate ground state, has been added for completeness.) This equation, first derived in a different manner by Sackur and Tetrode in 1912, is in excellent agreement with the experimental values of entropy determined calorimetrically (see Table 6.VII). As a matter of historic interest, Tetrode, from the calorimetric entropy of mercury vapor, obtained Planck's constant h to within 5% of the accepted value.

6.4. ROTATIONAL PARTITION FUNCTION

The power of statistical thermodynamics becomes obvious when the rotational degrees of freedom are considered. The simplest case is a heteronuclear molecule of moment of inertia I perpendicular to its axis. With spherical polar coordinates, the expression for the kinetic energy is $\mathcal{T} = \tfrac{1}{2}I(\dot\theta^2 + \sin^2\theta\dot\phi^2)$. The generalized momenta are $p_\theta = \partial\mathcal{T}/\partial\dot\theta = I\dot\theta$, $p_\phi = \partial\mathcal{T}/\partial\dot\phi = I\sin^2\theta\dot\phi$, and so the classical Hamiltonian is $\mathcal{H} = (p_\theta^2 + \sin^{-2}\theta p_\phi^2)/2I$. The transcription into quantum mechanical operators leads to the Schrödinger equation

$$\frac{\partial^2\psi}{\partial\theta^2} + \frac{1}{\sin^2\theta}\frac{\partial^2\psi}{\partial\phi^2} + \frac{8\pi^2 IE}{h^2}\psi = 0 \qquad (6.7)$$

The eigenfunctions of this equation are $\psi = P_j^{|m|}(\cos\theta)e^{im\phi}$, with $m = -j, -j+1, ..., j-1, j$, where $P_j^{|m|}(\cos\theta)$ are the associated Legendre functions. The energy levels are $\varepsilon_j = j(j+1)h^2/8\pi^2 I$, where $j = 0, 1, ...$. Each energy level j possesses $2j+1$ independent wave functions and so must be assigned a weight $2j+1$. Proceeding as before, the partition function is

$$Z = \frac{1}{N}(z)^N$$

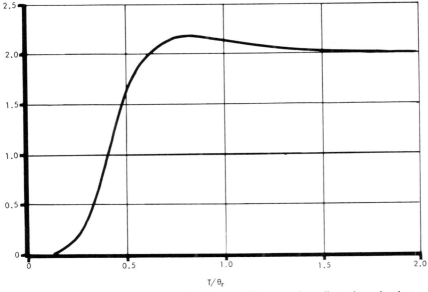

Fig. 6.1. Rotational heat capacity of a gas of heteronuclear diatomic molecules.

where the partition function z for a single molecule is

$$z = \sum_{j=0}^{\infty} (2j + 1) \exp\left[-\frac{j(j + 1)\theta_r}{T} \right] \qquad (6.8)$$

where $\theta_r = h^2/8\pi^2 Ik$. Over the entire range of temperatures, the summation has to be carried out by numerical methods[3,4], and the rotational specific heat has the values shown in Fig. 6.1. $C_v(\text{rot.})$ has a simple form at high or low temperatures:

$$C_v(\text{rot.}) = R\left[1 + \tfrac{1}{45}\left(\frac{\theta_r}{T}\right)^2 + \dots \right] \qquad \text{for } T \gg \theta_r \qquad (6.9)$$

$$= 12R\frac{\theta_r}{T}\exp\left(-\frac{\theta_r}{T}\right) + \dots \qquad \text{for } T \ll \theta_r \qquad (6.10)$$

The rotational heat capacity of diatomic molecules has the equipartition value $R \sim 2$ cal/mole·deg at high temperatures. As the temperature is lowered, $C_v(\text{rot.})$ attains a shallow maximum of about $1.1R$ at $T/\theta_r \sim 0.8$ and then drops down steeply. Below about $T/\theta_r \sim 0.2$, the rotational specific heat becomes too small to be resolved experimentally.

Table 6.IV. Rotational Characteristic Temperatures θ_r of Gases (in deg K)

	Gas									
	H_2	HD	HT	D_2	DT	T_2	HCl	N_2	O_2	CO	NH_3
θ_r	85.4	65.7	58.4	43.0	36.5	29.1	15.2	2.86	2.07	2.77	12.3

Clearly, θ_r is the characteristic temperature governing the behavior of C_v(rot.). Now a study of the band spectra enables the moment of inertia of the molecules to be determined,[5] and some values of θ_r calculated from such spectroscopic observations are given in Table 6.IV. For most gases, θ_r is in the region where the substances would have become liquids or solids, and so in the gaseous state they have the limiting value of R, thus accounting for the success of the equipartition law. Only in the case of the light hydrogeneous molecules is there any possibility of observing the "freezing" of the rotational degrees of motion. Hydrogen and deuterium are specially treated below because of the additional interesting effects arising from nuclear symmetry in the molecules. The rotational heat capacity of hydrogen deuteride (HD), obtained by subtracting the translational contribution $\frac{3}{2}R$ from the observed heat capacity, is in good agreement with the theoretical curve of Fig. 6.1 if θ_r is taken as 65.7°K. However, the observations are incomplete.

The treatment of polyatomic molecules is along similar lines, taking into account the possibility of rotation about all three axes and the molecular symmetry. For all polyatomic molecules, the equipartition value is reached in the gaseous state. The interest in the polyatomic gases is in calculating the entropy from the statistical partition function. The relevant formulas are analogous to the Sackur–Tetrode equation (6.6) and may be found in several treatises.[3,4,6] A comparison of the statistical entropy with the experimental value often gives information about the ordered state of the solid. This will be taken up in Section 6.7.

6.5. HOMONUCLEAR MOLECULES—ISOTOPES OF HYDROGEN

The heat capacity of homonuclear molecules, of which H_2 and D_2 are of great interest,[7] involves a consideration of the symmetry of the wave functions of the nuclei. Quantum mechanics shows that if the nuclei have an even mass number (for example, the deuteron), the wave function describing their motion must be symmetrical in nuclear coordinates, while if the nuclei have an odd mass number (for example, the proton) the wave functions must be antisymmetrical. Since the total wave function contains the product of the rotational and the nuclear spin functions, it is convenient to consider the two separately.

Interchanging the two nuclei of a diatomic molecule is equivalent to replacing θ by $\pi - \theta$ and ϕ by $\pi + \phi$ in the rotational eigenfunction $P_j^{|m|}(\cos \theta)e^{im\phi}$, that is, replacing the function by $(-1)^m P_j^{|m|}(-\cos \theta)e^{im\phi}$, which is equal to $(-1)^j P_j^{|m|}(\cos \theta)e^{im\phi}$ because $P_j^{|m|}(\cos \theta)$ is even or odd according to whether $j + |m|$ is even or odd. Hence the molecular rotational function is symmetric in the nuclear coordinates for even values of j and antisymmetrical for odd j. It is convenient to write

$$z_e = \sum_{j=0,2,4,\ldots} (2j + 1) \exp\left[-j(j + 1)\frac{\theta_r}{T}\right] \qquad (6.11)$$

$$z_0 = \sum_{j=1,3,5,\ldots} (2j + 1) \exp\left[-j(j + 1)\frac{\theta_r}{T}\right] \qquad (6.12)$$

If the nucleus has a spin I (in units of $\hbar$), there will be orientational quantization in an external magnetic field, with an eigenfunction for each of the $\rho = 2I + 1$ states. In the absence of a magnetic field, the orientated states become indistinguishable, but their number remains unaltered. Thus there are ρ spin wave functions $\psi_r(a)$, $\psi_s(b)$, where $r, s = 1, 2, \ldots, \rho$, for each nucleus a, b of a homonuclear diatomic molecule. From them, there are $\frac{1}{2}\rho(\rho - 1)$ combinations of the type $\psi_r(a)\psi_s(b) - \psi_r(b)\psi_s(a)$ (where $r \neq s$), which are antisymmetric in the nuclear coordinates, and there are $\frac{1}{2}\rho(\rho - 1)$ combinations of the type $\psi_r(a)\psi_s(b) + \psi_r(b)\psi_s(a)$ (where $r \neq s$), symmetric in the nuclei, as well as ρ products $\psi_r(a)\psi_r(b)$ also symmetric in the nuclei. In all, there are $\frac{1}{2}\rho(\rho - 1)$ antisymmetric and $\frac{1}{2}\rho(\rho + 1)$ symmetric spin wave functions of the molecule. These are the spin weight factors.

After these preliminaries, the rotational specific heat of hydrogen may be taken up. The hydrogen nucleus (proton spin $I = \frac{1}{2}$, $\rho = 2$) has an odd mass, and so the total wave function must be antisymmetric. This means that the symmetric rotational functions z_e must be combined with the antisymmetric spin functions, while the antisymmetric rotational functions z_0 are to be associated with the symmetric spin functions of degeneracy $\frac{1}{2}\rho(\rho + 1)$. If these weight factors $\frac{1}{2}\rho(\rho - 1) = 1$, $\frac{1}{2}\rho(\rho + 1) = 3$ are taken into account, the partition function for the equilibrium state of hydrogen becomes

$$z = z_e + 3z_0$$

and the specific heat will be

$$C_v(\text{rot.}) = \frac{d}{dT}\left[RT^2\frac{d}{dT}\ln(z_e + 3z_0)\right] \tag{6.13}$$

This formula, derived by Hund,[8] did not agree with the measured specific heats of hydrogen if the spectroscopic value of the moment of inertia, 4.67×10^{-40} g-cm^2, was used.

The reason was very soon pointed out by Dennison.[9] The transitions between the states of different nuclear spins are due to the very small interaction of the nuclear magnetic moment with the magnetic field produced by the rotation. The normal hazards of molecular collision do not affect the nuclear spins, and so the transitions between the two states are extremely rare. Therefore, hydrogen normally behaves as if it were a metastable mixture of two entirely separate species of molecules—parahydrogen and orthohydrogen. In parahydrogen, the nuclear spins are antiparallel (resultant spin and magnetic moment of the molecule are zero), and so this antisymmetric spin state is associated with even rotational states. Orthohydrogen has the spins of the nuclei parallel and corresponds to odd rotational states. In normal hydrogen, the relative abundance of the two types of molecules will be determined by the equilibrium conditions at room temperature. Since at high temperatures, z_0 is approximately equal to z_e, the relative abundance of para and ortho molecules will be in the ratio $p\text{-}H_2 : o\text{-}H_2 = 1:3$. The specific heat of normal hydrogen must be calculated by adding the contributions from the two species in this ratio, because during the course of an ordinary calorimetric measurement the ratio does not change appreciably. Thus

$$C_v(\text{rot.}) = \tfrac{1}{4}\frac{d}{dT}\left(RT^2\frac{d}{dT}\ln z_e\right) + \tfrac{3}{4}\frac{d}{dT}\left(RT^2\frac{d}{dT}\ln z_0\right) \tag{6.14}$$

This formula is in excellent agreement with the observations on ordinary hydrogen (for which the usual abbreviation is $n\text{-}H_2$).

Although the transitions between the ortho and para forms of hydrogen are so infrequent that the mixture retains its room-temperature composition of $o\text{-}H_2 : p\text{-}H_2 = 3:1$ during normal measurements of the specific heat, it is possible to catalyze the transitions by bringing the gas into contact with activated charcoal or paramagnetic salts. Substances such as ferric hydroxide are commonly used as catalysts. The lowest energy state of the ortho molecule is the $j = 1$ state, unlike the para molecule with a zero-energy $j = 0$ state. So, at low temperatures the equilibrium gas contains mostly para molecules. Typically, equilibrium hydrogen contains 25% $p\text{-}H_2$ at 300°K and over 99% $p\text{-}H_2$ at 20°K. This almost pure parahydrogen, or any

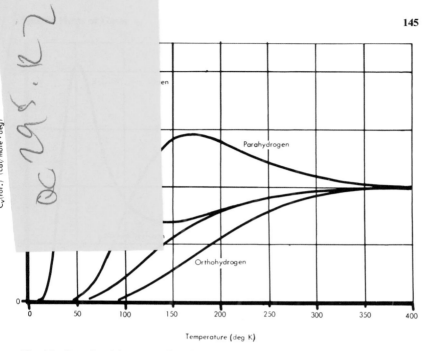

Fig. 6.2. Rotational heat capacity of ortho, para, normal, and equilibrium hydrogen ($\theta_r = 85.4°K$).

other mixture, will remain in metastable equilibrium if the temperature is changed in the absence of catalysts. Therefore, the specific heats of various ortho–para mixtures have been studied; the results are in excellent agreement with the theoretical calculations if θ_r is taken as 85.4°K. By selective adsorption of the ortho molecules on alumina, 99% pure orthohydrogen has been prepared recently[10] and its properties studied.

The rotational specific heat of the various forms (ortho, para, normal, and equilibrium states) of hydrogen are shown in Fig. 6.2.

For deuterium, the nuclear spin I is 1, and so $\rho = 3$. Since the deuteron contains two particles (proton and neutron), the total wave function must be symmetrical. The even rotational functions z_e are to be coupled to even nuclear spin functions of weight $\frac{1}{2}\rho(\rho + 1) = 6$, while the antisymmetrical rotational functions z_0 are to be associated with the antisymmetrical spin functions of weight $\frac{1}{2}\rho(\rho - 1) = 3$. So for a metastable mixture of deuterium (n-D_2),

$$C_v(\text{rot.}) = \frac{6}{9}\frac{d}{dT}\left(RT^2\frac{d}{dT}\ln z_e\right) + \frac{3}{9}\frac{d}{dT}\left(RT^2\frac{d}{dT}\ln z_0\right) \qquad (6.15)$$

The measurements on ordinary deuterium are in good agreement with this relation.

The para molecules have antiparallel nuclear spins. Therefore, paradeuterium is associated with odd rotational states, unlike parahydrogen, which is associated with even *j*-states because of the difference in nuclear mass and hence symmetry. The temperature variation of C_v(rot.) for paradeuterium is thus similar to that of orthohydrogen. The specific heat of orthodeuterium resembles the behavior of parahydrogen in having a maximum in C_v(rot.), but because of the increased moment of inertia, the peak occurs at about 85°K in orthodeuterium as compared to about 170°K in parahydrogen. Further, because of the higher percentage of even rotational states, normal deuterium shows a weak maximum in the specific heat at about 100°K. The theoretical variation of C_v(rot.) shown in Fig. 6.3 is in good agreement with experiments if θ_r is taken as 43.0°K. At low temperatures, orthodeuterium is the more favored

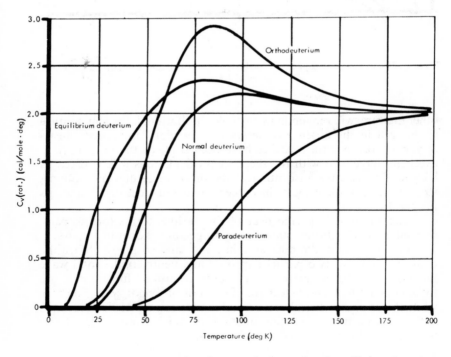

Fig. 6.3. Rotational heat capacity of para, ortho, normal, and equilibrium deuterium ($\theta_r = 43.0°K$).

state, and so almost pure metastable orthodeuterium can be prepared for experimental studies. Enrichment of paradeuterium requires a special process.[10]

Similar considerations apply to other cases such as that of CH_4, where the four hydrogen atoms are indistinguishable. However, these substances are no longer in the gaseous state when the deviations from the equipartition value are expected to arise. The study of tritium and its hydrides is barely possible.[11]

6.6. VIBRATIONAL AND ELECTRONIC SPECIFIC HEATS

The vibrational levels of molecules are 100 to 1000 times higher than the rotational levels; consequently, for many "permanent" gases the vibrational contribution becomes appreciable only at high temperatures. There are some substances, especially the organic vapors, which have rather low vibrational frequencies; for them, the vibrations are excited at room temperatures, as shown in Table 6.I.

The vibrational specific heat has been already calculated, in a different context. In Chapter 2, it was pointed out that a harmonic vibrator of frequency v has energy levels $\varepsilon_n = (n + \frac{1}{2})hv$, and so

$$z = \sum_{n=0}^{\infty} \exp\left[-\frac{(n + \frac{1}{2})hv}{kT}\right] = \frac{\exp(\frac{1}{2}hv/kT)}{1 - \exp(hv/kT)}$$

Thus

$$C_v(\text{vib.}) = R\left(\frac{\theta_v}{T}\right)^2 \frac{\exp(\theta_v/T)}{[\exp(\theta_v/T) - 1]^2} \tag{6.16}$$

where $\theta_v = hv/k$. This is the well-known Einstein function [equation (2.9)], and the temperature variation of C_v was represented in Fig. 2.1. (There is a small difference in that three-dimensional oscillators were considered in Chapter 2, whereas the present $C_v(\text{vib.})$ for the one-dimensional case is one-third the C_v considered in Section 2.4.) From spectroscopic studies of the vibrational frequencies, the values of θ_v may be calculated, some of which are given in Table 6.V. For simple molecules, the vibrational specific heat is barely excited at

Table 6.V. Vibrational Characteristic Temperatures θ_v (in $10^3 °K$)

	H_2	HD	D_2	HCl	HBr	CO	N_2	O_2	Cl_2	Br_2
θ_v	6.0	5.3	4.3	4.1	3.7	3.1	3.4	2.2	0.80	0.46

Table 6.VI. Vibrational Heat Capacity of Chlorine (in cal/mole·deg)

	Temperature (deg K)				
	243	270	319	391	452
Calculated	0.848	0.985	1.188	1.407	1.530
Experimental	0.840	0.977	1.148	1.459	1.557

300°K, i.e., at about one-tenth θ_v. Chlorine is an exception; the values, calculated from a band-spectrum value of $v = 16.95 \times 10^{12}$/sec, are compared with the experimental results[1] in Table 6.VI. There is indeed good agreement.

In polyatomic molecules, there are several vibrational frequencies, and the corresponding Einstein terms must be summed up. In many cases, to get full agreement with experiments, corrections have to be applied for the coupling between vibrational and rotational levels of the molecule and for the anharmonicity of the vibrations at higher temperatures. These problems are treated in several texts.[3,4]

Electronic energy levels, being of the order of 10^{4}°K apart, are not excited at room temperatures. In nitric oxide (NO) and a few free radicals, there are exceptionally low-lying levels with spacings of about 100°K. The excitations between such levels give rise to the Schottky type of specific heat (Section 4.9). Measurements in the gaseous state, which exists only at temperatures well above the specific-heat peak, are in reasonable accord with the calculations.[4]

6.7. CALORIMETRIC AND STATISTICAL ENTROPIES— DISORDER IN SOLID STATE

The study of the entropy of gases offers some interesting information about possible disorder in the solid state, which is of fundamental interest in connection with the third law of thermodynamics.[12] Statistical thermodynamics allows calculation of the absolute entropy of gases,[6] as was outlined for the case of translational degrees of freedom. The expressions involve, besides the fundamental constants h, k, m, etc., the frequencies of rotational and vibrational modes and the possible degeneracy of the states of the gas. These quantities can be determined from spectroscopic observations, and the entropy can be calculated.[5] On the other hand, from the measured specific heats of the solid and liquid phases as well as the latent heats of the phase changes, it is easy to calculate the entropy of the gas at, say, the normal boiling point. The calorimetrically determined values must agree with the statistically calculated values, if the conceptions

Table 6.VII. Statistical and Calorimetric Entropies (in cal/mole·deg)

	Gas and boiling point (deg K)									
	A 87.3	Kr 120.2	N_2 77.4	Cl_2 238.6	HCl 188.2	HI 237.5	CH_4 111.5	C_2H_4 169.3	CO_2 194.7	NH_3 239.7
Statistical	30.87	34.65	36.42	51.55	41.45	47.8	36.61	47.35	47.55	44.10
Calorimetric	30.85	34.63	36.53	51.56	41.3	47.8	36.53	47.26	47.59	44.13

of the third law and the statistical mechanics of the substances are correct. Table 6.VII, giving the relevant data at the boiling point of several simple substances, shows that the agreement is very good in most cases. This is indeed gratifying.

In some cases, calorimetric and statistical entropies do not agree so well as in Table 6.VII. Among the possible reasons for the discrepancy are (i) errors of calorimetry in the form of impure specimens, etc.; (ii) anomalous variations of specific heat below the temperatures up to which measurements have been made, resulting in an incorrect extrapolation to 0°K (compare Section 1.4); and (iii) inadequate knowledge of the molecular parameters or the equation of state. Even when these reasons are ruled out, differences between the statistical and calorimetric values persist in some cases.[13] Table 6.VIII shows that they are significantly greater than the limits of experimental error, which is of the order of ± 0.1 cal/mole·deg in the unfavorable cases involving specific-heat anomalies in the solid state. Although at one time there was considerable discussion about these discrepancies, it is now settled that in these substances the solid phases are not in internal equilibrium. As in the case of glassy materials discussed in Section 5.9, the solid state contains "frozen-in" configurational disorder not revealed in the calorimetric measurements of specific heats and hence in the evaluation of the entropy. Whereas the statistical calculations give the entropy difference between the gas at its boiling point and a perfectly ordered state at 0°K, calorimetry gives the entropy difference between the gas at its boiling point and a slightly disordered state at 0°K. Therefore, the calorimetric values must be *smaller* than the statistically calculated results, which is in fact one of the salient features of Table 6.VIII.

Carbon monoxide is a molecule with quite similar atoms; in an ideal solid state, the atoms should be arranged in the perfect order ... CO CO CO CO .... A disordered state ... CO CO OC CO ... will have a slightly higher energy Δ, dependent upon the difference between C and O atoms. If the temperature T is much larger than Δ/k, fluctuations in thermal energy of the order of Δ/k are possible,

Table 6.VIII. Discrepancies Between Statistical and Calorimetric Entropies[13]

	Gas and boiling point (deg K)							
	CO 83	N_2O 184.6	CH_3D 99.7	$FClO_3$ 226.5	SO_2F_2 217.8	NO 121.4	H_2O 298*	D_2O 298*
Statistical	38.32	48.50	39.49	62.59	64.14	43.75	45.10	46.66
Calorimetric	37.2	47.36	36.72	60.17	62.66	43.03	44.28	45.89
Statistical – Calorimetric	1.1	1.1	2.8	2.4	1.5	0.7	0.8	0.8

* H_2O and D_2O at room temperature.

and the molecule rotates freely from the CO to OC configuration and back. At very low temperatures ($T \ll \Delta/k$), the solid will become completely ordered if allowed to do so. However, in any solid there are always intermolecular potential barriers δ opposing the molecular motions. If these barriers are small compared to Δ, an ordered state sets in at $T \sim \Delta/k$. If, however, the potential barriers are much larger than Δ, then the high-temperature disordered state becomes frozen at $T \sim \delta/k$. The ordering at lower temperatures is not possible, because the mismatch energy Δ is not sufficient to overcome the potential barrier δ. If a molecule can take up one of two possible sites, the entropy of the frozen disorder is $R \ln 2$ per mole. The discrepancy in Table 6.VIII is 1.1 cal/mole·deg, which is slightly smaller than $R \ln 2 \sim 1.38$ units, suggesting that a part of the disorder had been removed before the potential barriers in the solid prevented any trend toward a perfect arrangement. Similar arguments apply to nitrous oxide. This is a linear molecule with the atoms nearly alike, so that its orientation in the solid state may be either NNO or ONN. The discrepancy, 1.1 units, is again a little smaller than $R \ln 2$. The same end-for-end disorder occurs in the long-chain 1-olefins with more than eleven carbon atoms,[14] while 1-decene and smaller molecules are fully ordered in the solid state.

The magnitude of the difference in CH_3D is about 2.7 cal/mole·deg, which immediately gives a clue to the nature of the disorder. In a completely ordered state, the CH_3D molecules may be expected to take up a position with the deuterium atoms in one particular site among the four tetrahedral carbon–hydrogen bonds. If the rotational motion has been frozen at relatively high temperatures, there will be a residual entropy of $R \ln 4 \sim 2.75$ units, which is very close to the experimental value. The same is the situation with the perchloryl fluoride $FClO_3$, where the crystal fails to distinguish between the oxygen and the fluorine atoms in orienting the molecule in the solid state. There are four possible positions for the fluorine atoms, giving a disorder entropy $R \ln 4 \sim 2.75$ units, which is close to the observed value of 2.42 units. In sulfuryl fluoride (SO_2F_2), the slightly asymmetric top molecules have two possible orientations in the solid state, resulting in an entropy difference of about 1.5 units.

The statistical entropy of nitric oxide is only 0.7 units higher than the calorimetric values. X-ray studies[15] show that nitric oxide is present as a dimer

$$\begin{array}{c} N..O \\ O..N \end{array}$$

with nitrogen–oxygen bonds of 1.1 and 2.4 Å, respectively. The X-ray diffraction patterns suggest that the dimer is distributed in the crystal without distinguishing between the corners occupied by the N atoms and those occupied by the O atoms. This randomness gives an entropy of $R \ln 2$ per mole of the dimer and so accounts for the observed difference $\frac{1}{2}R \ln 2 \sim 0.69$ units per mole of the monomer NO.

Ice provides a celebrated example of a more complicated type of disorder which was first elucidated by Pauling.[16] In gaseous H_2O, the HOH angle is about 105°, and the two H atoms are at a distance of 0.95 Å from the oxygen atom. In ice, the various molecules are bound together into a loose open structure by hydrogen bonds, and each O atom is surrounded by four other O, tetrahedrally situated at a distance of 2.76 Å. The water molecules retain their individuality to a large extent, but there is space only for one H atom along each tetrahedral O–O direction at a distance of 0.95 Å from either oxygen. In a mole of ice there are $2N$ H atoms, and if there are two possible positions along each O–O bond, the possible number of configurations is 2^{2N}. Of these, only a few are acceptable. Consider any O atom and the available sites along the four tetrahedral directions. There is one way of putting four hydrogens close to the O atom, giving $(OH_4)^{2+}$ ionic arrangement; there are four ways of getting $(OH_3)^+$, six ways of getting (OH_2), and four ways of getting $(OH)^-$; and there is one way of getting $(O)^{2-}$ ionic arrangement. Of these sixteen possibilities, only six yield the desired H_2O molecule; that is, only three-eighths of all possible configurations are acceptable to that O atom. Thus the total number of possible arrangements of a mole of the solid is $(2)^{2N} \cdot (\frac{3}{8})^N = (\frac{3}{2})^N$. Therefore, the entropy associated with this is $R \ln\frac{3}{2} = 0.81$ cal/mole·deg. This agrees very well with the difference of 0.8 units observed for both H_2O and D_2O. There is considerable evidence from neutron- and electron-diffraction studies for the essential correctness of the statistical disorder in ice, and the matter has been recently reviewed by Chidambaram.[17]

The hydrated sodium sulfate $Na_2SO_4 \cdot 10H_2O$ shows a residual entropy of about 1.5 units, which has been explained on the basis of X-ray structural work.[18] A four-member hydrogen-bonded ring exists in the structure, with the protons unsymmetrically located in the hydrogen bonds. Therefore, two arrangements,

are possible, and a random population of the two schemes gives a disorder entropy of $R \ln 2$. Isomorphous $Na_2 CrO_4 \cdot 10H_2O$ has the same structure and presumably would have the same residual entropy.

It was mentioned earlier that if the mismatch energy Δ is much larger than the intermolecular potential barriers, an ordered state is achieved at a temperature $T \sim \Delta/k$. Consider, for example, HI instead of CO. The atoms are so different that the energy difference Δ between HI and IH configurations is very large. Even at relatively high temperatures, there is insufficient thermal energy to permit such a disorder. As a matter of fact, such substances display the ordering process in spectacular specific-heat singularities, the typical example[19] of HI and DI being given in Fig. 6.4. These cooperative anomalies were first found in ammonium chloride by Simon in 1922 and have since been found in a large number of substances. They are discussed fully in the following chapter. The configurational entropy in these materials is removed at relatively high temperatures. Hence there should be no discrepancy between statistical and calorimetric entropies. The examples given in Table 6.VII confirm this.

6.8. HINDERED ROTATION

A molecule does not always rotate as a rigid body, as was implied in the calculations of Section 6.4. In many organic molecules, groups of atoms can rotate freely or partially about the bond directions. A classic example is the difference between ethane $H_3C–CH_3$ and dimethylacetylene $H_3C–C{\equiv}C–CH_3$. In ethane, the influence of the hydrogen atoms of one methyl group can be felt by the other CH_3

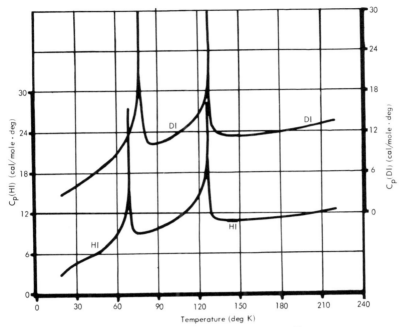

Fig. 6.4. Heat capacities of HI and DI.[19]

group, and so a rotation of one group about the C–C axis may be expected to have a potential of the form $V = V_0 (1 - \cos 3\phi)$. In dimethylacetylene, the CH_3 groups are far away, and so the methyl groups experience little, if any, potential barrier for rotation about the $C\equiv C$ bond. In fact, the entropy calculated by assuming a free rotation of the methyl group agrees well with the calorimetric value in the case of this substance. On the other hand, the measured entropy of ethane falls between the entropies calculated by assuming free or no rotation about the C–C bond. It is clear that from such entropy differences a knowledge of the potential barriers may be obtained.

The hindered rotation of the radicals in a molecule can also be studied from infrared and microwave spectra of the substance. Wilson[20] has recently reviewed the various methods of determining V_0. The thermodynamic method, though used first to obtain this information (mainly by Pitzer and his coworkers), is rather inaccurate because it depends upon the small difference between two large quantities, namely, the calorimetric entropy and the statistical contribution from translational, vibrational, and other modes. The spectroscopic determination is more accurate; V_0 thus determined can be used to interpret the calorimetric data. Methyl chloroform is one of the early substances for which spectroscopic data made possible the satisfactory interpretation of specific-heat measurements. Methanol has been studied extensively by various methods, and the results are in very good agreement with one another.[4]

6.9. ENTROPY OF HYDROGEN

The entropy of hydrogen depends upon its composition. Johnston and coworkers[21] calculated the entropy of parahydrogen by using the measured specific heats up to 12°K and then making a Debye-type extrapolation of the heat capacity of the solid down to absolute zero. At the boiling point (20.76°K), the entropy comes out to be

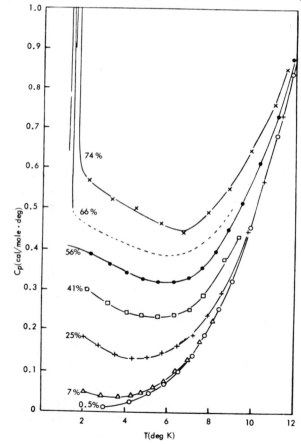

Fig. 6.5a. Heat capacities of mixtures of orthohydrogen and parahydrogen in the solid state.

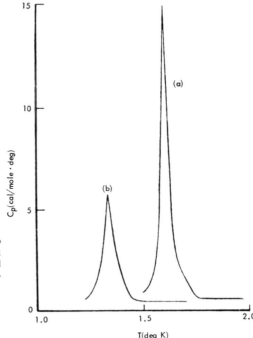

Fig. 6.5b. λ-peaks with ortho concentrations exceeding about 60%.[23] Curve (a) = 74% and curve (b) = 66% orthohydrogen.

14.8 ± 0.1 cal/mole·deg. The statistical entropy is easily calculated from the translational and rotational functions and a small vibrational partition function. The value 14.76 agrees very well with the calorimetric evaluation.

A similar statistical calculation of the entropy of normal hydrogen shows that it exceeds that of parahydrogen by 4.29 cal/mole·deg. This excess arises from three sources. Normal hydrogen is a mixture of orthohydrogen and parahydrogen in the ratio $o:p = 3:1$, and the entropy of mixing is equal to $-R(\frac{1}{4}\ln\frac{1}{4} + \frac{3}{4}\ln\frac{3}{4}) \sim 1.14$ units. A second source is the nuclear-spin entropy of orthohydrogen. The ortho molecules, with a resultant nuclear spin $I = 1$, have three possible orientations, and the degeneracy will not be revealed until the specific heats are measured down to about 10^{-6}°K. The excess entropy is $R\ln 3$ per mole of orthohydrogen, and so it contributes $\frac{3}{4}R\ln 3 \sim 1.64$ to the ordinary 3:1 mixture.

A third contribution comes from the ordering of the rotational axes of the molecules at low temperatures. As mentioned earlier, ortho–para transitions take place only slowly in liquid and solid states, which makes it possible to measure the thermal properties of the condensed phases with various ortho–para concentrations.

Such measurements were first performed by Simon, Mendelssohn, and Ruheman[22] and more recently by Hill and Ricketson[23] and by Ahlers and Orttung.[24] Measurements above helium temperatures (Fig. 6.5a) show that the specific heats of solid solutions of ortho-hydrogen considerably exceed those of pure parahydrogen. With ortho concentrations in excess of about 60%, the specific heat exhibits a pronounced λ-peak at about 2°K (Fig. 6.5b). The additional specific heat increases with increasing ortho concentration, and the entropy associated with the anomaly is only a little lower than $R \ln 3$ per mole of orthohydrogen.

The excess entropy is in fact what is expected. The ground state of the ortho-molecule is the $j = 1$ rotational state, which, because of the low moment of inertia, has considerable energy. Solid hydrogen has a very open structure, largely on account of the high zero-point energy; therefore, the potential barriers opposing rotation of the molecules are small. The ortho molecules may be rotating right down to 0°K. The rotational level $j = 1$ is threefold degenerate, but since the molecular field in the solid is cubic and not spherical, different relative orientations have slightly differing energies of interaction. The lowest energy of the system occurs for an ordered arrangement of the axis of rotation; indeed, NMR experiments[25] show that the ortho molecules become ordered in this way. The specific-heat anomaly is due to this cooperative ordering process, though recent investigations[24] show that the details of the ordering process are more complicated than was originally supposed. It is evident that the removal of the threefold degeneracy gives an extra entropy $R \ln 3$ per mole of orthohydrogen, or $\frac{3}{4}R \ln 3 \sim 1.64$ per mole of normal hydrogen. The sum of the three contributions $(1.14 + 1.64 + 1.64 \sim 4.4 \text{ cal/mole·deg})$ is in satisfactory agreement with the calculated difference of 4.3 units.

A similar entropy contribution due to the removal of the three-fold degeneracy of para molecules is present in deuterium. Following the earlier experiments,[26] which revealed anomalous specific heats similar to those shown in 6.5a, Grenier and White[27] detected λ-peaks (as in Fig. 6.5b) at about 3°K in the specific heat of solid deuterium, with para concentrations of more than approximately 65%. They used a special enrichment procedure[10] to get para concentrations greater than the normal $33\frac{1}{3}\%$. Taking into account the various contributions, there is satisfactory agreement between calorimetric and statistical entropies.

REFERENCES

1. J. R. Partington and W. G. Shilling. *The Specific Heats of Gases,* Benn, London, 1924. A. Eucken, *Handbuch der Experimental Physik, VIII(I)* (1929), chapter 10.

2. E. Justi, *Spezifische Warme, Entropie, und Dissoziation technischer Gase*, Springer, Berlin, 1938.

3. J. E. Mayer and M. G. Mayer, *Statistical Mechanics*, Wiley, New York, 1940, chapters 6, 7, and 8. J. G. Aston and J. J. Fritz, *Thermodynamics and Statistical Thermodynamics*, Wiley, New York, 1959, chapters 18, 19, and 20.

4. J. S. Rowlinson, *The Perfect Gas*, Pergamon, Oxford, 1963, chapter 3.

5. G. Herzberg, *Infrared and Raman Spectra of Polyatomic Molecules*, Van Nostrand, New York, 1945, p. 501; *Spectra of Diatomic Molecules*, Van Nostrand, New York, 1950, p. 466. K. S. Pitzer, *Quantum Chemistry*, Prentice-Hall, Englewood Cliffs, N.J., 1953, chapter 9.

6. L. S. Kassel, *Chem. Rev.* **18**, 277 (1936). E. B. Wilson, *Chem. Rev.* **27**, 17 (1940).

7. H. W. Woolley, R. B. Scott, and F. G. Brickwedde, *J. Res. Nat. Bur. Std.* **41**, 379 (1948).

8. F. Hund, *Z. Physik* **42**, 93 (1927).

9. D. M. Dennison, *Proc. Roy. Soc. (London)*, Ser. A **115**, 483 (1927).

10. C. M. Cunningham, D. S. Chapin, and H. L. Johnston, *J. Am. Chem. Soc.* **80**, 2382 (1958).

11. W. M. Jones, *J. Chem. Phys.* **16**, 1077 (1948); **17**, 1062 (1949).

12. J. Wilks, *Third Law of Thermodynamics*, Oxford University Press, Oxford, 1961, chapter 5.

13. J. O. Clayton and W. F. Giauque, *J. Am. Chem. Soc.* **54**, 2610 (1932). (Carbon monoxide.) K. Clusius, *Z. Elektrochem.* **40**, 99 (1934); R. W. Blue and W. F. Giauque, *J. Am. Chem. Soc.* **57**, 991 (1935). (Nitrous oxide.) K. Clusius, L. Popp, and A. Frank, *Physica* **4**, 1105 (1937). (Monodeutro methane.) J. K. Koehler and W. F. Giauque, *J. Am. Chem. Soc.* **80**, 2659 (1958). (Perchloryl fluoride.) F. J. Bockoff, R. V. Petrella, and E. L. Pace, *J. Chem. Phys.* **32**, 799 (1960); **36**, 3502 (1962). (Sulfuryl fluoride.) H. L. Johnston and W. F. Giauque, *J. Am. Chem. Soc.* **51**, 3194 (1929). (Nitric oxide.) W. F. Giauque and J. W. Stout, *J. Am. Chem. Soc.* **58**, 1144 (1936). (Water.) E. A. Long and J. D. Kemp, *J. Am. Chem. Soc.* **58**, 1829 (1936). (Heavy water.)

14. J. P. McCullough, H. L. Finke, M. E. Gross, J. F. Messerly, and G. Waddington, *J. Phys. Chem.* **61**, 289 (1957).

15. W. J. Dulmage, E. A. Meyers, and W. N. Lipscomb, *Acta cryst.* **6**, 760 (1953).

16. L. Pauling, *J. Am. Chem. Soc.* **57**, 2680 (1935); *Nature of the Chemical Bond*, Cornell University Press, Ithaca, N.Y., 1960, p. 464.

17. R. Chidambaram, *Acta cryst.* **14**, 467 (1961).

18. K. S. Pitzer and L. V. Coulter, *J. Am. Chem. Soc.* **60**, 1310 (1938); G. Brodale and W. F. Giauque, *J. Am. Chem. Soc.* **80**, 2042 (1958). H. W. Ruben, D. H. Templeton, R. D. Rosenstein, and I. Olovsson, *J. Am. Chem. Soc.* **83**, 820 (1961).

19. A. Eucken and E. Karwat, *Z. phys. Chem.* **112**, 467 (1924). W. F. Giauque and R. Wiebe, *J. Am. Chem. Soc.* **51**, 1441 (1929). K. Clusius and D. Wolf, *Z. Naturforsch.* **2a**, 495 (1947).

20. E. B. Wilson, *Advan. Chem. Phys.* **2**, 367 (1959).

21. H. L. Johnston, J. T. Clarke, E. B. Rifkin, and E. C. Kerr, *J. Am. Chem. Soc.* **72**, 3933 (1950).

22. K. Mendelssohn, M. Ruheman, and F. Simon, *Z. phys. Chem.* **B15**, 121 (1931).

23. R. W. Hill and B. W. A. Ricketson, *Phil. Mag.* **45**, 277 (1954).

24. G. Ahlers and W. H. Orttung, *Phys. Rev.* **133**, A1642 (1964).

25. J. Hatton and B. V. Rollin, *Proc. Roy. Soc. (London)*, Ser. A **199**, 222 (1949). F. Reif and E. M. Purcell, *Phys. Rev.* **91**, 631 (1953). T. Sugawara, Y. Masuda, T. Kanda, and E. Kanda, *Sci. Rept. Res. Inst. Tohoku, Univ.* **A7**, 67 (1955). G. W. Smith and R. N. Housley, *Phys. Rev.* **117**, 732 (1960).

26. O. D. Gonzalez, D. White, and H. L. Johnston, *J. Chem. Phys.* **61**, 773 (1957).

27. G. Grenier and D. White, *J. Chem. Phys.* **40**, 3015 (1964).

Chapter 7

Specific-Heat Anomalies

7.1. SPURIOUS AND GENUINE ANOMALIES

The idea that the specific heats of some materials show abnormal variations at certain temperatures was introduced as early as Chapter 1, and several examples of such uncommon behavior were mentioned in Chapters 3 to 6. Before embarking upon a systematic classification of such unusual specific-heat variations, it is worthwhile to digress a little upon what constitutes anomalous behavior. Any definition of an anomaly is to some extent negative in that it invokes the standards for normal behavior, which obviously depend upon the progress of our knowledge concerning the thermal properties of physical systems. Thus, deviations from Einstein and Debye models of specific heats, at one time considered to be anomalous variations of specific heats, are now taken as normal in the light of detailed lattice calculations. Similarly, the unexpected behavior of the specific heat of a superconductor is now viewed as a simple consequence of the onset of superconductivity in the electronic system. The possibility always exists that the puzzles of one era may become clarified in the succeeding years. Consequently, it is best to adopt as a pragmatic simplification that, in most substances and in many simple theoretical models of solids, the specific heat decreases continuously as the temperature is lowered. If there is an increase associated with reduction of temperatures, giving in effect a maximum in the heat capacity, the behavior is generally called a *specific-heat anomaly*. Although at one time such events were rarely observed, they are now known to occur in numerous substances. In general, if the origin of the effect is known, we shall call a finite small maximum a *peak* in the heat capacity and a large, nearly infinite, maximum a *singularity*. It appears best to reserve the term *anomaly* for the cases where the explanation is unknown.

158

It is useful to illustrate the above statements with some examples. For the majority of common solids, the typical low-temperature specific heat is that shown by the thick line in Fig. 7.1a, decreasing continuously to zero as 0°K is approached. A few substances exhibit a definite maximum as shown in Fig. 7.1b, a specific-heat peak. A practical case, that of nickel sulfate at low temperatures, was shown in Fig. 4.11. Here, on the basis of theoretical and experimental studies of thermal and other properties, it was possible to resolve the observations into a lattice contribution and a Schottky term, as shown schematically in Fig. 7.1b. Much effort has gone into the resolution of experimentally determined total specific heats into simple

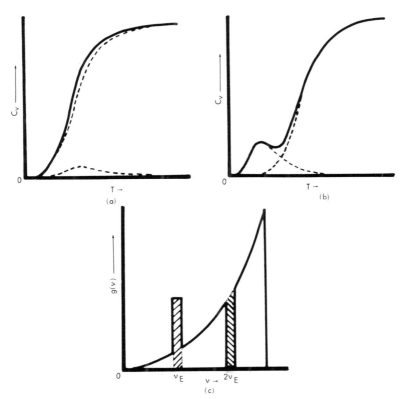

Fig. 7.1. (a) Typical specific-heat variation of many common solids (thick lines). Broken lines show a possible resolution into Debye and Schottky contributions. (b) Schematic picture of a specific heat peak. Broken lines show decomposition into lattice and Schottky contributions. (c) Frequency distribution for a combination of Debye and Schottky terms. The Schottky term is equivalent to removing frequencies at $2v_E$ and adding them at v_E shown as shaded portions.

lattice, electronic, and other contributions so that the anomalous part can be discussed independently. Unfortunately, this sort of decomposition game, played with numerical data, can be carried to extremes. It was noticed by Simon in 1930 that the specific heats of many solids could be fitted very well by a combination of a Debye and a Schottky term, somewhat as shown by the broken lines in Fig. 7.1a. It was then postulated that the lattice follows the Debye variation, while the electronic system follows the Schottky relation as a result of excitation between the ground state and a higher energy state. With several adjustable constants, the agreement in such cases is, as expected, very good.

The underlying physical reason for this kind of agreement is as follows.[1] A comparison of the Schottky equation (4.25) for the case $g_0 = g_1$ with the Einstein equation (2.9) reveals that the Schottky term is the same as the difference $C_v(T_E/T) - C_v(2T_E/T)$ between two Einstein models with frequencies v_E and $2v_E$. Thus, the above decomposition is equivalent to adding a number of frequencies at v_E and removing the same number at $2v_E$ in the Debye spectrum. The resulting $g(v)$ (thick line in Fig. 7.1c) has a slightly better resemblance to the actual frequency spectra of solids—compare Figs. 2.5 to 2.8— than a single Debye spectrum, and the better representation of the specific heats by such a frequency spectrum is not surprising. With other approximate representations of $g(v)$, such as those attempted by Raman and coworkers, the situation is similar.

It is now natural to ask whether a Schottky term obtained by such a decomposition justifies considering the specific-heat variation to be anomalous. At present, such specific-heat contributions are not called anomalous. The Debye spectrum is now known beyond all doubts to be nothing more than a good approximation to the $g(v)$ of solids; a judicious combination of Debye and other terms is at best a better approximation. Hence, any peak separated out from the observations is artificial and without proper theoretical justification; the actual specific heat can be represented equally well by an appropriate $g(v)$, which can be studied and confirmed by other independent methods such as neutron-diffraction studies. It is only when there is an actual maximum in the observed total specific heat that the lattice and electronic modes are insufficient for an explanation. Therefore, a practical criterion for a specific-heat anomaly is the presence of a maximum in the temperature variation of specific heat.

It is thus clear that what could have been considered a specific-heat anomaly in, say, 1930 is now taken to be normal behavior of the lattice. Another way in which later studies establish the presence of normal behavior is in bringing to light insidious experimental errors.

In particular, three sources of error in many early observations have been revealed. Where hydrogen or helium exchange gas is used to cool the specimen to low temperatures, the desorption of the gas at low temperatures vitiates calorimetric studies by preventing the easy attainment of good vacuum insulation and by causing liberation of the heat of desorption. Secondly, small amounts of impurities, especially of materials which have pronounced specific-heat peaks, often result in apparent anomalies. Magnetic materials showing transitions at low temperatures should be scrupulously avoided. Thirdly, uncertainties in temperature scales may cause errors in the evaluation of heat capacities. Several anomalies reported earlier in many common materials[1] have now proved to be results of these experimental shortcomings.

7.2. COOPERATIVE AND NONCOOPERATIVE ANOMALIES

In discussing the model systems which show specific-heat peaks it is convenient to start with a system of independent particles or modes. Indeed, the simple models of solids and gases in Chapters 2, 3, and 6 invoked only such independent modes of excitation, namely, independent phonons, electrons, and molecules. The simplicity of such a system is that the total energy is just the sum of the energies of the various independent modes. Since there is no mutual interdependence among the modes, the system is called a *noncooperative* one. Under these conditions, a rather complete theoretical analysis of the system is possible. The examples of Schottky effect (Section 4.9), rotational specific heat of gases (Section 4.5), and the heat capacity of some liquids and solutions[2] show that even in these noncooperative processes specific-heat maxima can occur. The practical examples of such peaks and their theoretical interpretation have been fully discussed elsewhere, and there is no need for further analysis in this chapter. As a matter of fact, the rotational specific heat of gases is so well understood that many authors do not classify its maximum as a specific-heat anomaly.

In some physical systems, the interactions among the constituents are so strong that the energy state of one constituent depends upon the energy states of its neighbors. For example, in a ferromagnet the probability of a given spin pointing along $+Z$ is large if the nearby spins also point along $+Z$ and small if they are aligned along $-Z$. Thus, the spin states are not mutually independent. The probability of transferring a particle to an excited state depends upon the degree to which the excited state is occupied. Under such conditions, the excited states are often too few until some critical mean energy, that is, some critical temperature, is approached. Then the process of excitation by mutual *cooperative* action takes over and the particles of the system are very rapidly transfered to the excited states in the vicinity of the transition temperature. Thus, the energy of the system is changed in a small interval of temperature. In consequence, the cooperative transition is revealed in the specific heat as a pronounced singularity at the transition temperature T_c.

Several categories of cooperative phenomena are now known. The alignment of magnetic dipoles (spins), superconductivity of electronic systems, superfluidity in liquid helium, order–disorder transitions, and the onset of molecular rotation are some topics mentioned earlier. The phenomenon of ferroelectricity is analogous to ferromagnetism. There are other specific-heat singularities in rare-earth metals and at liquid-gas critical points. The present chapter will be concerned with these cooperative effects.

Specific-heat singularities due to magnetic interactions are by far the most frequent peaks observed at low temperatures. There are many ions which are paramagnetic; the presence of any one of them in a substance gives rise to either noncooperative Schottky peaks or cooperative ordering singularities. In the latter case, the ordered state at low temperatures may be ferro-, ferri-, or antiferromagnetic. Even in diamagnetic solids, the nuclear moments, if any, become ordered at sufficiently low temperatures. The experimental and theoretical aspects of these phenomena were discussed at some length in Chapter 4. Here it suffices to remark that if the spins become noncooperatively ordered, there is a smooth Schottky maximum, whereas in cooperative ordering the specific heat is probably infinite at the transition temperature T_c. Where sufficiently careful measurements have been made, the specific heat shows a logarithmic infinity on the low-temperature side of T_c. On the high-temperature side, it is not settled whether the singularity is logarithmic or of the power-law type.

Cooperative transitions in superconductors and superfluids were also fully discussed in earlier chapters. The two processes differ from the other cooperative phenomena in that the ordering takes place in the momentum space rather than in the coordinate space. For instance, a ferromagnet becomes ordered with all spins along one direction in the ordinary coordinate space. On the other hand, the superfluid properties of liquid ^{4}He are basically the result of Bose condensation of the particles into zero-momentum states. The Cooper pairs, which are responsible for superconductivity, behave very much like condensed bosons. There are, however, differences between the specific-heat behavior of superfluids and superconductors. Liquid ^{4}He exhibits the famous λ-transition at 2.17°K, with the heat capacity showing logarithmic infinities both below and above T_λ (Section 5.5).

Superconductors show only a finite jump at the transition (Section 3.9). Further, liquid ^{4}He has a specific-heat tail on the high-temperature side of the transition, whereas at temperatures higher than T_c, superconductors give no clue about their dramatic properties below the transition. There have been suggestions that superconductors should also exhibit λ-type singularities, but careful experiments have up to now failed to reveal any such behavior.[3] The transition in liquid ^{3}He, if confirmed, should prove very interesting. Several authors have predicted a peculiar anisotropic state of the liquid below T_c.

With a variety of known cooperative effects, obviously no general theory of such processes can be given, and each effect is best treated on its own merits. Thereafter, it will be appropriate to show how cooperative phenomena can be interpreted in terms of simple models.

7.3. ORDER–DISORDER TRANSITIONS

In an ordinary alloy, the atoms are distributed at random over the available lattice sites. As the temperature is lowered, the third law of thermodynamics predicts that an ordered state having less entropy should result. However, in many cases the random arrangement is forcibly preserved by the interatomic potential barriers preventing the free movement of atoms. An illustration would be a typical tin–lead solder. This freezing-in of disorder has been mentioned earlier (Sections 5.9 and 6.7). In other cases, the material lowers its entropy by precipitating individual grains of the component pure metals. In a few cases, the alloy (say A_mB_n of metals A and B) lowers its entropy by taking up a structure appropriate to a crystalline chemical compound A_mB_n. This last transformation is the one under consideration here.

A classic example is the alloy β-brass, CuZn. At or below room temperature, the substance has perfect cubic symmetry. The Zn atoms occupy the corners of a cubic unit cell, and the Cu atoms occupy the cube center. Thus, in this state β-brass may be visualized as two interpenetrating simple cubic lattices of Cu and Zn. At a temperature of about 1000°K, the structure is disordered in the sense that the Cu and Zn atoms occupy sites at random. As the temperature is raised from 0°K, the ordered state (schematically shown in Fig. 7.2a) is gradually transformed into the disordered state (shown in Fig. 7.2b), although the process occurs very rapidly in the vicinity of the transition temperature $T_c \approx 469$°C. The change in lattice structure is most easily followed by X-ray or neutron scattering. Many alloys, among them AuCu, $AuCu_3$, CuPt, and AgZn, show order–disorder transformations.[4]

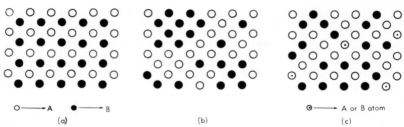

Fig. 7.2. Schematic view of order–disorder changes in an alloy AB: (a) ordered arrangement, (b) random arrangement, (c) illustration of the difference between long-range and short-range order.

The transformation is accompanied by changes in electrical, mechanical, and thermal properties. The specific heat of CuZn near its $T_c(\approx 469°C)$ is shown in Fig. 7.3a.[5] The λ-shaped peak characteristic of cooperative transitions is evident. The specific heat has a sharp rise below T_c and retains a small tail above T_c. Although we are not yet in a position to discuss the details of such specific-heat curves, a simple rule for the excess entropy is easily formulated. If the atoms have the possibility of choosing between r configurations, the associated entropy is

$$\Delta S = R \ln r \tag{7.1}$$

per mole. Thus in β-brass $r = 2$; indeed, the excess entropy in Fig. 7.3a is found to be very close to $R \ln 2$. Since the excess arises from the possibility of different configurations, ΔS is sometimes called the *configurational entropy*.

So far, the idea of order has been used in a qualitative manner. At this stage, we can introduce a quantitative description, used by Bragg and Williams in 1934, of what is strictly long-range order. Consider the alloy AB with an interpenetrating lattice of A and B. We may refer to the sites corresponding to one interpenetrating lattice as α-sites and the sites of the other lattice as β-sites. In a completely ordered state, let A atoms occupy α-sites and B atoms β-sites. Then, in a slightly disordered state, some atoms will be in right positions (A on α, B on β), while some will be in wrong positions (A on β, B on α). If there are R right atoms and W wrong atoms, the long-range order parameter σ_l may be defined as

$$\sigma_l = \frac{R - W}{R + W} \tag{7.2}$$

When $W = 0$, there is complete order and $\sigma_l = 1$. The case $R = 0$, $\sigma_l = -1$ also corresponds to a state of complete order, since by interchanging the names of α- and β-sites it becomes physically

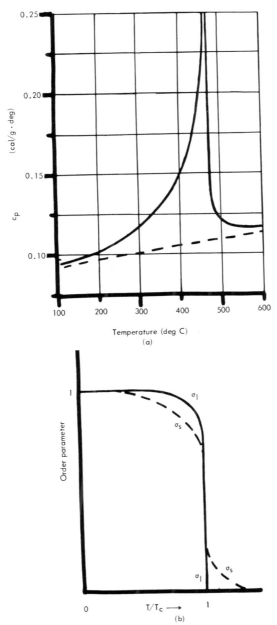

Fig. 7.3. (a) Specific heat of CuZn.[5] (b) Temperature variation of order parameters.

identical to the case $W = 0$. Complete disorder exists when there are as many right atoms as wrong ones, that is, when $R = W$ and $\sigma_l = 0$. Therefore, only the range between $\sigma_l = 1$ (complete order) and $\sigma_l = 0$ (complete disorder) is of physical interest. At very low temperatures, σ_l is unity, and it drops rapidly to zero when T_c is reached, as represented in Fig. 7.3b.

The short-range order parameter σ_s may also be easily introduced, following the work of Bethe in 1935. In many systems, the interaction among the atoms is significant only for the nearest neighbors. For instance, the spin exchange integrals of Section 4.6 are nearest-neighbor interactions. Therefore, as a criterion of order we may compare the number of right pairs (AB type) and the number of wrong (AA or BB) pairs of near neighbors. An illustration will clarify this concept. From the point of view of long-range order defined by equation (7.2), the lattice of Fig. 7.2c is highly disordered. Yet nearly all atoms have unlike atoms as nearest neighbors. So if the relative number of right and wrong neighbors is taken as a measure of the ordering in the vicinity of any atom, the lattice is only slightly disordered. Consider an A atom. Let the probability that a given neighbor is a B atom be $(1 + \sigma_s)/2$ and the probability that it is an A atom be $(1 - \sigma_s)/2$. For complete order $\sigma_s = 1$ and for complete disorder $\sigma_s = 0$. Therefore, σ_s is called the *short-range order parameter*. The temperature variation of σ_s is shown schematically in Fig. 7.3b. As T_c is approached, σ_s decreases rapidly from unity, but even above T_c short-range order persists for some temperatures.

7.4. ONSET OF MOLECULAR ROTATION

The nature of atomic motions in solids is obviously controlled by the interatomic forces. In rocksalt, the Na^+ ions are equally strongly bound to the six surrounding Cl^- atoms, and it is hard to identify a single NaCl molecule or the molecular frequencies. If the intramolecular forces are comparable to the intermolecular forces, it is sometimes possible to identify distorted motions of parts of the molecules, for example, the CO_3 vibrations in solid $CaCO_3$. In the extreme case of loosely bonded molecules, the molecular motions are practically unaffected at high temperatures; it was mentioned in Section 6.7 that under such circumstances the molecules or radicals may be freely rotating. Consider as an example solid methane, in which the spherical CH_4 molecules are loosely held together by Van der Waals forces. The methane molecules are freely rotating at "high" temperatures. On reducing the energy content of the solid by cooling it to "low" temperatures, the rotational motion is found to die down in a cooperative way. The specific heat of methane,[6]

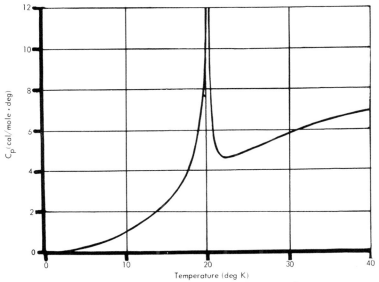

Fig. 7.4. Heat capacity of methane.[6]

given in Fig. 7.4, shows the familiar λ-peak. Structural studies,[7] in particular those in which magnetic resonance and neutron diffraction were used, reveal that the CH_4 molecules are freely rotating above $T_c = 20°K$. At lower temperatures, they perform hindered rotations or torsional oscillations backward and forward about a mean position.

The transition in solid hydrogen, treated in Section 6.9, is another well-known example of a cooperative onset of molecular rotation. In orthohydrogen, the axis of rotation, which is not unique above T_c, becomes ordered below the transition. Similar specific-heat singularities in hydrogen halides and in various ammonium salts were mentioned in Section 6.7. As a matter of fact, the specific-heat singularity in solid NH_4Cl, observed by Simon in 1922, was the first true λ-anomaly to be discovered. In many cases, the precise nature of molecular rotations is not yet clear, and the available evidence suggests that they differ from substance to substance. However, a discussion of the various individual cases[7] is not appropriate here.

7.5. FERROELECTRICITY

Solids belonging to ten of the thirty-two crystallographic classes lack inversion symmetry. They can exhibit electric polarization in the absence of an electric field, owing to the spontaneous alignment of electric dipoles. In contrast to the magnetic case, this electric polarization cannot be observed under ordinary static conditions, because it is compensated by free charges on the surfaces. However, the polarization is temperature-dependent, and so changes in it can be deduced from the current flowing in a closed circuit when the temperature of the crystal is changed. For this reason, substances belonging to the ten noncentrosymmetric classes are called *pyroelectric*.

Some pyroelectrics have the additional property that the spontaneous polarization can be reversed in sense by an applied electric field. The material is then said to be *ferroelectric*. Thus, in ferroelectrics the polarization can be measured simply by reversing the applied electric field. In nonferroelectric pyroelectrics, dielectric breakdown occurs well before a field large enough to reverse the polarization can be applied. The dielectric behavior of a ferroelectric is complex. Not only is the relation between the polarization P and the applied field E nonlinear, but there is also a hysteresis loop, analogous to the ferromagnetic case. The alignment of the dipoles is opposed by thermal agitation. On increasing the temperature, the ordering is disturbed, and at a critical temperature, the ferroelectric Curie point, it breaks up. The crystal loses its ferroelectricity and becomes an ordinary dielectric (paraelectric state). Rochelle salt, ammonium dihydrogen phosphate, barium titanate, and triglycine sulfate are among the well-known ferroelectrics. There are several excellent reviews of this field.[8]

The onset of ferroelectric ordering gives rise to λ-type peaks in the heat capacity. The behavior of potassium dihydrogen phosphate (KDP), which is ferroelectric below $123°K$, is typical of the specific-heat studies.[9] Superimposed on the usual lattice contribution is the configurational specific heat associated with ferroelectric ordering at $123°K$ (Fig. 7.5). The detailed behavior near the Curie point is slightly uncertain in most ferroelectrics because of the existence of thermal hysteresis; that is, the specific heat on cooling is slightly different from that on warming. The entropy associated with the excess specific heat is about 0.7 cal/mole·deg, which is close to the value $\frac{1}{2}R \ln 2$. The spontaneous polarization P_s decreases slowly as the temperature is raised from $0°K$, but drops rapidly as T_c is approached. Just as in the magnetic case [equation (4.17)], the excess specific heat should be proportional to dP_s^2/dT. This relationship is approximately obeyed in KDP.[10] Further, there is evidence[10a] that the specific heat near T_c may be fitted to logarithmic singularities, of the type discussed in Sections 4.6 and 4.7.

The similarity between ferroelectricity and ferromagnetism extends to other forms of ordering as well. Ferroelectricity and

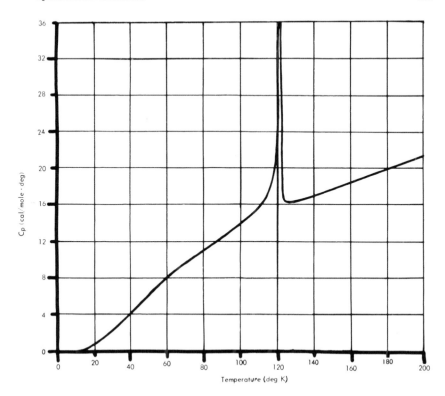

Fig. 7.5. Heat capacity of KH_2PO_4.[9]

antiferroelectricity are also known; these topics are discussed in the many reviews on the subject.[8] In spite of these similarities, the molecular basis of the electric phenomenon is apparently very different. Taking the example of KH_2PO_4, the deuterated KD_2PO_4 has a transition temperature ($\sim 213°K$) nearly double that of KDP. Yet the entropy associated with the transition is nearly the same in the two salts. The entropy excess suggests some form of order–disorder process, while the dependence on the mass of hydrogen shows that the hydrogen atoms are involved in the ordering. Indeed, the theoretical explanations of ferroelectricity, originally advanced by Mueller, Slater, and others, invoke an ordering of the hydrogen bonds. For a large number of compounds, order–disorder structures of the hydrogen bonds are possible.[8] In ionic ferroelectrics such as $BaTiO_3$, another mechanism has been suggested by Anderson, Cochran, and others.[11] This is based on the idea that in an optical mode (Section 2.8) the adjacent charges vibrate out of phase. If the restoring forces and hence the frequency tend to zero, a spontaneous separation of charges, which is nothing but the spontaneous polarization under consideration here, is possible. Thus, it is suggested that as the temperature is lowered the frequency of some optical mode decreases rapidly and becomes zero at T_c. Such a mechanism, which is supported by neutron-diffraction studies on $SrTiO_3$, explains many observations on $BaTiO_3$-type ferroelectrics. These questions are treated at length in the reviews already cited.

7.6. TRANSITIONS IN RARE-EARTH METALS

The rare-earth metals, lanthanum (atomic number $Z = 57$) to lutetium ($Z = 71$), can be isolated and purified only with some special techniques developed in the last twenty years. Much of the work done before 1950 was on impure metals; as seen earlier, the impurities often have very disturbing effects on specific heats. Recent studies[12] on relatively pure metals have shown very complicated thermal and magnetic properties. The rare-earth metals show unusual types of ferro- and antiferromagnetic orderings[13] which give rise to these complicated phenomena. Thus, a discussion of the heat capacity of rare-earth metals should belong to Chapter 4. However, on account of the variety of abnormal effects observed and the very large gaps in our knowledge, these matters are considered here.

The electronic structure of the rare-earth metals may be written as Xe core—$4f^n$; $5s^2$, $5p^6$; $6s^2$, $5d^1$—although some exchange between the $4f$; and $5d$-shells takes place. As the atomic number Z increases from 57 to 71, n increases from 0 to 14. The $4f$-shells are largely screened by the closed $5s$- and $5p$-shells, so that magnetic and Stark interactions are weak. As a result of the subtle balance between these interactions and the normal thermal energy, the metals show very complicated thermal, magnetic, and other properties. A brief account of the specific-heat behavior will highlight the challenging problems in the study of these metals.

Lanthanum ($Z = 57$, $n = 0$) has no $4f$-electron, is a superconductor, and behaves in a normal way.

Cerium has one $4f$-electron and exhibits the complex specific-heat behavior shown in Fig. 7.6. As the specimen is cooled from room temperature, the specific heat follows the curve A in the region $200 > T > 120°K$. On warming from a low temperature, the specific heat follows the curve B, exhibiting a pronounced thermal hysteresis. Some latent heat is also evolved in the region L around $100°K$. At $13°K$, there is a large peak in the specific heat, which is due to the onset of antiferromagnetism at lower temperatures. At about $200°K$,

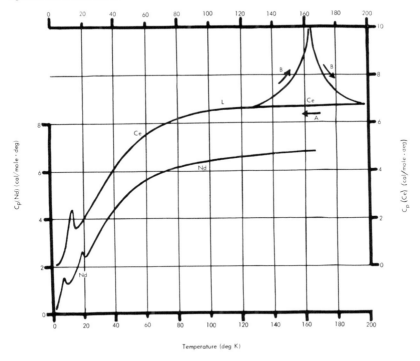

Fig. 7.6. Heat capacities of cerium and neodymium.[14]

the fcc lattice of cerium starts to undergo a transition into a compressed fcc' lattice of about 15 % less volume. Besides the fcc' phase, there is another hcp phase at low temperatures.[15] Apparently the fcc ⇌ fcc' transition is an electronic one in which the magnetic 4 f-electron goes over into the 5d conduction band. These phase changes involve very little rearrangement of atoms and show a pronounced dependence upon the stresses and strains in the crystal, past thermal history, and the state of crystalline imperfections. Thus, on repeated cooling to 20°K and warming to 300°K, the hysteresis loop at 160°K collapses and the peak at 13°K is enhanced. Such a sluggish dependence upon thermal history is characteristic of martensitic transformations,[16] of which another example, namely, that of sodium, was mentioned in Section 2.10. At the present time, however, there is no quantitative explanation of the hysteresis effects.

Praseodymium has a large specific-heat bump distributed around 40°K. Neodymium ($Z = 60$) has two peaks, one at 8°K and another at 19°K (Fig. 7.6). Below 8°K, there is an ordering into the ordinary antiferromagnetic state discussed in Section 4.2. The peak at 19°K is due to the onset of a special type of antiferromagnetism, which will be mentioned later (Fig. 7.8e). The peak in praseodymium also arises from a similar special type of antiferromagnetic ordering.[17]

The heat capacity of promethium, an element which has to be produced artificially, has not been studied so far. Samarium ($Z = 62$) has a sharp singularity at 15°K due to antiferromagnetic ordering. There is a second peak at 106°K, but as yet no corresponding anomaly in the magnetic behavior has been found. Europium is antiferromagnetic below about 90°K.

The ferromagnetism of gadolinium below 289°K is very well known. The specific heat has a large λ-singularity at that temperature (Fig. 7.7). The next five metals, in which n runs from 8 to 12, show complex ferro- and antiferromagnetic states. Terbium is paramagnetic down to 230°K, where it becomes ferromagnetic. Dysprosium (Fig. 7.7) is paramagnetic down to 175°K, when it becomes antiferromagnetic, and then at 85°K it becomes ferromagnetic. There is a large λ-peak at 175°K and a symmetrical peak at 85°K. Holmium behaves in a similar manner, with a λ-peak at the Néel point (132°K) and a symmetrical peak at the ferromagnetic Curie point of 20°K. In between the two temperatures, the specific heat rises rather nonuniformly, a feature which is aggravated in erbium (Fig. 7.7). Between its Néel point of 80°K and its Curie point of 19°K, there is a rounded maximum at 54°K, just discernible in the scale of Fig. 7.7. This arises from complications in magnetic ordering, which are discussed below. Thulium becomes antiferromagnetic on cooling to 15°K. With these metals, the specific heat at the ferromagnetic transition shows considerable hysteresis.

In yttrium ($Z = 70$), the $5d$-electron goes into the $4f$-shell, which otherwise should have $n = 13$, and completes it. Therefore, the metal does not exhibit any striking magnetic or thermal phenomena. Likewise, lutetium, which has a closed shell ($n = 14$) of $4f$-electrons, behaves normally.

Even this sketchy summary is enough to show that nearly every type of specific-heat abnormality is present in these metals. This complex behavior corresponds to the complicated magnetic structure, which is being slowly unravelled as a result of careful neutron-diffraction and magnetic measurements. Although the details of such studies[13] go beyond the scope of the present discussion, an indication of the complexity of the problem is appropriate here.

Simple cases of magnetic ordering were outlined in Section 4.2. Ferromagnetism corresponds to parallel alignment of adjacent spins and antiferromagnetism to antiparallel alignment. This simple arrangement holds good, for example, in ferromagnetic dysprosium,

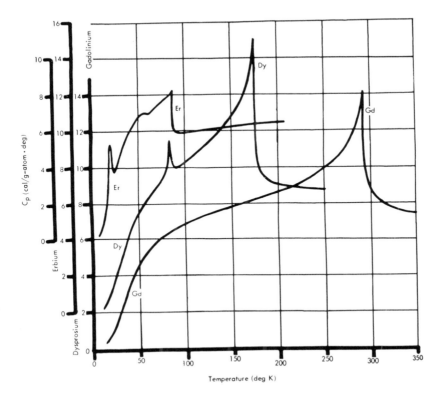

Fig. 7.7. Heat capacities of gadolinium, dysprosium, and erbium.[18] Note off-set scales for the ordinates.

$T < 85°$K, when the magnetic moments lie parallel in the basal plane (Fig. 7.8a). In the antiferromagnetic phase $(85° < T < 175°$K), the resultant moment in each plane is rotated by an angle α with respect to the moment in the next plane (Fig. 7.8b), the angle α changing with T. It is evident that the magnetic moments in the hexagonal lattice lie on a spiral, the characteristic helicoidal structure, and that this ordering has no net moment on a bulk scale. The same helicoidal arrangement is found in terbium, also.

Holmium is more complex. In the ferromagnetic state, the magnetic moment has a common component normal to the hexagonal planes and a helicoidally ordered component in the basal plane (Fig. 7.8c). Thus, the ferromagnetic moment of holmium below 20°K

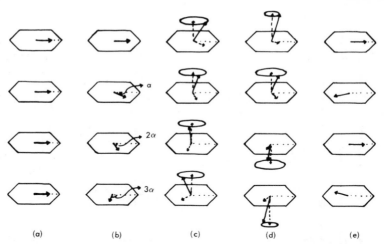

Fig. 7.8. Complex magnetic ordering in rare-earth metals: (a) collinear ferro-magnetism—dysprosium, (b) helicoidal antiferromagnetism—dysprosium, (c) helicoidal ferromagnetism—holmium and erbium, (d) cycloidal antiferro-magnetism—erbium, (e) transverse oscillatory antiparallel ordering—praseo-dymium and neodymium. The drawings are based on projections of regular hexagons. In (a), the vector (arrow) always points toward the horizontal vertex. In (b), the arrow moves uniformly in the plane, the rotation angles α, 2α, and 3α being shown. In (c), the arrow rotates uniformly in the ellipse so that its pro-jection in the plane (broken line) rotates uniformly in the plane while the projection perpendicular to the plane is constant. In (d), the projection in the plane rotates uniformly while the ellipses move up and down. In (e), the vector is always in the plane and lies on either side of the main diagonal in the second and fourth rows.

is due only to the component parallel to the hexagonal c-axis. This component decreases with the increase of T, and in the antiferro-magnetic state ($20 < T < 132°K$), only the helical structure remains.

Ferromagnetic erbium has a structure similar to that shown in Fig. 7.8c, a constant component along the c-axis and helicoidally arranged components in the basal plane. In the antiferromagnetic region ($19 < T < 80°K$), the magnitude and sign of the moment along c vary periodically from layer to layer in accordance with a sine law (Fig. 7.8d). Below about $52°K$, the moments in the basal plane are helicoidally ordered, but at higher temperatures they become dis-ordered. This change of the basal components makes itself felt in specific heats as a small bump at approximately $54°K$, which was mentioned earlier.

There remains one more type of magnetic ordering, which in the absence of any better name may be called *transverse oscillatory anti-*

parallel ordering. Neodymium below 7°K has the usual type of collinear antiparallel ordering of the moments, which lie on the basal plane. Between 7 and 19°K, there is a superimposed sinusoidal modulation of the basal moments in a direction perpendicular to the usual ordering direction (Fig. 7.8e). This ordering disappears above 19°K and gives rise to a specific-heat bump at 19°K. A similar situation exists in praseodymium, also.

Any theoretical discussion of such types of magnetic ordering is bound to be complicated,[13] though considerable progress has been made recently. With a very delicate balance between thermal and magnetic forces, the situation offers a challenge to theoreticians and experimenters alike to improve the existing knowledge of the phenomenon.

7.7. LIQUID–GAS CRITICAL POINTS

A perusal of the specific-heat singularities mentioned earlier brings out the fact that they are associated with some change in the ordered state or a phase change. The close relation of the thermal properties to molecular ordering has been the aim of the discussions, while the relation of phase changes to phenomenological considerations has been left to Section 8.1. The liquid–gas phase equilibrium is historically important for having been the source of the idea of the equation of state. At the liquid–gas critical point (for convenience simply called *critical point* in this section), the isothermal bulk modulus vanishes, differences between liquid and gaseous states disappear, and the region is dominated by molecular fluctuations. Obviously, unusual effects in thermal properties should be expected. Early experiments showed a large peak as the critical point was approached. In the related case of critical liquid–liquid mixtures, the existence of singular behavior in specific heat[19] and other properties has also been known for some time. Nevertheless, it is only recently that specific heats have been measured near enough to the critical point to reveal the unusual behavior. Since the compressibility of the system is high in the critical region, a direct measurement of the specific heat at constant volume C_v is possible using containers strong enough to withstand the critical pressure.

The first experiments of this kind were completed by Bagatskii, Voronel', and Gusak[20] on argon near its critical point; they showed that C_v had a tendency to become infinite at T_c. Subsequent work[20] by Voronel' and coworkers on oxygen and by Little and Muldover on ^{4}He has abundantly verified that C_v tends to an infinite value at T_c. In the helium case, experiments to within 10^{-4}°K of T_c show that the approach to infinity is logarithmic in $|T - T_c|$ both below and above T_c. The situation is very similar to the λ-transition at 2.17°K in liquid ^{4}He (Section 5.5), and the coefficient of the logarithmic term is of the same order in both cases. The behavior of argon and oxygen appears to be more complicated. The original discussion indicated a logarithmic approach both below and above T_c with the same slope (Fig. 7.9). Fisher[21] has analyzed the data again to show that although below T_c the approach is certainly logarithmic, above T_c it may be a power law of the form $c \propto (T - T_c)^{-1/5}$. Figure 7.9 shows the situation in the case of argon. Obviously, only further work can settle the exact nature of the approach to infinity on the high-temperature side.

The singularity in the specific heat at constant volume is of special interest. The experiments quoted earlier to show the possibility of infinite specific heats at some transitions all refer to the heat capacity at constant pressure or at constant saturation. Other parameters such as the coefficient of thermal expansion also show

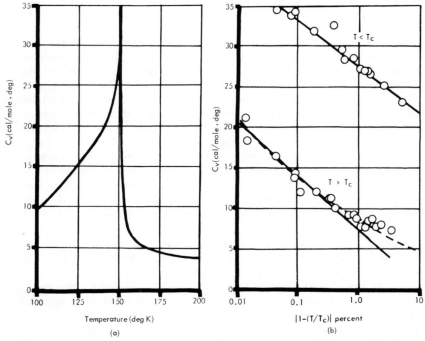

Fig. 7.9. (a) Heat capacity C_v of argon. (b) Behavior near its liquid–gas critical temperature $T_c = 150.5$°K. Full lines refer to logarithmic singularity both above and below T_c. Broken line is a power-law fit above T_c with an exponent $-\frac{1}{5}$.

singularities, and it was believed that though C_p is infinite, C_v remains finite. The phenomenological theories of phase transitions based on an expansion of some order parameters in powers of $|T - T_c|$, as originally done by Landau and Lifshitz, are based on such ideas. The experiments at the critical point show that, in some cases at least, such assumptions are not valid. The thermodynamic consequences of infinite singularities in C_v have been considered by several authors.[22] It is found, for instance, that the adiabatic compressibility should tend to zero at T_c; experiments on sound propagation in ^{4}He near the critical region verify this prediction.[23] It is somewhat amusing that while the theoretical two-dimensional Ising model gives a logarithmic infinity in C_v, it is only for an ideal incompressible lattice. The introduction of lattice compressibility results in a finite specific heat together with a latent heat at the transition.[24]

One might at first expect that the properties of gases are so well known that a satisfactory theory of the condensation into a liquid could easily be formulated. Unfortunately, it is not so. The interatomic forces in a gas normally play only a secondary role and may therefore be treated as small corrections to ideal gases. On the other hand, the phenomenon of condensation arises solely from the cohesive forces; in this limiting case, the usual methods of calculation do not work well. The principal theoretical contribution of sufficient generality is Mayer's demonstration of the existence of a condensation in the theory of nonideal gases.[7] Calculations based on simple models have been rather more successful. Mention should be made of Lee and Yang's analysis showing that the properties of a weakly interacting gas have some similarity to those of an Ising lattice (Section 4.6). The ferromagnetic ordering and the random paramagnetic arrangement are the respective formal analogs of the condensed and gaseous phases.[25] Near the transition temperature, the specific heats of ferromagnets and liquids show similar singularities, which lends some credence to this view, although it is not possible here to go into the details of the calculations.

7.8. MODELS OF COOPERATIVE TRANSITIONS

Having seen the variety of possible cooperative effects, it is obvious that no general theory of such phenomena is possible. The main difficulty in developing a theory of strongly interacting systems is that the total energy of the system can no longer be calculated from the simple sum of the energies of the individual particles, as was done earlier with systems of noninteracting particles. A natural way under such circumstances is to ask how the system is altered when a new particle is added to the existing N particles—in other words, to determine the response of the system to small perturbations. This approach is usually called the method of *Green's functions*; it is along these lines that much recent progress has been made. The mathematical techniques involved in such computations are quite esoteric. Even so, except for the case of superconductivity of electronic systems, no complete theory, applicable right up to the transition temperature, has been worked out for the phenomena of interest. Therefore, in an elementary text it is instructive to mention how the cooperative effect may be incorporated in simple models.

It turns out that the Ising lattice, introduced in connection with magnetic ordering (Section 4.6), is a reasonable model of many types of cooperative phenomena. In this model, spins are placed at lattice sites, and each spin can point along $+ Z$ or $- Z$. The interactions, which extend to nearest neighbors only, have two possible values, corresponding to parallel or antiparallel alignment of a pair of adjacent spins. It is not hard to see that the same model can be applied to order–disorder transformations, also. In such case, the atoms are at lattice sites and the atomic interactions have two possible values, corresponding to right or wrong pairing of nearest neighbors. Further, it was mentioned in the preceding section that the liquid–gas transformation can also be brought into the general scheme of Ising models. Other association problems, such as the ordering of hydrogen bonds, lead to similar mathematical calculations. Indeed, cooperative phenomena in quite different fields, such as traffic flow or melting of polymers, can be viewed against the same framework. Because of such varied applications, the Ising model has received considerable attention from theoreticians.[26]

It was mentioned in Section 4.6 that the exact solution of the three-dimensional Ising lattice has not been obtained so far. For two dimensions, Onsager showed in 1944 that the specific heat exhibits a logarithmic approach to infinity both above and below T_c. In three dimensions, approximate calculations show that the specific heat has the form

$$c \sim A \ln (T_c - T) + ... \qquad T < T_c$$
$$\sim B (T - T_c)^{-\alpha} + ... \qquad T > T_c, \alpha \sim \tfrac{1}{5}$$

although the behavior on the high-temperature side is not quite settled. The mathematical details of even these calculations are too specialized to be proper here.

The experimental evidence for a variety of transitions is consistent with the predicted variation in the lower temperature $(T < T_c)$ region. For $T > T_c$, the data can be fitted well by a power law in some cases and by a logarithmic term in some others. This remains a challenging unsolved problem.

Although the Ising lattice gives a workable model of configurational ordering, the complexity of the mathematical calculations has led to several further approximate models. The Weiss model of ferromagnetism and the Bragg–Williams model of order–disorder transitions and its extensions are some of the well-known simplifications of the Ising problem. All these calculations are still not quantitatively applicable to real physical systems, because of the restriction to nearest-neighbor interactions. Any consideration of more realistic interatomic forces appears to be too formidable a problem to be attempted at present.

So far, most λ-type specific-heat singularities have been ascribed to configurational ordering. The possibility exists, however, that the singularities may arise from the vibrational modes of the lattice. If some optical branch of the vibration spectrum approaches zero frequency, a λ-type of specific-heat singularity can result.[27] As mentioned in Section 7.5, if the frequency of an optical mode vanishes in an ionic crystal, it can give rise to ferroelectric polarization.

REFERENCES

1. D. H. Parkinson, *Rept. Progr. Phys.* **21**, 226 (1958).
2. L. A. K. Staveley, K. R. Hart, and W. I. Tupman, *Dis. Faraday Soc.* **15**, 130 (1953). G. N. Lewis, M. Randall, K. S. Pitzer, and L. Brewer, *Thermodynamics*, McGraw Hill, New York, 1961, chapter 25.
3. J. F. Cochran, *Ann. Phys. (N.Y.)* **19**, 186 (1962).
4. H. Lipson, *Progr. Metal Phys.* **2**, 1 (1950). T. Muto and Y. Takagi, *Solid State Phys.* **1**, 193 (1955). L. Guttman, *Solid State Phys.* **3**, 145 (1956). E. W. Elcock, *Order–Disorder Phenomena*, Methuen, London, 1956.
5. H. Moser, *Phys. Z.* **37**, 737 (1936). C. Sykes and H. Wilkinson, *J. Inst. Metals* **61**, 223 (1937). C. W. Garland, *Phys. Rev.* **135**, A1696 (1964).
6. K. Clusius, *Z. phys. Chem.* **B3**, 41 (1929). K. Clusius and A. Perlick, *Z. phys. Chem.* **B24**, 313 (1934). J. H. Colwell, E. K. Gill, and J. A. Morrison, *J. Chem. Phys.* **36**, 2223 (1962).
7. H. N. V. Temperley, *Changes of State*, Cleaver-Hume, London, 1956.
8. E. T. Jaynes, *Ferroelectricity*, Princeton University Press, Princeton, 1953. A. F. Devonshire, *Advan. Phys.* **3**, 85 (1954). P. W. Forsberg, *Handbuch der Physik*, *XVII*, 264 (1956). W. Kanzig, *Solid State Phys.* **4**, 1 (1957). H. D. Megaw, *Ferroelectricity in Crystals*, Methuen, London, 1957. F. Jona and G. Shirane, *Ferroelectric Crystals*, Pergamon, Oxford, 1962. W. J. Merz, *Progr. Dielectrics* **4**, 101 (1962). A. F. Devonshire, *Rept. Progr. Phys.* **27**, 1 (1964).
9. J. Mendelssohn and K. Mendelssohn, *Nature* **144**, 595 (1939). C. C. Stephenson and J. G. Hooley, *J. Am. Chem. Soc.* **66**, 1397 (1944).
10. A. von Arx and W. Bantle, *Helv. phys. acta* **16**, 211 (1943).
10a. B. A. Strukov, *Soviet Phys. Solid State* **6**, 2278 (1965). J. Grindlay, *Phys. Letters* **18**, 239 (1965).
11. W. Cochran, *Advan. Phys.* **9**, 387 (1960); **10**, 401 (1961).
12. F. H. Spedding, S. Levigold, A. H. Daane, and L. D. Jennings, *Progr. Low Temp. Phys.* **2**, 368 (1957).
13. K. P. Belov, R. Z. Levitin, and S. A. Nikitin, *Soviet Phys. Uspekhi* **7**, 179 (1964). K. Yosida, *Progr. Low Temp. Phys.* **4**, 265 (1964). W. C. Koehler, *J. Appl. Phys.* **36**, 1078 (1965).

14. D. H. Parkinson, F. E. Simon, and F. H. Spedding, *Proc. Roy. Soc. (London),* *Ser. A* **207**, 137 (1951). D. H. Parkinson and L. M. Roberts, *Proc. Phys. Soc. (London), Ser. B* **70**, 471 (1957). O. V. Lounasmaa, *Phys. Rev.* **133**, A502 (1964).
15. C. J. McHargue and H. L. Yakel, *Acta Met.* **8**, 637 (1960). M. K. Wilkinson, H. R. Child, C. J. McHargue, W. C. Koehler, and E. O. Wollan, *Phys. Rev.* **122**, 1409 (1961). K. A. Gschneidner, R. O. Elliot, and R. R. McDonald, *J. Phys. Chem. Solids* **23**, 555 (1962).
16. C. S. Barrett and M. Cohen, in: *Phase Transformations in Solids* (R. Smoluchowski, J. E. Mayer, and W. A. Weyl, editors), Wiley, New York, 1951, chapters 13 and 17. M. A. Jaswon, *Research* **11**, 315 (1958).
17. R. M. Moon, J. W. Cable, and W. C. Koehler, *J. Appl. Phys.* **35**, 1041 (1964). J. W. Cable, R. M. Moon, W. C. Koehler, and E. O. Wollan, *Phys. Rev. Letters* **12**, 553 (1964).
18. M. Griffel, R. E. Skochdopole, and F. H. Spedding, *Phys. Rev.* **93**, 657 (1954); *J. Chem. Phys.* **23**, 2258 (1955); **25**, 75 (1956).
19. M. Fixman, *J. Chem. Phys.* **36**, 1957 (1962).
20. M. I. Bagatskii, A. V. Voronel', and V. G. Gusak, *Soviet Phys. JETP* **16**, 517 (1963). A. V. Voronel', Ya. R. Chashkin, V. A. Popov, and V. G. Simkin, *Soviet Phys. JETP* **18**, 568 (1964). W. A. Little and M. Moldover, *Proceedings of the Ninth International Conference on Low Temperature Physics* (Columbus, Ohio, 1964), Plenum Press, New York, 1965, p. 653.
21. M. E. Fisher, *Phys. Rev.* **136**, A1599 (1964).
22. M. Ya. Azbel, A. V. Voronel', and M. Sh. Giterman, *Soviet Phys. JETP* **19**, 457 (1964). C. N. Yang and C. P. Yang, *Phys. Rev. Letters* **13**, 303 (1964). R. B. Griffiths, *Phys. Rev. Letters* **14**, 623 (1965).
23. C. E. Chase, R. C. Williamson, and L. Tisza, *Phys. Rev. Letters* **13**, 467 (1964).
24. O. K. Rice, *J. Chem. Phys.* **22**, 1535 (1954). C. Domb, *J. Chem. Phys.* **25**, 783 (1956).
25. T. L. Hill, *Statistical Mechanics*, McGraw-Hill, New York, 1956, chapters 5 and 7.
26. G. F. Newell and E. W. Montroll, *Rev. Mod. Phys.* **25**, 353 (1953). H. S. Green and C. A. Hurst, *Order–Disorder Phenomena*, Interscience, New York, 1964.
27. H. B. Rosenstock, *J. Chem. Phys.* **35**, 420 (1961).

Chapter 8

Miscellaneous Problems in Specific Heats

8.1. SPECIFIC HEAT NEAR PHASE TRANSITIONS

In the previous chapters, various aspects of specific heats of solids, liquids, and gases have been discussed. It is a common experience to find that two phases can coexist over a range of pressure and temperature. Consider, for instance, water and its vapor contained in a vessel of volume V. If the temperature is raised slightly, a small quantity of water is converted into steam, absorbing latent heat in the process, and a new equilibrium pressure is established. In a P–T plane (Fig. 8.1), this will be represented as an equilibrium curve. Quantities such as the density, specific heat, and compressibility remain finite but different in the two phases. An interesting relation among the thermodynamic quantities at such an equilibrium curve is furnished by the Clausius–Clapeyron equation. To derive this, apply Maxwell's relation $(\partial P/\partial T)_v = (\partial S/\partial V)_T$ [equation (1.11)] to the

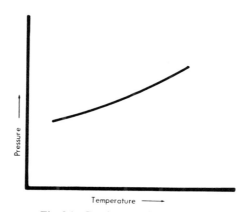

Fig. 8.1. Coexistence of two phases.

181

system. The latent heat L_{12} is equal to $T\,dS$ at the phase boundary, and so

$$\frac{DP}{DT} = \frac{S_2 - S_1}{V_2 - V_1} = \frac{L_{12}}{T(V_2 - V_1)} \qquad (8.1)$$

where D/DT stands for the derivative along the equilibrium curve. This simple equation, in which all the quantities can be determined experimentally, forms a rigorous practical test of the first and second laws of thermodynamics. Nowadays, it is often used to calculate or check the latent heat when the vapor pressure of the liquid is known.

It turns out that this type of equilibrium among the phases is only one of the many possible types of phase changes.[1] The superconducting phase transition at zero field (Section 3.9) shows no latent heat or volume change. Then the right-hand side of equation (8.1), being of the form 0/0, is indeterminate, whereas the left-hand side is found to have a definite value in practice. The Weiss model of ferromagnetism (Section 4.5) and the Bragg–Williams model of order–disorder transition (Section 7.3) show a similar behavior. There are other phase changes where the specific heats become infinite. Magnetic transitions (Section 4.7) and the λ-transition in liquid ^{4}He (Section 5.5) show logarithmic infinities in specific heats. It is obvious that the above simple considerations of phase equilibria must be generalized to include these possibilities.

It is convenient to start from the general thermodynamic condition for phase equilibrium, namely, the equality of the Gibbs' function of the two phases:

$$G_1 = G_2 \qquad (8.2)$$

Further, $(\partial G/\partial T)_p = -S$ and $(\partial G/\partial P)_T = V$ [equation (1.10)]. In the ordinary phase change considered above, there are changes in V and S, that is, in the first derivatives of G. Ehrenfest suggested that such changes should be called *transitions of the first order*. The condition for equilibrium along the equilibrium line (Fig. 8.1) is

$$\left(\frac{\partial G_1}{\partial P}\right)_T \delta P + \left(\frac{\partial G_1}{\partial T}\right)_P \delta T = \left(\frac{\partial G_2}{\partial P}\right)_T \delta P + \left(\frac{\partial G_2}{\partial T}\right)_P \delta T$$

or, rearranging,

$$\frac{DP}{DT} = \frac{S_2 - S_1}{V_2 - V_1}$$

which is the Clausius–Clapeyron equation. In the superconducting transition, there is no volume or entropy change, but the specific heat and compressibility are different; that is to say, the first derivatives of G are continuous but the second derivatives are not. Therefore, they are called *phase changes of the second order*. For such changes, consider the equilibrium along segments of S and V curves:

$$\left(\frac{\partial S_1}{\partial P}\right)_T \delta P + \left(\frac{\partial S_1}{\partial T}\right)_P \delta T = \left(\frac{\partial S_2}{\partial P}\right)_T \delta P + \left(\frac{\partial S_2}{\partial T}\right)_P \delta T$$

$$\left(\frac{\partial V_1}{\partial P}\right)_T \delta P + \left(\frac{\partial V_1}{\partial T}\right)_P \delta T = \left(\frac{\partial V_2}{\partial P}\right)_T \delta P + \left(\frac{\partial V_2}{\partial T}\right)_P \delta T$$

so

$$\frac{DP}{DT} = \frac{1}{TV} \frac{C_{p2} - C_{p1}}{\beta_2 - \beta_1} = \frac{\beta_2 - \beta_1}{k_{T2} - k_{T1}} \tag{8.3}$$

where β is the volume expansion coefficient and k_T is the isothermal compressibility. Equations (8.3) are called *Ehrenfest relations* for second-order phase changes and can also be obtained by applying L'Hospital's rule to equation (8.1) under these conditions. The super-conducting phase change at zero field is a practical example of a second-order phase change. The available evidence (Section 3.9) is in reasonable agreement with the Ehrenfest relations. Theoretically, still higher order phase changes can exist, but so far no such cases have been experimentally observed.

In some situations, quantities such as the specific heat and volume expansion become infinite, when equation (8.3) reduces to an indeterminacy of the form ∞/∞. A simple way of handling these λ-transitions was suggested by Pippard in 1956. Since C_p becomes very large near T_λ, the entropy–temperature curve must have an almost vertical tangent at T_λ. On the other hand, S_λ will be a smooth function of P, so that we may take S as a function of T and P to be cylindrical in shape near T_λ. Thus,

$$S(P,T) = S_\lambda + f(P - \alpha T)$$

where α is the pressure coefficient of the λ-point $(DP/DT)_\lambda$ and f is some function describing how the curve approaches the λ-point. Then

$$\left(\frac{\partial^2 S}{\partial P^2}\right)_T = f'' \qquad \left(\frac{\partial^2 S}{\partial T \partial P}\right) = -\alpha f'' \qquad \left(\frac{\partial^2 S}{\partial T^2}\right)_p = \alpha^2 f''$$

so that

$$\alpha = \frac{DP}{DT} = -\frac{(\partial^2 S/\partial T^2)_p}{\partial^2 S/\partial T \partial P} = -\frac{\partial^2 S/\partial T \partial P}{(\partial^2 S/\partial P^2)_T}$$

Making use of the Maxwell's relation [equation (1.11)],

$$\frac{\partial}{\partial T}\left(\frac{\partial S}{\partial T}\right)_p = \alpha\frac{\partial}{\partial T}\left(\frac{\partial V}{\partial T}\right)_p$$

and

$$\frac{\partial}{\partial P}\left(\frac{\partial S}{\partial T}\right)_p = \alpha\ \frac{\partial}{\partial P}\left(\frac{\partial V}{\partial T}\right)_p$$

Physically, these equations mean that in the vicinity of the λ-line $(\partial S/\partial T)_p$ is a linear function of $(\partial V/\partial T)_p$, and so

$$C_p = \left(\frac{DP}{DT}\right)_\lambda TV\beta + \text{constant} \tag{8.4a}$$

If $V(P,T)$ is treated in the same manner as $S(P,T)$, $(\partial V/\partial T)_p$ is seen to be a linear function of $(\partial V/\partial p)_T$ near the λ-point, and so

$$\beta = \left(\frac{DP}{DT}\right)_\lambda k_T + \text{constant} \tag{8.4b}$$

The relations (8.4) are called *Pippard's relations* for the λ-transition, and the cylindrical approximation should hold good very near the transition temperature. For several λ-type phase changes, the relations are found to be obeyed reasonably well. Figure 8.2 shows

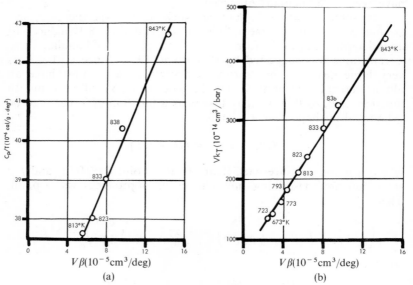

Fig. 8.2. Pippard's relations near $\alpha \rightleftharpoons \beta$ transition of quartz[2] at 574°C: (a) c_p/T versus $V\beta$ [equation (8.4a)], (b) $V\beta$ versus Vk_T [equation (8.4b)].

how closely ordinary α-quartz follows equations (8.4) slightly below its transition temperature ($\sim$ 574°C) to the β-form.[2] More detailed studies on liquid ^{4}He (Section 5.5) and ammonium chloride[3] show that equations (8.4) are obeyed quite well, but that its range of validity is much smaller above the transition than at lower temperatures.

In solids, other general relations are possible,[4] but so far they have found little use. Simple discussions of the various models of phase transitions and their application to physical systems are available elsewhere,[1,5] rendering a further analysis unnecessary here.

8.2. SPECIFIC HEAT AT SATURATED VAPOR PRESSURE

The discussion of the specific-heat behavior at coexistent phases leads naturally to an important mode of calorimetry, namely, the measurement of specific heat at constant saturation. Consider again the example of a liquid in contact with its saturated vapor in a closed vessel. C_p and C_v may easily be defined for the pure phases, but not for the total system. The heat applied at constant pressure is utilized as latent heat for evaporating the liquid without any rise of temperature, and an indeterminate infinite value of C_p will be calculated. Under such conditions, it is best to consider what happens if the heating is done with the assumption that the pressure on the liquid is not constant but equal to the saturated vapor pressure corresponding to the temperature of the liquid. Using once again the notation D/DT for heating along the liquid–vapor equilibrium curve, as in Fig. 8.1,

$$C_{\text{sat}} = T\frac{DS}{DT} \tag{8.5}$$

The relation between C_{sat} and C_p of a liquid or vapor is easily found. For any quantity x, the variations at constant P and along the P–T equilibrium curve are connected by

$$\frac{Dx}{DT} = \left(\frac{\partial x}{\partial T}\right)_p + \left(\frac{\partial x}{\partial P}\right)_T \frac{DP}{DT}$$

Using Maxwell's relation $(\partial S/\partial P)_T = -(\partial V/\partial T)_p$ [equation (1.11)], it follows that

$$\frac{DS}{DT} = \left(\frac{\partial S}{\partial T}\right)_p - \left(\frac{\partial V}{\partial T}\right)_p \frac{DP}{DT}$$

Hence

$$C_{\text{sat}} = C_p - TV\beta\frac{DP}{DT} \tag{8.6}$$

which was the relation mentioned in Section 5.2. For a solid in contact with its vapor, C_{sat}, defined as for a liquid, may be taken equal to C_p for most practical purposes because the expansion coefficient and vapor pressure are both very small. In a liquid, $(C_p - C_{sat})/C_p$ is nearly zero at low temperatures and becomes about 10 to 20% near the boiling point. For a vapor, the situation is very different, because the volume expansion β is 10 to 100 times larger than that of the liquid. In fact, C_{sat} becomes negative at temperatures near the boiling point. Thus, superheated steam gets hotter if expanded adiabatically, a fact which is of importance in practical engineering applications.

If C_{s1} denotes the specific heat of the liquid at constant saturation and C_{s2} that of the vapor,

$$\frac{DL_{12}}{DT} = \frac{D}{DT}[T(S_2 - S_1)] = S_2 - S_1 + T\left(\frac{DS_2}{DT} - \frac{DS_1}{DT}\right)$$

$$= \frac{L_{12}}{T} + C_{s2} - C_{s1}$$

or

$$C_{s2} - C_{s1} = \frac{DL_{12}}{DT} - \frac{L_{12}}{T} \tag{8.7}$$

Equations (8.6) and (8.7) are of use in evaluating the specific heats if the liquid and its vapor are placed in a closed vessel to which heat is applied. Under these conditions, which are quite common in the calorimetry of liquids, the heat is used not only in heating the liquid and vapor but also in supplying latent heat. A full discussion of the procedures to be adopted under such conditions is given by Rowlinson.[6]

8.3. RELAXATION OF ROTATIONAL AND VIBRATIONAL SPECIFIC HEATS

It was mentioned in Section 4.8 that in paramagnetic salts the magnetic susceptibility shows dispersion as a function of the frequency of measurements. This paramagnetic relaxation arises basically because the magnetic dipoles require a finite time, of the order of 10^{-6} to 10^{-3} sec at room temperature, to attain thermal equilibrium with the lattice. So the susceptibility changes gradually from its isothermal low-frequency value to the adiabatic high-frequency value when the period of the applied AC signal scans the region of the relaxation time. A very similar phenomenon occurs if the ratio of the specific heats $\gamma = C_p/C_v$ is determined from the velocity of sound,

$c = (\gamma P/\rho)^{1/2}$. From its normal value at low frequencies, it increases to a limiting high-frequency value as the frequency of the sound wave becomes greater than the reciprocal of some relaxation time. For example, in hydrogen at STP, the velocity of sound increases by about 9% as the frequency becomes approximately 100 Mcps, which is just what is expected if C_p/C_v increases from 1.40 to 1.67. The obvious interpretation of this acoustic relaxation would be that the rotational degrees of freedom require a finite time, of the order of 10^{-7} sec at STP, to come to equilibrium with the translatory motion.

Since the original observations on carbon dioxide in 1925 by Pierce, acoustical relaxation has been observed in numerous gases, liquids, solutions, and gas mixtures at frequencies from 10 to 10^9 cps. However, the velocity does not always increase with the relaxation of all the rotational degrees of freedom as in the simple case considered above. Rotations about different axes may have different relaxation times τ. Further, each vibrational mode has its characteristic τ, and it is found that structural relaxation is possible in liquids, because the disturbances of the atomic structure caused by a sound wave take a finite time to attain the new values. Therefore, the interest in the field has been not so much concerned with the study of specific heats as with the molecular processes in liquids and gases. The rather extensive literature on the subject is adequately summarized in several places.[7]

8.4. DEFECTS IN SOLIDS

The solidified inert gases are often regarded as particularly simple solids. The interatomic forces are known reasonably well; therefore, a calculation of the heat capacity of the lattice, as in Chapter 2, should completely explain their specific heats. It turns out that this is not quite the case. The specific heat of solid argon,[8] shown in Fig. 8.3a, reveals a peculiar feature. As the melting point is approached, the specific heat rises very much above the Dulong–Petit value of about 6.5 cal/mole·deg. Solid krypton,[8] solid ^{3}He,[9] and in fact a variety of solids[10] show a similar marked upward trend in specific heat below the melting point.

Such an increase above the classical value may arise from three causes: anharmonicity, the phenomenon of premelting, or generation of defects in the solid state. Detailed calculations show that in most cases anharmonic effects give an increase of C_p no more than about a tenth of the observed excess. Premelting of solids[11] is a term applied to the phenomenon of abnormally large values of heat capacity and other properties sometimes observed very close to the melting point T_M. In these cases, the liquids also exhibit abnormally large values of

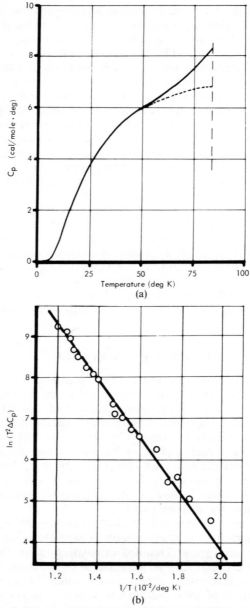

Fig. 8.3. (a) Heat capacity of solid argon (full line). Broken line is the value expected from the behavior below 40°K. (b) Plot of $\ln(T^2 \Delta C_p)$ against $1/T$.[8]

the various parameters as the freezing point is approached, the phenomenon of aftermelting in liquids.[10] They may arise from actual melting, at temperatures slightly different from the nominal T_M, in the regions of singularities such as dislocations and grain boundaries, where impurities have segregated. Then the latent heat associated with such regions may be measured as a pseudo specific heat. The subject appears to be somewhat controversial, because some authors[12] have carefully looked for these anomalies but did not find any. All the same, the magnitude and range of the excess specific heat in Fig. 8.3a rule out premelting as the cause of the observed behavior; there is now growing evidence that the explanation is to be sought in the thermal excitation of defects in the solid state.

Studies of diffusion, optical properties, and other phenomena in solids indicate that at temperatures above $T \approx \theta$, the perfect lattice arrangement is disturbed by various kinds of defects.[13] For example, an atom may have moved away from its lattice position, leaving a hole at its site, a vacancy defect, and an atom may occupy a nonlattice vacant space amid other atoms which are at their lattice positions, an interstitial atom. In a simple way, if ε_d is the energy needed to form a defect, the number of defects n_d at any temperature T will be given by a Boltzmann factor

$$n_d = n_0 \exp\left(-\frac{\varepsilon_d}{kT}\right)$$

and the specific-heat contribution from such defects will be

$$\Delta C_v = \frac{d}{dT}(n_d \varepsilon_d) = \frac{n_0 \varepsilon_d^2}{kT^2} \exp\left(-\frac{\varepsilon_d}{kT}\right) \tag{8.8}$$

Thus, a plot of $\ln(T^2 \Delta C_v)$ against $1/T$ should be a straight line with a slope $-\varepsilon_d/k$. Similarly, a plot of $\ln(T^2 \Delta C_p)$ against $1/T$ will be a straight line with a slope $-h_d/k$, where h_d is the enthalpy of formation of a defect. Figure 8.3b shows such a plot; the observations do fit the theoretical linear relationship with $h_d \sim 1250$ cal/mole in solid argon. The value is uncertain to about $\pm 5\%$, because ΔC_p depends slightly upon the method used to extrapolate the specific heat from below about $40°K$ in Fig. 8.3a. Similar $\Delta C_p = AT^{-2} \exp(-B/T)$ variations have been observed in solid ^3He and other substances.

Since the atomic forces and crystal structure of solidified inert gases are well known, several attempts have been made to calculate the values of h_d from theoretical models; the values come out to be about 30% higher than the experimental results. The discrepancy arises from the fact that in the earlier models no relaxation of the stress field was assumed. On the other hand, it is more plausible that the atoms surrounding a vacancy defect move in slightly to reduce the void, so that the volume of the vacancy is less than that of the atom which left that site. When this is taken into account,[14] there is better agreement with the experiments.

Similar specific-heat effects resulting from the presence of defects in the lattice structure are produced by heavy mechanical deformation,[15] neutron irradiation,[16] and self-irradiation in radioactive materials. In some cases, the specific heat is reduced, for example, by defects acting as traps for charge carriers in semiconductors and thereby reducing the number of "free" electrons or holes.

8.5. SURFACE EFFECTS

In the simple discussion of specific heats so far, it has been generally assumed that the internal energy, and hence the specific heat, is proportional to the mass of the substance; that is, they are extensive quantities (Section 1.2). As a matter of fact, statistical mechanics shows that this is a very good approximation (Section 2.5). Nevertheless, in special circumstances, as with finely divided powders, a contribution proportional to the surface area must be considered. It is qualitatively easy to visualize the nature of the effects, taking for simplicity the Debye model for an enumeration of the frequency distribution. In a finite solid, besides the longitudinal and transverse waves which propagate through the solid as if in an infinite medium, there are surface waves of the type considered by Rayleigh, Love, and others. The enumeration of the number of frequencies in a three-dimensional volume V, as in Section 2.5, gives the number of frequencies below v as being proportional to Vv^3, while it is evident that a similar calculation for a two-dimensional surface of area S will give a term proportional to Sv^2. Thus, the addition of surface contributions to the Debye term will result in

$$g(v)\, dv = \alpha_1 V v^2\, dv + \alpha_2 S v\, dv$$

The corresponding low-temperature specific heat will be

$$C_v = \beta_1 V T^3 + \beta_2 S T^2 \tag{8.9}$$

This behavior is indeed found in the specific heat of powdered materials. Figure 8.4 shows the specific heat, in the liquid-helium range, of MgO powder with an area of about 160 M^2/g, which corresponds to an edge length of about 100 Å if all the particles are in the form of cubes.[17] The specific heat is represented well by an equation $C = 0.00459 T^3 + 0.163 T^2$ mJ/mole·deg, in which the T^3-term is the usual Debye term.

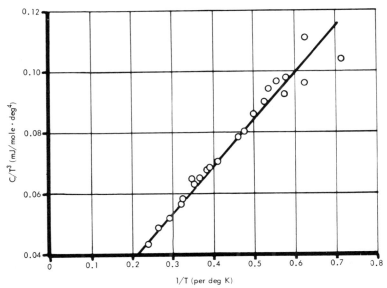

Fig. 8.4. Heat capacity of powdered magnesium oxide with grains of about 100 Å size.[17]

The full calculation of the surface contribution is a complex problem which as yet has not been solved satisfactorily. In the continuum model, it is possible to calculate with some difficulty the surface and volume modes of plates and rectangular parallelopipeds.[18] Apart from the usual shortcomings of a continuum model, there is a further assumption that the elastic behavior is not affected by the size of the specimen. On the other hand, it is obvious that the atoms near the surfaces are acted upon by forces very different from those exerted upon the atoms in the interior. Therefore, there is a spatial inhomogeneity of the lattice. The calculations with models of finite lattices are so involved that only beginnings have been made.[19] They show that, apart from the low-temperature effect given by equation (8.9), there should be very small differences at higher temperatures, because of the change in optical frequencies resulting from the presence of surface boundaries. The experimental observations are scanty, but it appears that the ST^2-term in equation (8.9) is two to three times larger than the theoretical estimates.[18] A full comparison between theory and experiment is not easy, because under the experimental conditions, in addition to the total surface area, the shape of the individual particles may also have some influence. Further, the possibility of thermal motions of whole grains of the substance, behaving as though they were giant macromolecules, cannot be eliminated. The experiments also suffer from the fact that attaining thermal equilibrium in a fine powder is difficult. There is a real need for further experimental and theoretical studies.

8.6. COMPILATIONS OF SPECIFIC-HEAT DATA

A knowledge of specific heat is useful in so many fields of study that the literature on heat capacities is very extensive and is reported in diverse publications. Without the abstracting services of *Chemical Abstracts* and *Physics Abstracts*, the task of searching for the data on any particular material would be inordinately laborious. Apart from these sources, perhaps the best single reference, if the heat capacity of any substance is needed, is the sixth edition of *Landolt–Börnstein Zahlenwerte and Funktionen, Vol. 2, Part* 4 (Springer-Verlag, Berlin, 1961, 863 pages). This gives an exhaustive listing of the heat capacities of almost all materials investigated before 1958-1959. Special data of cryogenic interest are collected in the various publications of the National Bureau of Standards Cryogenic Engineering Laboratory, Boulder, Colorado. For example, *A Compendium of the Properties of Materials at Low Temperatures* (V. J. Johnson, editor, 1957) and *Specific Heats and Enthalpies of Technical Solids at Low Temperatures* (by R. J. Corruccini and J. J. Gniewek, 1960) contain useful information about the specific heat and other properties below 300°K. There are, of course, other reports by several groups of workers on various aspects of specific-heat studies, such as Debye temperatures or the properties of metals and gases; the references to them may be found without difficulty from the recent reviews cited at the end of the earlier chapters.

In the construction of calorimeters and other pieces of cryogenic equipment, various low-melting solders, glues, varnishes, and technical solids are often used. Their specific heats are needed for the design of such apparatus, especially because weight-for-weight they may contribute more thermal capacity than the standard construction materials such as copper, brass, and stainless steel. Unfortunately, the heat capacity depends upon the purity, method of preparation, and composition of these substances, so that for accurate work each sample must be individually investigated. For many other purposes, it is convenient to have some approximate values. Even so, no handy tabulation of the many measurements is available, and hence Table 8.I is given here as a summary of the properties of several such auxiliary materials used in cryogenic equipment.

The specific heats of several materials are quite high compared to those of, say, copper. In particular, if the heat capacity of some

Table 8.I. Specific Heats c_p (in mJ/g·deg K)

T (deg K)	Cu	W.M.	So.So.	Aral.	Gly.	Bak.	G.E.	Pyr.
2	0.03	0.06	0.06	0.24	0.4	—	0.31	0.025
5	0.16	1.39	1.17	4.6	4.8	5.3	6.1	0.38
10	0.86	13.4	11.7	27.2	22	19.2	—	4.2
20	7.7	46.0	47.5	81.1	110	66.7	—	27.4
50	99	—	—	—	380	237	—	—
100	254	—	—	—	1150	—	—	—
300	386	—	—	—	—	—	—	—

T (deg K)	Sil.	Cons.	Man.	Mon.	St.St.	Tef.	Poly.	GR-S
2	0.02	0.23	0.15	0.22	0.03	0.3	—	—
5	0.35	0.56	0.5	0.55	0.2	2.4	1.2	4.2
10	4.0	1.69	—	1.7	0.8	18	9.6	28
20	24.4	6.8	—	7.1	6	76	67.2	113
50	111	83	—	—	74	202	330	338
100	268	238	—	240	251	386	657	612
300	738	—	—	430	490	1010	2370	1900

W.M. Wood's Metal (12.5 wt-% Sn, 12.5% Cd, 25% Pb, 50% Bi; m.p. 68°C). D. H. Parkinson and J. E. Quarrington, *Brit. J. Appl. Phys.* **5**, 219 (1954). Superconducting below $\sim$ 5°K.

So.So. Soft solder (40 wt-% Pb, 60% Sn; m.p. $\sim$ 185°C). J. de Nobel and F. J. du Chatenier, *Physica* **29**, 1231 (1963). Superconducting below $\sim$7°K. Other compositions also investigated.

Aral. Araldite Type I (baked according to instructions from manufacturers). D. H. Parkinson and J. E. Quarrington, *Brit. J. Appl. Phys.* **5**, 219 (1954).

Gly. Glyptal varnish (air-dried at room temperature). N. Pearlman and P. H. Keesom, *Phys. Rev.* **88** 398 (1952). P. H. Keesom and G. Seidel, *Phys. Rev.* **113**, 33 (1959).

Bak. Formite bakelite varnish V11105. R. W. Hill and P. L. Smith, *Phil. Mag.* **44**, 636 (1953).

G.E. G.E. varnish 7031. N. E. Phillips, *Phys. Rev.* **114**, 676 (1959).

Pyr. Pyrex glass. P. L. Smith and N. M. Wolcott, *Phil. Mag.* **1**, 854 (1956). Between 1.5 and 4.2°K, $c \approx 3.1 \times 10^{-3} T^3$ mJ/g·deg.

Sil. Silica glass (vitreous silica or fused quartz). F. E. Simon and F. Lange, *Z. Physik* **38**, 227 (1926). E. F. Westrum, quoted in R. C. Lord and J. C. Morrow, *J. Chem. Phys.* **26**, 230 (1957). P. Flubacher, A. J. Leadbetter, J. A. Morrison, and B. Stoicheff, *J. Phys. Chem. Solids* **12**, 53 (1959).

Cons. Constantan (60 wt-% Cu, 40% Ni). A. Eucken and H. Werth, *Z. anorg. allgem. Chem.* **188**, 152 (1930). W. H. Keesom and B. Kurrelmeyer, *Physica* **7**, 1003 (1940). J. C. Ho, H. R. O'Neal, and N. E. Phillips, *Rev. Sci. Instr.* **34**, 782 (1963), find a T^{-2} increase of specific heat below 0.3°K.

Man. Manganin (87% Cu, 13% Mn). J. C. Ho, H. R. O'Neal, and N. E. Phillips, *Rev. Sci. Instr.* **34**, 782 (1963). Between 0.25 and 1.5°K, $c \sim 0.0580T + 0.0112T^{-2}$ mJ/g·deg K.

Mon.   Monel (67 wt-% Ni, 30% Cu, 1.5% Fe, 1% Mn). W. F. Hampton and J. H.
        Mennie, *Can. J. Res.* **7**, 677 (1932). W. H. Keesom and B. Kurrelmeyer,
        Physica **7**, 1003 (1940).

St.St. Stainless steel. R. Kohlhass and M. Braun, *Arch. Eisenhüttenw.* **34**, 391 (1963).
        F. J. du Chatenier, B. M. Boerstoel, and J. de Nobel, *Physica* **31**, 1061 (1965).
        Below $\sim 300°K$, values are nearly the same for γ-iron, manganese steel, and
        chrome–nickel steel.

Tef.   Teflon (polytetrafluoroethylene). Material has a transition around 160°K.
        G. T. Furukawa, R. E. McCoskey, and G. J. King, *J. Res. Nat. Bur. Std.* **49**, 273
        (1952). Between 1.4 and 4.2°K, R. J. Noer, C. W. Dempsey, and J. E. Gordon,
        Bull. Am. Phys. Soc. **4**, 108 (1959), give $c \sim 40 \times 10^{-3}T^3$ mJ/g·deg for teflon,
        $c \sim 63 \times 10^{-3}T^3$ for polystyrene, and $c \sim 35 \times 10^{-3}T^3$ for lucite. W. Reese
        and J. E. Tucker, *J. Chem. Phys.* **43**, 105 (1965), give values for teflon, nylon, and
        Kel–F (1 to 4°K) also.

Poly.   Amorphous polyethylene. Glassy transition 200°K. B. Wunderlich, *J. Chem.
        Phys.* **37**, 1203 (1962). (Material with various degrees of crystallinity also
        investigated.) I. V. Sochava and O. N. Trepeznikova, *Soviet Phys. Doklady* **2**,
        164 (1957). (Data for polyvinyl alcohol also given.)

GR-S.   GR-S (Buna S) rubber (1,3-butadiene with 25 wt-% styrene). Second-order
        transition with hysteresis around 210°K. R. D. Rands, W. F. Ferguson, and
        J. L. Prather, *J. Res. Nat. Bur. Std.* **33**, 63 (1944). Natural rubber studied by
        N. Bekkedahl and H. Matheson, *J. Res. Nat. Bur. Std.* **15**, 505 (1934).

substance with low specific heat is to be measured, the thermal
capacity of a small amount of glue or solder used for attaching the
heater or thermometer may be comparable to that of the specimen
under study. Further, constantan and manganin, widely used for
winding heaters, are quite unsuitable below about 0.5°K because
of the T^{-2} increase. At 0.1°K, for example, the specific heat of
manganin is nearly 10^3 times that of copper.

8.7. TABULATIONS OF SPECIFIC-HEAT FUNCTIONS

The Einstein and Debye functions are widely used in calculating
the thermodynamic properties of gases and solids, as discussed in
detail elsewhere in this monograph. The Debye function for the
internal energy is also useful in cryogenic practice for calculating the
amount of refrigeration needed to cool an apparatus. For example,
let us calculate the amount of liquid ^{4}He spent if its latent heat, equal
to 0.62 cal/cc, is used to cool 1 gram-atom of copper (1 gram-atom =
63.6 g of copper, Debye temperature of copper $\approx 310°K$) from 300,
90, or 20°K to 4.2°K. Strictly, it is the change in enthalpy $\Delta H = \int C_p dT$
of copper which must be used for this purpose rather than an estimate
of the change in the internal energy $\Delta E = \int C_v dT$. However, $C_p - C_v$,
which depends upon the expansion coefficient and compressibility
and hence is not easily tabulated as a function of T/θ, is usually small
enough to permit the calculation to be done using ΔE without any
serious error. Further, copper has no specific-heat anomaly in this

Table 8.II

T	$\dfrac{\theta}{T}$	$\dfrac{E(\text{Debye})}{3RT}$	$E(\text{Debye})$ cal/mole
300	1.03	0.666	1200
90	3.44	0.233	126
20	15.5	0.005	0.6
4.2	74	0.00004	0.001

region. So for various values of θ/T, we look up the values of the Debye energy function $E(\text{Debye})/3RT$ in the *Appendix* and write out a table (Table 8.II), taking for simplicity $R \approx 2$ cal/mole·deg.

The change in internal energy between room temperature and liquid-helium temperature is about 1200 cal/mole. If the latent heat of liquid helium is used to bring about this reduction of temperature, about 2000 cc will be spent. A similar calculation shows that 200 cc is needed to cool 63.6 g of copper from 90 to 4.2°K, and only 1 cc from 20 to 4.2°K. The tremendous advantage of precooling any apparatus with liquid air and liquid hydrogen in order to conserve the supply of liquid helium was mentioned even in the *Introduction*.

Many tabulations of the Einstein and Debye functions were mentioned in Chapter 2. Some of these tables, especially the older ones, should be used with caution since the value of R different from the present accepted 8.314 J/mole·deg = 1.987 cal/mole·deg has been used in them. The error caused by this is serious only at high temperatures, where the Debye specific heat approaches its limiting value of 3R. A 1% error in the specific heat at $T \sim \theta$ gives an error of nearly 10% in the calculated value of θ. One way to make the tables permanently useful is to give the values in a dimensionless form, that is, give $C_v/3R$ rather than C_v. Then, to find the specific heat at any given T/θ, the entries must be multiplied by 3R, but the tables themselves need not be changed every time an improvement in our knowledge of the value of R takes place. This is the procedure followed in the tabulations of Overton and Hancock for the Einstein functions and those of Beattie for the Debye functions, which are at present the most accurate ones available. For rough calculations, a table to three figures is often sufficient, but for a variety of refined calculations it is necessary to have more accurate tables. Unfortunately, six-figure tables are not easily accessible. Beattie's six-figure tables were published in 1926, though they have been recently checked for accuracy, while the eight-figure tables of Overton and Hancock and the detailed tables of Hilsenrath and Ziegler are contained in laboratory reports rather than professional journals.

Therefore, six-figure tables of Einstein and Debye functions are given in a suitable form as an *Appendix* (with the permission of Professors Beattie and Overton).

REFERENCES

1. H. N. V. Temperley, *Changes of States*, Cleaver-Hume, London, 1956. A. B. Pippard, *Elements of Classical Thermodynamics*, Cambridge University Press, Cambridge, 1957, chapters 8 and 9.
2. A. J. Hughes and A. W. Lawson, *J. Chem. Phys.* **36**, 2098 (1962).
3. C. W. Garland and J. S. Jones, *J. Chem. Phys.* **39**, 2874 (1963).
4. R. Viswanathan and E. S. R. Gopal, *Physica* **27**, 765, 981 (1961); **29**, 18 (1963). C. W. Garland, *J. Chem. Phys.* **41**, 1005 (1964). M. P. Mokhnatkin, *Soviet Phys.-Solid State* **5**, 1495 (1964).
5. D. Turnbull, *Solid State Phys.* **3**, 225 (1956).
6. J. S. Rowlinson, *Liquids and Liquid Mixtures*, Butterworth, London, 1959, p.40.
7. J. J. Markham, R. T. Beyer, and R. B. Lindsay, *Rev. Mod. Phys.* **23**, 353 (1951). R. O. Davies and J. Lamb, *Quart. Rev. Chem. Soc. (London)* **11**, 134 (1957). G. S. Verma, *Rev. Mod. Phys.* **31**, 1052 (1959). K. F. Herzfeld and T. A. Litovitz, *Absorption and Dispersion of Ultrasonic Waves*, Academic, New York, 1959.
8. P. Flubacher, A. J. Leadbetter, and J. A. Morrison, *Proc. Phys. Soc. (London)* **78**, 1449 (1961). R. H. Beaumont, H. Chihara, and J. A. Morrison, *Proc. Phys. Soc. (London)* **78**, 1462 (1961).
9. E. C. Heltemes and C. A. Swenson, *Phys. Rev. Letters*, **7**, 363 (1961); *Phys. Rev.* **128**, 1512 (62). D. O. Edwards, A. S. McWilliams, and J. G. Daunt, *Phys. Letters* **1**, 218 (1962). F. W. de Wette, *Phys. Rev.* **129**, 1160 (1963).
10. G. Borelius, *Solid State Phys.* **15**, 1 (1963).
11. A. R. Ubbelohde, *Quart. Rev. Chem. Soc.* (London) **4**, 356 (1950).
12. J. D. Hoffman and B. F. Decker, *J. Phys. Chem.* **57**, 520 (1953). R. E. Meyer and N. H. Nachtrieb, *J. Chem. Phys.* **23**, 405 (1955).
13. A. B. Lidiard, *Handbuch der Physik*, *XX (II)*, 246 (1957).
14. A. J. E. Foreman and A. B. Lidiard, *Phil. Mag.* **8**, 97 (1963). G. F. Nardelli and N. Terzi, *J. Phys. Chem. Solids* **25**, 815 (1964).
15. A. Eucken and H. Werth, *Z. anorg. allgem. Chem.* **188**, 152 (1930). C. G. Maier and C. T. Anderson, *J. Chem. Phys.* **2**, 513 (1934). D. L. Martin, *Can. J. Phys.* **38**, 17 (1960). F. A. Otter and D. E. Mapother, *Phys. Rev.* **125**, 1171 (1962).
16. P. H. Keesom, K. Lark-Horovitz, and N. Pearlman, *Science* **116**, 630 (1952). W. DeSorbo and W. W. Tyler, *J. Chem. Phys.* **26**, 244 (1957). B. B. Goodman, L. Montpetit, and L. Weil, *Compt. rend. acad, sci (Paris)* **248**, 956 (1959).
17. W. H. Lien and N. E. Phillips, *J. Chem. Phys.* **29**, 1415 (1958).
18. M. Dupuis, R. Mazo, and L. Onsager, *J. Chem. Phys.* **33**, 1452, (1960). R. Stratton, *J. Chem. Phys.* **37**, 2972 (1962).
19. A. A. Maradudin, E. W. Montroll, and G. H. Weiss, *Theory of Lattice Dynamics in the Harmonic Approximation*, Academic, New York, 1963, chapter 6.

Appendix

The six-figure tables give the values of the internal energy E and heat capacity at constant volume C_v of solids in the Einstein and Debye models. The functions are tabulated in a dimensionless form as follows to make them permanently useful:

A. Einstein internal energy function [equation (2.9a)]:

$$\frac{E\,(\text{Einstein})}{3RT} = \frac{x}{e^x - 1} \qquad x = \frac{h v_E}{kT} = \frac{T_E}{T}$$

B. Einstein specific-heat function [equation 2.7)]:

$$\frac{C_v\,(\text{Einstein})}{3R} = \frac{x^2 e^x}{(e^x - 1)^2} \qquad x = \frac{T_E}{T}$$

C. Debye internal energy function [equation (2.16a)]:

$$\frac{E\,(\text{Debye})}{3RT} = \frac{3}{x^3} \int_0^x \frac{x^3\,dx}{e^x - 1} \qquad x = \frac{h v_D}{kT} = \frac{\theta}{T}$$

D. Debye specific-heat function [equation (2.17)]:

$$\frac{C_v\,(\text{Debye})}{3R} = \frac{3}{x^3} \int_0^x \frac{x^4 e^x\,dx}{(e^x - 1)^2} \qquad x = \frac{\theta}{T}$$

The presently accepted value of R is 1.987 cal/mole · deg, or 8.314 J/mole·degK.

The functions A to D are tabulated at intervals of 0.01 over the useful range, namely, $T_E/T < 16$ in the Einstein functions and $\theta/T < 24$ in the Debye functions. Over most of the range, a linear interpolation gives an accuracy of nearly three to four units in the sixth significant figure. However, interpolation with second differences is recommended for accurate work. Following the usual procedure, a reduction by one unit of the fixed "characteristic" part is indicated by an underscoring

197

of the varying "mantissa" part. For example,

$$x = 1.61 \qquad \frac{E\,(\text{Einstein})}{3RT} = 0.4\,02217$$

$$= 1.62 \qquad\qquad\qquad = 0.3\,99695$$

$$= 3.48 \qquad\qquad\qquad = 0.11\,0618$$

$$= 3.49 \qquad\qquad\qquad = 0.10\,9797$$

Over wider ranges of x, the following approximations can be used with an error of about one unit in the sixth significant figure. At high temperatures,

$$\frac{E\,(\text{Einstein})}{3RT} \approx 1 - \frac{x}{2} + \frac{x^2}{12} - \frac{x^4}{720} \qquad x = \frac{T_E}{T} \gtrsim 0.1$$

$$\frac{C_v\,(\text{Einstein})}{3R} \approx 1 - \frac{x^2}{12} + \frac{x^4}{240}$$

$$\frac{E\,(\text{Debye})}{3RT} \approx 1 - \frac{3x}{8} + \frac{x^2}{20} - \frac{x^4}{1680} \qquad x = \theta/T \gtrsim 0.1$$

$$\frac{C_v\,(\text{Debye})}{3R} \approx 1 - \frac{x^2}{20} + \frac{x^4}{560}$$

while at low temperatures

$$\frac{E\,(\text{Einstein})}{3RT} \approx xe^{-x} \qquad x = \frac{T_E}{T} > 16$$

$$\frac{C_v\,(\text{Einstein})}{3R} \approx x^2 e^{-x}$$

$$\frac{E\,(\text{Debye})}{3RT} \approx \frac{19.481818}{x^3} \qquad x = \theta/T > 24$$

$$\frac{C_v\,(\text{Debye})}{3R} \approx \frac{77.92727}{x^3}$$

A. Einstein Internal Energy Function E (Einstein)/3RT

x	0	1	2	3	4	5	6	7	8	9
0.0	1.0 00000	95008	90033	85075	80133	75208	70300	65408	60533	55675
0.1	.9 50833	46008	41200	36408	31633	26874	22132	17407	12699	08007
0.2	9 03331	98672	94030	89404	84795	80203	75627	71068	66525	61999
0.3	8 57489	52996	48519	44059	39615	35188	30777	26382	22004	17643
0.4	.8 13298	08969	04657	00361	96082	91818	87571	83341	79127	74929
0.5	7 70747	66582	62432	58299	54183	50082	45998	41930	37877	33841
0.6	7 29822	25818	21830	17858	13903	09963	06039	02131	98240	94364
0.7	.6 90504	86660	82831	79019	75222	71441	67676	63927	60193	56475
0.8	6 52773	49086	45415	41760	38120	34496	30887	27293	23715	20153
0.9	6 16606	13074	09558	06057	02571	99101	95646	92206	88781	85371
1.0	0.5 81977	78597	75233	71884	68549	65230	61926	58636	55361	52102
1.1	5 48857	45627	42411	39211	36025	32853	29697	26554	23427	20314
1.2	5 17215	14131	11062	08006	04965	01939	98927	95929	92945	89975
1.3	4 87020	84078	81151	78238	75339	72453	69582	66724	63881	61051
1.4	.4 58235	55433	52644	49870	47108	44361	41627	38906	36199	33506
1.5	4 30825	28159	25505	22865	20238	17624	15024	12436	09862	07301
1.6	4 04753	02217	99695	97186	94689	92205	89734	87276	84831	82398
1.7	.3 79978	77570	75175	72792	70422	68064	65719	63386	61065	58757
1.8	3 56461	54176	51904	49645	47397	45161	42937	40725	38525	36337
1.9	3 34160	31996	29843	27701	25572	23453	21347	19252	17168	15096
2.0	0.3 13035	10986	08948	06921	04905	02900	00907	98925	96953	94993
2.1	.2 93044	91105	89178	87261	85355	83459	81575	79701	77838	75985
2.2	2 74143	72311	70490	68679	66879	65088	63308	61539	59779	58030
2.3	2 56291	54562	52842	51133	49434	47745	46065	44396	42736	41086
2.4	.2 39445	37814	36193	34581	32979	31386	29803	28229	26665	25110
2.5	2 23564	22027	20500	18981	17472	15972	14480	12998	11525	10061
2.6	2 08605	07158	05721	04291	02871	01459	00056	98661	97275	95897
2.7	.1 94528	93167	91815	90471	89135	87808	86488	85177	83874	82579
2.8	1 81293	80014	78743	77480	76225	74978	73738	72507	71283	70067
2.9	1 68858	67658	66464	65279	64101	62930	61767	60611	59462	58321
3.0	0.15 7187	6060	4941	3829	2724	1626	0535	9451	8374	7304
3.1	.14 6241	5184	4135	3092	2057	1028	0005	8989	7980	6978
3.2	13 5982	4993	4010	3033	2063	1099	0142	9191	8246	7308
3.3	12 6376	5449	4530	3616	2708	1806	0910	0021	9137	8259
3.4	.11 7387	6520	5660	4805	3957	3113	2276	1444	0618	9797
3.5	10 8982	8172	7368	6569	5776	4988	4206	3429	2657	1890
3.6	10 1129	0372	96214	88756	81348	73991	66685	59429	52223	45067
3.7	.09 37960	30902	23893	16933	10020	03156	96339	89569	82847	76171
3.8	08 69542	62959	56421	49930	43484	37083	30727	24415	18147	11924
3.9	08 05744	99608	93515	87465	81458	75493	69570	63689	57849	52051

x		0	1	2	3	4	5	6	7	8	9
4.0	0.07	46294	40578	34903	29268	23673	18117	12602	07126	01688	96290
4.1	.06	90930	85609	80326	75080	69872	64702	59569	54472	49413	44389
4.2	06	39402	34451	29536	24656	19812	15002	10228	05488	00782	96111
4.3	05	91473	86870	82299	77763	73259	68788	64349	59943	55569	51228
4.4	.05	46918	42639	38392	34176	29991	25837	21714	17620	13557	09524
4.5	05	05521	01547	97602	93687	89801	85943	82114	78313	74541	70796
4.6	04	67079	63390	59729	56094	52487	48907	45353	41826	38325	34850
4.7	.04	31402	27979	24582	21210	17863	14542	11246	07974	04727	01504
4.8	03	98306	95132	91981	88855	85752	82672	79616	76583	73572	70585
4.9	03	67620	64678	61758	58860	55984	53130	50298	47487	44698	41930
5.0	0.03	39183	36457	33752	31067	28403	25759	23136	20532	17949	15385
5.1	.03	12841	10317	07812	05326	02859	00412	97983	95572	93181	90808
5.2	02	88453	86116	83797	81496	79213	76948	74700	72470	70257	68061
5.3	02	65882	63720	61574	59446	57334	55238	53159	51095	49048	47017
5.4	.02	45002	43002	41018	39050	37097	35159	33236	31329	29436	27558
5.5	02	25695	23846	22012	20192	18387	16596	14819	13056	11306	09571
5.6	02	07849	06141	04446	02764	01096	99441	97799	96170	94554	92951
5.7	.01	91360	89782	88217	86664	85123	83594	82078	80573	79081	77600
5.8	01	76131	74674	73229	71795	70372	68961	67561	66172	64794	63427
5.9	01	62071	60726	59392	58068	56755	55453	54160	52879	51607	50346
6.0	0.014	9095	7854	6622	5401	4190	2988	1796	0613	9440	8277
6.1	.013	7122	5977	4842	3715	2598	1490	0390	9300	8218	7145
6.2	012	6081	5025	3978	2939	1909	0887	9873	8868	7870	6881
6.3	011	5900	4927	3962	3004	2054	1113	0178	9252	8332	7421
6.4	.010	6517	5620	4730	3848	2973	2105	1244	0390	95436	87037
6.5	009	78707	70445	62250	54123	46062	38067	30138	22274	14474	06738
6.6	008	99066	91457	83910	76425	69002	61640	54338	47096	39914	32792
6.7	.008	25727	18721	11773	04882	98048	91270	84548	77882	71271	64714
6.8	007	58212	51763	45367	39025	32735	26497	20311	14175	08091	02057
6.9	006	96073	90139	84254	78418	72630	66891	61199	55554	49956	44405
7.0	0.006	38900	33441	28027	22658	17334	12054	06818	01626	96477	91372
7.1	.005	86308	81287	76308	71370	66474	61619	56804	52029	47294	42599
7.2	005	37943	33327	28748	24208	19707	15242	10816	06426	02073	97757
7.3	004	93477	89232	85024	80851	76712	72609	68540	64505	60505	56537
7.4	.004	52604	48703	44835	41000	37197	33426	29687	25979	22303	18657
7.5	004	15043	11459	07905	04381	00887	97422	93987	90581	87203	83854
7.6	003	80534	77241	73976	70739	67530	64347	61192	58063	54961	51885
7.7	.003	48835	45811	42813	39840	36892	33969	31071	28198	25349	22525
7.8	003	19724	16948	14194	11465	08758	06075	03414	00776	98160	95567
7.9	002	92996	90447	87919	85413	82929	80465	78023	75601	73201	70820

x	0	1	2	3	4	5	6	7	8	9
8.0	0.002 68460	66120	63800	61500	59220	56959	54717	52495	50292	48107
8.1	.002 45941	43794	41665	39555	37462	35387	33330	31291	29269	27265
8.2	002 25278	23308	21354	19418	17498	15595	13708	11837	09982	08143
8.3	002 06320	04513	02721	00945	99184	97438	95707	93991	92290	90603
8.4	.001 88931	87273	85630	84001	82386	80785	79197	77623	76063	74517
8.5	001 72983	71463	69956	68462	66981	65513	64058	62615	61184	59766
8.6	001 58360	56966	55585	54215	52857	51511	50177	48854	47543	46243
8.7	.001 44954	43676	42410	41154	39909	38676	37452	36240	35038	33846
8.8	001 32665	31494	30333	29183	28042	26911	25790	24688	23577	22485
8.9	001 21403	20330	19266	18211	17166	16130	15103	14084	13075	12074
9.0	**0.0011 1083**	**0099**	9125	8158	7201	6251	5310	4377	3453	2536
9.1	.0010 1627	0726	98336	89485	80711	72014	63393	54848	46377	37980
9.2	0009 29656	21406	13227	05120	97084	89118	81222	73395	65637	57946
9.3	0008 50323	42767	35277	27852	20492	13197	05966	98799	91694	84651
9.4	.0007 77671	70751	63892	57094	50355	43675	37054	30491	23985	17537
9.5	0007 11146	04810	98530	92306	86136	80020	73959	67950	61995	56091
9.6	0006 50240	44440	38691	32993	27345	21747	16198	10698	05246	99842
9.7	.0005 94486	89178	83915	78700	73530	68406	63327	58293	53303	48358
9.8	0005 43456	38597	33781	29008	24277	19587	14939	10332	05766	01240
9.9	0004 96754	92308	87901	83533	79204	74913	70659	66444	62266	58125
10.0	0.0004 54020	49952	45919	41923	37962	34036	30144	26287	22465	18676
10.1	.0004 14921	11199	07510	03853	00229	96638	93078	89550	86053	82587
10.2	0003 79151	75747	72372	69028	65713	62427	59171	55944	52745	49575
10.3	0003 46433	43318	40232	37173	34141	31136	28158	25206	22281	19381
10.4	.0003 16507	13659	10837	08039	05266	02518	99795	97095	94420	91769
10.5	0002 89141	86536	83955	81397	78861	76348	73858	71390	68944	66519
10.6	0002 64116	61735	59375	57036	54717	52420	50143	47886	45650	43433
10.7	.0002 41236	39059	36901	34763	32644	30543	28461	26398	24354	22327
10.8	0002 20319	18329	16356	14402	12464	10544	08641	06755	04886	03034
10.9	0002 01198	99379	97576	95789	94019	92264	90524	88801	87092	85400
11.0	0.0001 83722	82059	80411	78778	77160	75556	73966	72391	70830	69283
11.1	.00016 7749	6230	4724	3231	1752	0287	8834	7395	5968	4554
11.2	00015 3153	1765	0388	9025	7673	6334	5007	3691	2388	1096
11.3	00013 9816	8547	7290	6044	4809	3585	2373	1171	9980	8800
11.4	.00012 7630	6471	5322	4184	3056	1938	0830	9732	8644	7566
11.5	00011 6497	5438	4389	3349	2319	1297	0285	9282	8289	7304
11.6	00010 6328	5360	4402	3452	2511	1578	0653	97374	88296	79300
11.7	.00009 70385	61550	52796	44120	35523	27003	18560	10194	01903	93686
11.8	00008 85544	77476	69481	61557	53706	45925	38215	30574	23002	15499
11.9	00008 08064	00696	93394	86159	78989	71883	64842	57865	50951	44100

E(Einstein)/3 RT

x	0	1	2	3	4	5	6	7	8	9
12.0	0.00007 37310	30582	23915	17308	10761	04273	97844	91473	85160	78904
12.1	.00006 72705	66562	60474	54442	48464	42541	36671	30854	25090	19379
12.2	00006 13719	08110	02552	97045	91588	86180	80821	75511	70248	65034
12.3	00005 59867	54747	49673	44646	39664	34727	29835	24987	20184	15424
12.4	.00005 10707	06033	01402	96812	92265	87758	83293	78868	74483	70139
12.5	00004 65833	61567	57340	53151	49000	44887	40811	36772	32770	28805
12.6	00004 24875	20982	17123	13300	09512	05758	02038	98352	94700	91080
12.7	.00003 87494	83941	80419	76930	73473	70047	66652	63288	59955	56653
12.8	00003 53380	50137	46924	43740	40585	37458	34361	31291	28249	25236
12.9	00003 22249	19290	16358	13453	10574	07721	04894	02094	99318	96568
13.0	0.00002 93843	91143	88468	85817	83190	80588	78009	75453	72921	70412
13.1	.00002 67926	65462	63021	60603	58206	55832	53479	51147	48837	46548
13.2	00002 44280	42032	39806	37599	35413	33246	31100	28973	26865	24777
13.3	00002 22708	20658	18626	16613	14619	12643	10685	08744	06822	04917
13.4	.00002 03030	01159	99306	97470	95651	93848	92062	90292	88539	86801
13.5	00001 85080	83374	81684	80009	78350	76705	75076	73462	71863	70278
13.6	00001 68708	67152	65610	64083	62569	61070	59584	58112	56653	55207
13.7	.00001 53775	52356	50950	49557	48177	46809	45454	44112	42781	41463
13.8	00001 40157	38863	37581	36311	35052	33805	32569	31345	30132	28930
13.9	00001 27739	26558	25389	24231	23083	21946	20819	19702	18596	17500
14.0	0.000011 6414	5338	4272	3216	2169	1132	0105	9087	8078	7078
14.1	.000010 6088	5107	4135	3172	2218	1272	0335	94071	84874	75762
14.2	000009 66734	57789	48926	40145	31444	22824	14283	05820	97436	89128
14.3	000008 80897	72742	64662	56656	48724	40865	33079	25364	17720	10146
14.4	.000008 02643	95208	87842	80544	73313	66148	59050	52017	45049	38145
14.5	000007 31304	24527	17812	11159	04568	98037	91566	85156	78804	72510
14.6	000006 66275	60097	53977	47912	41904	35951	30053	24209	18420	12683
14.7	.000006 07000	01369	95790	90263	84786	79360	73984	68658	63381	58153
14.8	000005 52973	47840	42755	37717	32726	27781	22881	18027	13217	08452
14.9	000005 03731	99053	94419	89828	85279	80772	76306	71882	67499	63156
15.0	0.000004 58854	54591	50367	46183	42037	37930	33861	29829	25834	21877
15.1	.000004 17956	14071	10222	06409	02631	98888	95180	91506	87866	84260
15.2	000003 80687	77147	73639	70165	66722	63311	59932	56584	53268	49981
15.3	000003 46726	43500	40304	37138	34001	30893	27814	24764	21742	18747
15.4	.000003 15781	12842	09930	07045	04187	01355	98550	95770	93017	90289
15.5	000002 87586	84908	82255	79626	77022	74442	71886	69354	66845	64360
15.6	000002 61897	59457	57040	54646	52273	49923	47594	45287	43001	40737
15.7	.000002 38493	36271	34069	31887	29726	27584	25463	23361	21279	19216
15.8	000002 17172	15147	13141	11154	09185	07234	05302	03387	01490	99611
15.9	000001 97749	95905	94077	92267	90473	88696	86936	85192	83464	81752
16.0	0.000001 80056									

$$E / 3RT = x\,e^{-x} \quad \text{when} \quad x > 16 .$$

B. Einstein Specific Heat Function
C_v (Einstein)/3R

x	0	1	2	3	4	5	6	7	8	9
0.0	1.0 00000	99992	99967	99925	99867	99792	99700	99592	99467	99325
0.1	.9 99167	98992	98801	98593	98368	98127	97869	97595	97304	96997
0.2	9 96673	96333	95976	95603	95214	94808	94386	93947	93492	93021
0.3	9 92534	92030	91510	90974	90422	89854	89270	88669	88053	87421
0.4	.9 86773	86109	85429	84733	84022	83295	82552	81793	81019	80230
0.5	9 79425	78604	77768	76917	76050	75168	74271	73359	72432	71490
0.6	9 70532	69560	68573	67571	66555	65523	64477	63417	62341	61252
0.7	.9 60148	59030	57897	56750	55589	54415	53226	52023	50806	49575
0.8	9 48331	47073	45801	44516	43218	41906	40581	39242	37891	36526
0.9	9 35148	33758	32354	30938	29509	28068	26614	25147	23668	22177
1.0	0.9 20674	19158	17630	16091	14540	12976	11401	09815	08217	06607
1.1	.9 04986	03354	01710	00056	98390	96714	95026	93328	91619	89900
1.2	8 88170	86430	84679	82918	81147	79366	77575	75774	73964	72144
1.3	8 70314	68474	66626	64768	62900	61024	59139	57244	55341	53429
1.4	.8 51509	49580	47642	45696	43742	41780	39809	37831	35844	33850
1.5	8 31849	29839	27822	25798	23766	21728	19682	17629	15569	13502
1.6	8 11429	09349	07262	05169	03070	00964	98852	96734	94610	92481
1.7	.7 90345	88204	86057	83905	81747	79584	77416	75243	73064	70881
1.8	7 68693	66500	64303	62101	59894	57684	55469	53249	51026	48799
1.9	7 46568	44333	42094	39852	37606	35356	33104	30848	28589	26327
2.0	0.7 24062	21794	19523	17249	14973	12694	10413	08130	05844	03556
2.1	.7 01266	98974	96680	94384	92086	89787	87486	85184	82880	80575
2.2	6 78269	75961	73652	71343	69032	66721	64408	62096	59782	57468
2.3	6 55154	52839	50524	48209	45893	43578	41262	38947	36632	34317
2.4	.6 32002	29688	27374	25061	22748	20437	18125	15815	13506	11197
2.5	6 08890	06584	04279	01975	99673	97372	95072	92774	90477	88183
2.6	5 85890	83598	81309	79021	76736	74452	72171	69892	67615	65340
2.7	.5 63068	60798	58530	56265	54003	51743	49486	47232	44980	42732
2.8	5 40486	38244	36004	33767	31534	29304	27077	24853	22633	20416
2.9	5 18203	15993	13786	11584	09385	07189	04997	02810	00625	98445
3.0	0.4 96269	94097	91929	89764	87604	85448	83296	81149	79006	76867
3.1	.4 74732	72602	70476	68355	66238	64125	62018	59915	57816	55722
3.2	4 53633	51549	49470	47395	45325	43260	41200	39145	37095	35050
3.3	4 33010	30975	28946	26921	24901	22887	20878	18874	16876	14882
3.4	.4 12894	10912	08935	06963	04996	03036	01080	99130	97186	95247
3.5	3 93313	91386	89463	87547	85636	83731	81831	79937	78049	76167
3.6	3 74290	72419	70554	68695	66841	64993	63152	61316	59486	57661
3.7	.3 55843	54031	52224	50424	48629	46840	45058	43281	41510	39746
3.8	3 37987	36234	34488	32747	31012	29284	27562	25845	24135	22431
3.9	3 20733	19041	17355	15675	14001	12333	10672	09017	07367	05724

x	0	1	2	3	4	5	6	7	8	9
4.0	0.3 04087	02456	00832	99213	97601	95995	94394	92800	91213	89631
4.1	.2 88055	86486	84923	83365	81814	80270	78731	77198	75672	74152
4.2	2 72637	71129	69627	68132	66642	65158	63681	62210	60744	59285
4.3	2 57832	56385	54944	53509	52081	50658	49241	47831	46426	45027
4.4	.2 43635	42248	40868	39494	38125	36763	35406	34056	32711	31372
4.5	2 30040	28713	27392	26077	24768	23465	22168	20877	19591	18312
4.6	2 17038	15770	14508	13252	12001	10757	09518	08285	07057	05836
4.7	.2 04620	03410	02205	01006	99813	98626	97444	96268	95097	93933
4.8	1 92773	91620	90471	89329	88192	87060	85934	84814	83699	82589
4.9	1 81485	80387	79294	78206	77123	76046	74975	73909	72848	71792
5.0	0.17 0742	9697	8657	7623	6594	5570	4551	3537	2529	1526
5.1	.16 0528	9535	8547	7564	6587	5614	4647	3685	2727	1775
5.2	15 0827	9885	8948	8015	7087	6165	5247	4334	3426	2523
5.3	14 1624	0731	9842	8958	8078	7204	6334	5469	4608	3752
5.4	.13 2901	2055	1213	0376	9543	8715	7891	7072	6257	5447
5.5	12 4642	3840	3044	2251	1463	0680	9901	9126	8355	7589
5.6	11 6827	6070	5317	4568	3823	3082	2346	1613	0885	0161
5.7	.10 9442	8726	8014	7307	6603	5904	5208	4517	3829	3146
5.8	10 2466	1791	1119	0451	97875	91275	84713	78189	71704	65257
5.9	09 58847	52475	46140	39843	33583	27359	21173	15023	08910	02832
6.0	0.08 96791	90786	84816	78882	72984	67121	61293	55499	49741	44017
6.1	.08 38327	32672	27051	21464	15910	10390	04904	99451	94031	88644
6.2	07 83289	77967	72678	67421	62196	57004	51843	46713	41615	36549
6.3	07 31513	26509	21536	16593	11681	06799	01948	97126	92335	87573
6.4	.06 82841	78139	73465	68821	64206	59620	55063	50534	46034	41561
6.5	06 37117	32701	28313	23953	19620	15314	11036	06784	02560	98363
6.6	05 94192	90048	85930	81838	77772	73733	69719	65731	61768	57831
6.7	.05 53919	50032	46171	42334	38521	34734	30970	27231	23516	19826
6.8	05 16159	12516	08896	05300	01728	98178	94652	91149	87668	84210
6.9	04 80775	77363	73972	70604	67258	63934	60632	57351	54092	50854
7.0	0.04 47638	44443	41269	38116	34984	31873	28782	25712	22662	19632
7.1	.04 16623	13633	10663	07714	04783	01873	98982	96110	93257	90423
7.2	03 87609	84813	82036	79277	76538	73816	71113	68428	65761	63112
7.3	03 60481	57868	55273	52695	50134	47591	45065	42556	40064	37590
7.4	.03 35132	32690	30266	27857	25466	23090	20731	18388	16061	13750
7.5	03 11454	09175	06911	04662	02429	00212	98009	95822	93650	91493
7.6	02 89350	87223	85110	83012	80928	78858	76803	74762	72736	70723
7.7	.02 68725	66740	64769	62812	60868	58938	57021	55118	53228	51351
7.8	02 49487	47636	45799	43974	42162	40362	38575	36801	35039	33290
7.9	02 31553	29828	28115	26414	24725	23049	21384	19730	18089	16459

x	0	1	2	3	4	5	6	7	8	9
8.0	0.02 14840	13233	11638	10053	08480	06918	05367	03827	02298	00780
8.1	.01 99273	97776	96291	94815	93350	91896	90452	89018	87595	86182
8.2	01 84779	83385	82002	80629	79266	77912	76568	75234	73909	72594
8.3	01 71288	69992	68705	67427	66159	64900	63649	62408	61176	59952
8.4	.01 58738	57532	56335	55147	53967	52796	51633	50479	49333	48195
8.5	01 47066	45945	44832	43727	42630	41541	40460	39387	38322	37265
8.6	01 36215	35173	34138	33111	32092	31080	30076	29079	28089	27106
8.7	.01 26131	25163	24202	23247	22300	21360	20427	19501	18582	17669
8.8	01 16763	15864	14971	14085	13205	12332	11466	10606	09752	08904
8.9	01 08063	07228	06399	05577	04760	03950	03145	02347	01554	00767
9.0	0.009 99866	92116	84423	76788	69210	61688	54222	46812	39457	32157
9.1	.009 24911	17720	10582	03498	96466	89488	82561	75687	68864	62092
9.2	008 55370	48700	42079	35508	28986	22513	16089	09714	03386	97106
9.3	007 90873	84687	78547	72454	66407	60406	54449	48538	42671	36849
9.4	.007 31071	25336	19645	13997	08391	02828	97307	91828	86391	80994
9.5	006 75639	70324	65050	59815	54621	49466	44350	39273	34235	29235
9.6	006 24273	19348	14462	09612	04800	00024	95285	90582	85915	81283
9.7	.005 76687	72126	67600	63108	58651	54228	49839	45484	41161	36872
9.8	005 32616	28393	24202	20043	15916	11820	07757	03724	99722	95752
9.9	004 91811	87901	84022	80172	76351	72561	68799	65066	61363	57687
10.0	0.004 54041	50422	46831	43268	39733	36225	32744	29290	25862	22461
10.1	.004 19087	15739	12416	09120	05849	02603	99383	96187	93016	89870
10.2	003 86749	83651	80578	77529	74503	71501	68522	65567	62634	59725
10.3	003 56838	53973	51131	48311	45513	42737	39982	37249	34538	31847
10.4	.003 29178	26529	23901	21294	18707	16141	13594	11068	08561	06074
10.5	003 03606	01158	98729	96319	93928	91555	89202	86866	84549	82251
10.6	002 79970	77708	75463	73236	71026	68834	66659	64501	62360	60236
10.7	.002 58129	56038	53964	51906	49865	47839	45830	43836	41858	39896
10.8	002 37950	36018	34102	32201	30316	28445	26589	24747	22921	21108
10.9	002 19310	17527	15757	14002	12260	10532	08818	07118	05431	03758
11.0	0.002 02097	00450	98816	97195	95587	93992	92410	90840	89282	87737
11.1	.001 86205	84684	83176	81679	80195	78722	77261	75812	74375	72949
11.2	001 71534	70130	68738	67357	65987	64628	63280	61942	60615	59299
11.3	001 57994	56699	55414	54139	52875	51621	50377	49143	47919	46704
11.4	.0014 5500	4305	3119	1944	0777	9620	8473	7334	6205	5084
11.5	0013 3973	2871	1777	0693	9617	8550	7491	6441	5399	4366
11.6	0012 3341	2324	1316	0316	9323	8339	7363	6395	5434	4481
11.7	.0011 3536	2598	1669	0746	9831	8924	8024	7131	6245	5366
11.8	0010 4495	3631	2773	1923	1079	0243	94130	85898	77733	69635
11.9	0009 61602	53635	45732	37893	30118	22407	14757	07170	99645	92181

$C_v(\text{Einstein})/3R$

x	0	1	2	3	4	5	6	7	8	9
12.0	0.0008 84777	77434	70151	62927	55761	48654	41605	34613	27678	20800
12.1	.0008 13977	07211	00499	93842	87240	80691	74196	67754	61364	55026
12.2	0007 48741	42506	36323	30190	24107	18074	12090	06155	00268	94430
12.3	0006 88640	82897	77201	71551	65948	60391	54879	49412	43990	38613
12.4	.0006 33279	27990	22744	17540	12380	07262	02185	97151	92158	87205
14.5	0005 82294	77423	72592	67800	63048	58335	53661	49025	44427	39867
12.6	0005 35345	30860	26411	22000	17624	13285	08982	04713	00481	96282
12.7	.0004 92119	87990	83895	79834	75806	71811	67850	63921	60024	56160
12.8	0004 52327	48527	44757	41019	37312	33635	29989	26373	22786	19230
12.9	0004 15703	12205	08736	05295	01883	98500	95144	91816	88516	85243
13.0	0.0003 81997	78779	75586	72421	69281	66168	63080	60018	56981	53970
13.1	.0003 50983	48022	45085	42172	39284	36419	33579	30761	27968	25197
13.2	0003 22450	19725	17023	14344	11687	09052	06439	03847	01278	98729
13.3	0002 96202	93696	91211	88746	86302	83879	81475	79092	76728	74384
13.4	.0002 72060	69755	67470	65203	62955	60726	58516	56324	54151	51995
13.5	0002 49858	47738	45637	43552	41486	39436	37404	35388	33390	31408
13.6	0002 29443	27494	25561	23645	21745	·19860	17992	16139	14301	12479
13.7	.0002 10672	08881	07104	05342	03596	01863	00145	98442	96753	95078
13.8	0001 93417	91770	90137	88518	86912	85320	83741	82175	80623	79083
13.9	0001 77557	76043	74542	73054	71578	70114	68663	67224	65798	64383
14.0	0.00016 2980	1589	0209	8842	7485	6141	4807	3485	2174	0874
14.1	.00014 9585	8306	7039	5782	4536	3300	2075	0860	9655	8461
14.2	00013 7276	6102	4937	3783	2638	1502	0377	9261	8154	7056
14.3	00012 5968	4889	3820	2759	1707	0664	9630	8605	7588	6580
14.4	.00011 5581	4590	3607	2633	1666	0708	9759	8817	7883	6957
14.5	00010 6039	5129	4226	3332	2444	1564	0692	98272	89696	81193
14.6	00009 72762	64403	56114	47896	39748	31669	23658	15715	07840	00032
14.7	.00008 92290	84614	77003	69457	61975	54556	47201	39908	32677	25508
14.8	00008 18400	11352	04364	97435	90566	83755	77002	70306	63667	57085
14.9	00007 50559	44089	37674	31313	25007	18754	12554	06408	00314	94271
15.0	0.00006 88281	82341	76452	70613	64824	59085	53394	47752	42158	36612
15.1	.00006 31113	25662	20256	14897	09584	04316	99093	93915	88781	83690
15.2	00005 78648	73640	68679	63761	58885	54050	49257	44505	39793	35122
15.3	00005 30490	25899	21346	16833	12358	07922	03523	99162	94839	90552
15.4	.00004 86303	82089	77912	73771	69665	65594	61558	57557	53590	49657
15.5	00004 45758	41892	38060	34260	30493	26758	23055	19384	15745	12137
15.6	00004 08560	05013	01497	98011	94555	91129	87732	84365	81026	77716
15.7	.00003 74435	71181	67956	64758	61588	58446	55330	52241	49178	46142
15.8	00003 43132	40148	37190	34257	31349	28467	25609	22775	19967	17182
15.9	00003 14421	11685	08971	06281	03615	00971	98350	95752	93176	90622
16.0	0.00002 88090									

$$C_v/3R = x^2 e^{-x} \quad \text{when} \quad x > 16.$$

C. Debye Internal Energy Function
$E\,(Debye)/3RT$

x	0	1	2	3	4	5	6	7	8	9
0.0	1.0 00000	96255	92520	88795	85080	81375	77680	73995	70320	66655
0.1	.9 63000	59355	55720	52095	48480	44875	41280	37695	34119	30554
0.2	9 26999	23454	19919	16393	12878	09373	05877	02392	98916	95451
0.3	8 91995	88550	85114	81688	78272	74866	71470	68084	64708	61341
0.4	.8 57985	54638	51302	47975	44658	41351	38053	34766	31489	28221
0.5	8 24963	21715	18477	15248	12030	08821	05622	02433	99253	96083
0.6	7 92923	89773	86633	83502	80381	77270	74168	71076	67994	64921
0.7	.7 61858	58805	55762	52728	49703	46689	43684	40688	37702	34726
0.8	7 31759	28802	25854	22916	19987	17068	14159	11259	08368	05487
0.9	7 02615	99753	96900	94057	91223	88398	85583	82777	79981	77193
1.0	0.6 74415	71647	68888	66138	63397	60666	57944	55231	52527	49833
1.1	.6 47148	44472	41805	39147	36498	33859	31228	28607	25995	23392
1.2	6 20798	18213	15637	13070	10512	07963	05422	02891	00369	97856
1.3	5 95351	92856	90369	87891	85422	82962	80511	78068	75634	73209
1.4	.5 70793	68386	65987	63596	61215	58842	56478	54122	51775	49437
1.5	5 47107	44785	42472	40168	37872	35585	33306	31036	28774	26520
1.6	5 24275	22038	19809	17589	15377	13174	10979	08792	06613	04442
1.7	.5 02280	00126	97980	95842	93712	91590	89477	87371	85274	83184
1.8	4 81103	79030	76964	74907	72857	70816	68782	66756	64738	62728
1.9	4 60726	58731	56745	54766	52794	50831	48875	46927	44987	43054
2.0	0.4 41128	39211	37301	35398	33503	31616	29736	27864	25999	24141
2.1	.4 22291	20448	18613	16785	14965	13151	11345	09547	07755	05971
2.2	4 04194	02424	00661	98906	97157	95416	93682	91955	90235	88522
2.3	3 86816	85117	83425	81740	80062	78390	76726	75068	73418	71774
2.4	.3 70137	68507	66883	65266	63656	62053	60456	58866	57283	55706
2.5	3 54136	52572	51015	49465	47921	46383	44852	43328	41810	40298
2.6	3 38793	37294	35801	34315	32835	31361	29893	28432	26977	25528
2.7	.3 24086	22649	21219	19795	18377	16965	15559	14159	12765	11377
2.8	3 09995	08619	07249	05885	04527	03174	01828	00487	99152	97823
2.9	2 96500	95182	93870	92564	91264	89969	88680	87397	86119	84847
3.0	0.28 3580	2319	1063	9813	8568	7329	6095	4867	3644	2427
3.1	.27 1215	0008	8807	7610	6419	5234	4054	2879	1709	0544
3.2	25 9385	8230	7081	5937	4798	3664	2535	1412	0293	9179
3.3	24 8070	6966	5868	4774	3684	2600	1521	0447	9377	8312
3.4	.23 7252	6197	5146	4101	3060	2023	0991	9964	8942	7924
3.5	22 6911	5903	4899	3899	2904	1914	0928	9947	8970	7998
3.6	21 7030	6066	5107	4152	3201	2255	1313	0376	9442	8513
3.7	.20 7589	6668	5752	4840	3932	3028	2128	1233	0341	9454
3.8	19 8571	7692	6817	5945	5078	4215	3356	2501	1650	0803
3.9	18 9959	9120	8284	7452	6624	5800	4980	4164	3351	2542

x	0	1	2	3	4	5	6	7	8	9
4.0	0.18 1737	0935	0138	9344	8553	7767	6984	6204	5428	4656
4.1	.17 3888	3123	2361	1603	0849	0098	9351	8607	7866	7129
4.2	16 6396	5666	4939	4216	3496	2779	2066	1356	0649	9946
4.3	15 9246	8549	7856	7166	6479	5795	5114	4437	3763	3092
4.4	.15 2424	1759	1097	0439	9783	9131	8482	7835	7192	6552
4.5	14 5914	5280	4649	4021	3395	2773	2153	1537	0923	0312
4.6	13 9704	9099	8497	7898	7301	6707	6116	5528	4943	4360
4.7	.13 3780	3203	2628	2057	1488	0921	0357	9796	9238	8682
4.8	12 8129	7579	7031	6485	5942	5402	4864	4329	3797	3267
4.9	12 2739	2214	1691	1171	0653	0138	9625	9114	8606	8101
5.0	0.11 7598	7097	6598	6102	5608	5116	4627	4140	3656	3174
5.1	.11 2694	2216	1740	1267	0796	0327	9861	9396	8934	8474
5.2	10 8016	7561	7107	6656	6206	5759	5314	4871	4430	3992
5.3	10 3555	3120	2688	2257	1829	1402	0978	0555	0135	97163
5.4	.09 92997	88852	84726	80619	76531	72463	68414	64384	60373	56381
5.5	09 52408	48453	44517	40600	36701	32821	28958	25114	21288	17480
5.6	09 13690	09917	06162	02425	98706	95004	91319	87652	84002	80369
5.7	.08 76753	73155	69573	66007	62459	58927	55412	51913	48431	44965
5.8	08 41515	38082	34664	31263	27877	24508	21154	17815	14493	11186
5.9	08 07894	04618	01357	98112	94881	91666	88466	85280	82110	78954
6.0	0.07 75813	72687	69575	66478	63395	60327	57273	54233	51208	48196
6.1	.07 45198	42215	39245	36289	33347	30419	27504	24603	21715	18841
6.2	07 15980	13132	10297	07476	04668	01873	99090	96321	93564	90821
6.3	06 88090	85371	82665	79972	77291	74623	71967	69323	66691	64072
6.4	.06 61465	58869	56286	53715	51155	48607	46071	43547	41034	38533
6.5	06 36043	33565	31098	28643	26199	23766	21344	18934	16534	14146
6.6	06 11768	09402	07046	04701	02366	00043	97730	95428	93136	90854
6.7	.05 88583	86323	84073	81833	79603	77384	75174	72975	70785	68606
6.8	05 66437	64277	62127	59987	57857	55737	53626	51525	49433	47351
6.9	05 45278	43214	41160	39115	37080	35053	33036	31028	29029	27039
7.0	0.05 25059	23087	21123	19169	17224	15287	13359	11440	09530	07628
7.1	.05 05734	03849	01973	00105	98245	96394	94551	92716	90890	89071
7.2	04 87261	85459	83665	81879	80101	78331	76569	74815	73068	71329
7.3	04 69598	67875	66160	64452	62752	61059	59374	57696	56026	54363
7.4	.04 52707	51059	49418	47785	46158	44539	42927	41322	39725	38134
7.5	04 36550	34974	33404	31841	30285	28736	27194	25658	24129	22607
7.6	04 21092	19583	18081	16586	15097	13615	12139	10669	09206	07750
7.7	.04 06299	04855	03418	01987	00562	99143	97730	96323	94923	93529
7.8	03 92140	90758	89382	88011	86647	85289	83936	82590	81249	79914
7.9	03 78584	77261	75943	74631	73324	72023	70728	69439	68155	66876

x	0	1	2	3	4	5	6	7	8	9
8.0	0.036 5603	4335	3073	1816	0565	9319	8078	6843	5613	4388
8.1	.035 3169	1954	0745	9541	8342	7149	5960	4776	3598	2424
8.2	034 1256	0092	8933	7780	6631	5487	4348	3213	2084	0959
8.3	032 9839	8724	7613	6507	5406	4310	3218	2130	1048	9970
8.4	.031 8896	7827	6762	5702	4646	3594	2547	1505	0467	9433
8.5	030 8403	7378	6357	5340	4328	3319	2315	1315	0319	9328
8.6	029 8340	7357	6378	5402	4431	3464	2500	1541	0586	9634
8.7	.028 8687	7744	6804	5868	4936	4008	3084	2163	1247	0334
8.8	027 9424	8519	7617	6719	5825	4934	4047	3163	2283	1407
8.9	027 0534	9665	8799	7937	7078	6223	5371	4523	3678	2837
9.0	0.026 1999	1164	0333	9505	8681	7859	7041	6227	5416	4608
9.1	.025 3803	3001	2203	1408	0616	9827	9041	8259	7479	6703
9.2	024 5930	5160	4393	3629	2868	2110	1355	0603	9854	9108
9.3	023 8365	7625	6888	6154	5423	4694	3969	3246	2526	1809
9.4	.023 1095	0384	9676	8970	8267	7567	6869	6174	5482	4793
9.5	022 4107	3423	2741	2063	1387	0714	0043	9375	8709	8046
9.6	021 7386	6728	6073	5421	4771	4123	3478	2835	2195	1558
9.7	.021 0923	0290	9659	9031	8406	7783	7162	6544	5928	5315
9.8	020 4704	4095	3488	2884	2282	1683	1085	0490	9897	9307
9.9	019 8719	8133	7549	6967	6388	5811	5236	4663	4092	3524
10.0	0.019 2958	2393	1831	1271	0714	0158	9604	9053	8503	7956
10.1	.018 7410	6867	6326	5787	5249	4714	4181	3650	3120	2593
10.2	018 2068	1544	1023	0504	9986	9470	8957	8445	7935	7427
10.3	017 6921	6416	5914	5413	4915	4418	3923	3430	2938	2449
10.4	.017 1961	1475	0991	0508	0027	9548	9071	8596	8122	7650
10.5	016 7180	6711	6244	5779	5316	4854	4394	3936	3479	3024
10.6	016 2570	2118	1668	1220	0773	0328	9884	9442	9001	8562
10.7	.015 8125	7689	7255	6822	6391	5962	5534	5107	4682	4259
10.8	015 3837	3416	2997	2580	2164	1749	1336	0925	0515	0106
10.9	014 9699	9293	8889	8486	8084	7684	7286	6888	6492	6098
11.0	0.014 5705	5313	4923	4534	4146	3760	3375	2992	2610	2229
11.1	.014 1849	1471	1094	0719	0345	9972	9600	9230	8861	8493
11.2	013 8126	7761	7397	7034	6673	6313	5954	5596	5239	4884
11.3	013 4530	4177	3826	3475	3126	2778	2431	2085	1741	1398
11.4	.013 1056	0715	0375	0036	9699	9362	9027	8693	8360	8029
11.5	012 7698	7368	7040	6713	6387	6061	5737	5415	5093	4772
11.6	012 4452	4134	3816	3500	3184	2870	2557	2245	1934	1623
11.7	.012 1314	1006	0699	0393	0088	9784	9481	9179	8878	8578
11.8	011 8279	7982	7685	7389	7094	6799	6506	6214	5923	5633
11.9	011 5344	5055	4768	4482	4196	3912	3628	3346	3064	2783

x	0	1	2	3	4	5	6	7	8	9
12.0	0.011 2503	2224	1946	1669	1393	1118	0843	0570	0297	0025
12.1	.010 9754	9484	9215	8947	8679	8413	8147	7882	7618	7355
12.2	010 7093	6832	6571	6311	6052	5794	5537	5281	5025	4770
12.3	010 4516	4263	4011	3759	3509	3259	3010	2761	2514	2267
12.4	.010 2021	1776	1531	1288	1045	0803	0561	0321	0081	98419
12.5	009 96036	93661	91293	88932	86579	84233	81895	79564	77240	74923
12.6	009 72614	70312	68017	65730	63449	61176	58909	56650	54398	52153
12.7	.009 49915	47683	45459	43241	41031	38827	36630	34440	32257	30080
12.8	009 27910	25747	23591	21441	19298	17161	15031	12907	10790	08680
12.9	009 06576	04478	02387	00302	98224	96152	94086	92027	89974	87927
13.0	0.008 85886	83851	81823	79801	77785	75775	73771	71774	69782	67796
13.1	.008 65817	63843	61875	59914	57958	56008	54064	52125	50193	48266
13.2	008 46345	44430	42521	40617	38719	36827	34941	33060	31184	29314
13.3	008 27450	25592	23739	21891	20049	18212	16381	14555	12735	10920
13.4	.008 09111	07306	05507	03714	01926	00143	98365	96592	94825	93063
13.5	007 91306	89554	87807	86066	84330	82598	80872	79151	77435	75724
13.6	007 74017	72316	70620	68929	67242	65561	63884	62213	60546	58884
13.7	.007 57226	55574	53927	52284	50646	49012	47384	45760	44140	42526
13.8	007 40916	39310	37710	36114	34522	32935	31353	29775	28201	26632
13.9	007 25068	23508	21953	20402	18855	17313	15775	14242	12713	11188
14.0	0.007 09668	08152	06640	05132	03629	02130	00636	99145	97659	96177
14.1	.006 94699	93225	91755	90290	88829	87371	85918	84469	83024	81583
14.2	006 80146	78713	77285	75860	74439	73022	71609	70200	68795	67394
14.3	006 65996	64603	63213	61828	60446	59068	57694	56323	54957	53594
14.4	.006 52235	50880	49528	48180	46836	45496	44159	42826	41497	40171
14.5	006 38849	37531	36216	34905	33597	32293	30992	29695	28402	27112
14.6	006 25826	24543	23264	21988	20716	19447	18181	16919	15661	14405
14.7	.006 13153	11905	10660	09418	08180	06945	05714	04485	03260	02039
14.8	006 00820	99605	98393	97185	95979	94777	93578	92383	91190	90001
14.9	005 88815	87632	86452	85275	84102	82932	81764	80600	79439	78281
15.0	0.0057 7126	5975	4826	3680	2537	1398	0261	9128	7997	6869
15.1	.0056 5745	4623	3504	2388	1276	0166	9059	7955	6853	5755
15.2	0055 4660	3567	2478	1391	0307	9226	8147	7072	5999	4929
15.3	0054 3862	2798	1736	0677	9621	8568	7518	6470	5425	4382
15.4	.0053 3342	2305	1271	0239	9210	8184	7160	6139	5121	4105
15.5	0052 3092	2081	1073	0068	9065	8065	7067	6072	5080	4090
15.6	0051 3102	2117	1135	0155	9177	8202	7230	6260	5292	4327
15.7	.0050 3365	2405	1447	0492	9539	8588	7640	6694	5751	4810
15.8	0049 3872	2936	2002	1070	0141	9215	8290	7368	6448	5531
15.9	0048 4616	3703	2792	1884	0978	0074	9173	8274	7377	6482

x	0	1	2	3	4	5	6	7	8	9
16.0	0.0047 5589	4699	3811	2925	2042	1160	0281	<u>9404</u>	<u>8529</u>	<u>7656</u>
16.1	.0046 6786	5917	5051	4187	3325	2465	1607	0752	<u>9898</u>	<u>9047</u>
16.2	0045 8198	7350	6505	5662	4821	3982	3146	2311	1478	0647
16.3	0044 9819	8992	8167	7345	6524	5706	4889	4075	3262	2451
16.4	.0044 1643	0836	0031	<u>9229</u>	<u>8428</u>	<u>7629</u>	<u>6832</u>	<u>6037</u>	<u>5244</u>	<u>4453</u>
16.5	0043 3664	2876	2091	1307	0526	<u>9746</u>	<u>8968</u>	<u>8192</u>	<u>7418</u>	<u>6646</u>
16.6	0042 5875	5107	4340	3575	2812	2051	1292	0534	<u>9778</u>	<u>9024</u>
16.7	.0041 8272	7522	6774	6027	5282	4539	3797	3058	2320	1584
16.8	0041 0849	0117	<u>9386</u>	<u>8656</u>	<u>7929</u>	<u>7203</u>	<u>6479</u>	<u>5757</u>	<u>5037</u>	<u>4318</u>
16.9	0040 3601	2885	2171	1459	0749	0040	<u>9333</u>	<u>8628</u>	<u>7924</u>	<u>7222</u>
17.0	0.0039 6521	5822	5125	4430	3736	3044	2353	1664	0977	0291
17.1	.0038 9606	8924	8243	7563	6885	6209	5535	4862	4190	3520
17.2	0038 2852	2185	1519	0855	0193	<u>9532</u>	<u>8873</u>	<u>8216</u>	<u>7560</u>	<u>6905</u>
17.3	0037 6252	5600	4950	4301	3654	3009	2365	1722	1081	0441
17.4	.0036 9803	9166	8531	7897	7264	6633	6004	5376	4749	4124
17.5	0036 3500	2878	2257	1637	1019	0403	<u>9787</u>	<u>9173</u>	<u>8561</u>	<u>7950</u>
17.6	0035 7340	6732	6125	5519	4915	4312	3711	3110	2512	1914
17.7	.0035 1318	0723	0130	<u>9538</u>	<u>8947</u>	<u>8358</u>	<u>7770</u>	<u>7183</u>	<u>6598</u>	<u>6014</u>
17.8	0034 5431	4849	4269	3690	3113	2536	1961	1388	0815	0244
17.9	0033 9674	9106	8538	7972	7408	6844	6282	5721	5161	4602
18.0	0.0033 4045	3489	2934	2380	1828	1277	0727	0178	<u>9631</u>	<u>9084</u>
18.1	.0032 8539	7995	7453	6911	6371	5832	5294	4757	4221	3687
18.2	0032 3154	2622	2091	1561	1033	0505	<u>9979</u>	<u>9454</u>	<u>8930</u>	<u>8407</u>
18.3	0031 7886	7365	6846	6327	5810	5294	4779	4266	3753	3241
18.4	.0031 2731	2222	1714	1206	0700	0196	<u>9692</u>	<u>9189</u>	<u>8687</u>	<u>8187</u>
18.5	0030 7687	7189	6692	6195	5700	5206	4713	4221	3730	3240
18.6	0030 2752	2264	1777	1291	0807	0323	<u>9841</u>	<u>9359</u>	<u>8879</u>	<u>8399</u>
18.7	.0029 7921	7443	6967	6492	6017	5544	5072	4600	4130	3661
18.8	0029 3192	2725	2258	1793	1329	0865	0403	<u>9942</u>	<u>9481</u>	<u>9022</u>
18.9	0028 8563	8106	7649	7193	6739	6285	5832	5381	4930	4480
19.0	0.0028 4031	3583	3136	2690	2245	1800	1357	0915	0473	0033
19.1	.0027 9593	9155	8717	8280	7844	7409	6975	6542	6109	5678
19.2	0027 5247	4818	4389	3961	3534	3108	2683	2259	1835	1413
19.3	0027 0991	0570	0151	<u>9732</u>	<u>9313</u>	<u>8896</u>	<u>8480</u>	<u>8064</u>	<u>7649</u>	<u>7235</u>
19.4	.0026 6822	6410	5999	5588	5179	4770	4362	3955	3549	3143
19.5	0026 2738	2335	1932	1530	1128	0728	0328	<u>9929</u>	<u>9531</u>	<u>9134</u>
19.6	0025 8738	8342	7947	7553	7160	6768	6376	5985	5595	5206
19.7	.0025 4817	4430	4043	3657	3272	2887	2503	2120	1738	1357
19.8	0025 0976	0596	0217	<u>9839</u>	<u>9461</u>	<u>9084</u>	<u>8708</u>	<u>8333</u>	<u>7958</u>	<u>7585</u>
19.9	0024 7212	6839	6468	6097	5727	5358	4989	4621	4254	3888

$E(\text{Debye})/3\,RT$

x	0	1	2	3	4	5	6	7	8	9
20.0	0.0024 3522	3157	2793	2429	2067	1705	1343	0983	0623	0264
20.1	.0023 9905	9548	9191	8834	8479	8124	7770	7416	7064	6712
20.2	0023 6360	6010	5660	5310	4962	4614	4266	3920	3574	3229
20.3	0023 2884	2540	2197	1855	1513	1172	0832	0492	0153	9814
20.4	.0022 9476	9139	8803	8467	8132	7797	7463	7130	6798	6466
20.5	0022 6135	5804	5474	5145	4816	4488	4161	3834	3508	3182
20.6	0022 2857	2533	2210	1887	1564	1242	0921	0601	0281	9962
20.7	.0021 9643	9325	9008	8691	8375	8059	7744	7430	7116	6803
20.8	0021 6491	6179	5867	5556	5246	4937	4628	4319	4012	3705
20.9	0021 3398	3092	2786	2481	2177	1874	1571	1268	0966	0665
21.0	0.0021 0364	0064	9764	9465	9166	8868	8571	8274	7978	7682
21.1	.0020 7387	7092	6798	6505	6212	5920	5628	5337	5046	4756
21.2	0020 4466	4177	3889	3601	3313	3026	2740	2454	2169	1884
21.3	0020 1600	1316	1033	0750	0468	0187	9906	9625	9345	9066
21.4	.0019 8787	8509	8231	7953	7676	7400	7124	6849	6574	6300
21.5	0019 6026	5753	5480	5208	4936	4665	4394	4124	3854	3585
21.6	0019 3316	3048	2780	2513	2246	1980	1714	1449	1184	0920
21.7	.0019 0656	0393	0130	9867	9605	9344	9083	8823	8563	8303
21.8	0018 8044	7786	7528	7270	7013	6756	6500	6244	5989	5734
21.9	0018 5480	5226	4973	4720	4467	4215	3964	3713	3462	3212
22.0	0.0018 2962	2713	2464	2216	1968	1720	1473	1227	0981	0735
22.1	.0018 0490	0245	0001	9757	9513	9270	9028	8786	8544	8303
22.2	0017 8062	7821	7581	7342	7103	6864	6626	6388	6150	5913
22.3	0017 5677	5441	5205	4970	4735	4501	4267	4033	3800	3567
22.4	.0017 3335	3103	2871	2640	2409	2179	1949	1720	1491	1262
22.5	0017 1034	0806	0578	0351	0125	9899	9673	9447	9222	8998
22.6	0016 8774	8550	8326	8103	7880	7658	7436	7215	6994	6773
22.7	.0016 6553	6333	6113	5894	5675	5457	5239	5021	4804	4587
22.8	0016 4371	4155	3939	3724	3509	3294	3080	2866	2653	2440
22.9	0016 2227	2015	1803	1591	1380	1169	0958	0748	0539	0329
23.0	0.0016 0120	9911	9703	9495	9288	9080	8873	8667	8461	8255
23.1	.0015 8050	7845	7640	7435	7231	7028	6824	6621	6419	6217
23.2	0015 6015	5813	5612	5411	5210	5010	4810	4611	4412	4213
23.3	0015 4014	3816	3619	3421	3224	3027	2831	2635	2439	2243
23.4	.0015 2048	1854	1659	1465	1271	1078	0885	0692	0499	0307
23.5	0015 0116	9924	9733	9542	9352	9162	8972	8782	8593	8404
23.6	0014 8215	8027	7839	7652	7464	7277	7091	6904	6718	6533
23.7	.0014 6347	6162	5977	5793	5609	5425	5241	5058	4875	4693
23.8	0014 4510	4328	4147	3965	3784	3603	3423	3243	3063	2883
23.9	0014 2704	2525	2346	2168	1990	1812	1634	1457	1280	1104
24.0	0.0014 0928									

$$E/3RT = 19.481818/x^3 \quad \text{when } x > 24.$$

D. Debye Specific Heat Function
$C_v (Debye)/3R$

x	0	1	2	3	4	5	6	7	8	9
0.0	1.0 00000	99995	99980	99955	99920	99875	99820	99755	99680	99595
0.1	.9 99500	99395	99280	99156	99021	98876	98721	98556	98382	98197
0.2	9 98003	97798	97584	97360	97126	96882	96628	96364	96091	95808
0.3	9 95514	95211	94899	94576	94244	93902	93550	93188	92817	92436
0.4	.9 92045	91645	91235	90816	90387	89948	89500	89042	88574	88097
0.5	9 87611	87115	86610	86095	85571	85037	84494	83942	83380	82809
0.6	9 82229	81639	81041	80433	79816	79190	78554	77910	77256	76594
0.7	.9 75922	75242	74552	73854	73147	72430	71705	70971	70229	69477
0.8	9 68717	67948	67171	66385	65590	64787	63975	63155	62326	61489
0.9	9 60643	59789	58927	58056	57177	56290	55395	54491	53580	52660
1.0	0.9 51732	50796	49853	48901	47941	46974	45999	45016	44025	43026
1.1	.9 42020	41006	39985	38956	37919	36875	35824	34765	33699	32626
1.2	9 31545	30457	29362	28259	27150	26033	24910	23779	22642	21498
1.3	9 20346	19188	18024	16852	15674	14489	13298	12100	10895	09684
1.4	.9 08467	07243	06013	04777	03534	02286	01031	99770	98503	97230
1.5	8 95951	94666	93375	92078	90775	89467	88153	86834	85509	84178
1.6	8 82842	81500	80153	78800	77442	76079	74711	73337	71959	70575
1.7	.8 69186	67792	66394	64990	63581	62168	60750	59327	57900	56468
1.8	8 55031	53590	52144	50694	49239	47780	46317	44850	43378	41902
1.9	8 40423	38939	37451	35959	34463	32963	31460	29952	28441	26926
2.0	0.8 25408	23886	22361	20832	19299	17763	16224	14681	13135	11586
2.1	.8 10034	08479	06920	05359	03794	02227	00656	99083	97507	95928
2.2	7 94347	92763	91176	89586	87994	86400	84803	83203	81602	79998
2.3	7 78391	76783	75172	73559	71944	70327	68708	67087	65464	63839
2.4	.7 62212	60584	58954	57322	55688	54053	52416	50777	49137	47496
2.5	7 45853	44209	42563	40916	39268	37619	35968	34316	32664	31010
2.6	7 29355	27699	26042	24385	22726	21067	19407	17746	16084	14422
2.7	.7 12759	11095	09431	07766	06101	04436	02770	01104	99437	97770
2.8	6 96103	94435	92768	91100	89432	87764	86096	84428	82760	81092
2.9	6 79424	77757	76089	74422	72754	71087	69421	67755	66089	64423
3.0	0.6 62758	61093	59429	57766	56103	54440	52778	51117	49456	47796
3.1	.6 46137	44479	42821	41165	39509	37854	36200	34546	32894	31243
3.2	6 29593	27944	26296	24649	23003	21359	19715	18073	16432	14792
3.3	6 13154	11517	09881	08247	06614	04983	03353	01724	00097	98472
3.4	.5 96848	95226	93605	91986	90369	88753	87139	85526	83916	82307
3.5	5 80700	79095	77491	75889	74290	72692	71096	69502	67910	66320
3.6	5 64732	63146	61562	59980	58400	56823	55247	53674	52102	50533
3.7	.5 48966	47401	45839	44279	42721	41165	39611	38060	36511	34965
3.8	5 33421	31879	30340	28803	27268	25736	24207	22680	21155	19633
3.9	5 18113	16596	15082	13570	12061	10554	09050	07548	06049	04553

C_v(Debye)/3 R

x	0	1	2	3	4	5	6	7	8	9
4.0	0.5 03059	01568	00080	98595	97112	95632	94154	92679	91207	89738
4.1	.4 88272	86808	85347	83889	82434	80982	79532	78086	76642	75201
4.2	4 73763	72328	70896	69466	68040	66616	65196	63778	62363	60952
4.3	4 59543	58137	56734	55334	53938	52544	51153	49765	48380	46999
4.4	.4 45620	44244	42872	41502	40136	38772	37412	36055	34701	33350
4.5	4 32002	30657	29315	27976	26641	25308	23979	22653	21330	20010
4.6	4 18693	17380	16069	14762	13458	12157	10859	09565	08273	06985
4.7	.4 05700	04418	03139	01864	00591	99322	98056	96794	95534	94278·
4.8	3 93025	91775	90528	89284	88044	86807	85573	84342	83114	81890
4.9	3 80669	79451	78237	77025	75817	74612	73410	72211	71016	69824
5.0	0.36 8635	7449	6267	5087	3911	2738	1568	0402	9239	8079
5.1	.35 6922	5768	4618	3470	2326	1186	0048	8913	7782	6654
5.2	34 5529	4408	3289	2174	1062	9953	8847	7744	6645	5549
5.3	33 4456	3366	2279	1195	0115	9038	7963	6892	5825	4760
5.4	.32 3698	2640	1585	0533	9484	8438	7395	6355	5319	4285
5.5	31 3255	2228	1203	0182	9164	8149	7138	6129	5123	4121
5.6	30 3121	2125	1131	0141	9154	8169	7188	6210)	5235	4262
5.7	.29 3293	2327	1364	0404	9447	8493	7541	6593	5648	4706
5.8	28 3767	2830	1897	0967	0039	9115	8193	7275	6359	5446
5.9	27 4536	3629	2725	1824	0926	0031	9138	8249	7362	6478
6.0	0.26 5597	4719	3843	2971	2101	1234	0370	9509	8651	7795
6.1	.25 6943	6093	5246	4401	3559	2721	1885	1051	0221	9393
6.2	24 8568	7745	6926	6109	5295	4483	3674	2868	2065	1264
6.3	24 0466	9670	8878	8088	7300	6515	5733	4954	4177	3403
6.4	.23 2631	1862	1095	0331	9570	8811	8055	7302	6551	5802
6.5	22 5056	4313	3572	2834	2098	1364	0633	9905	9179	8456
6.6	21 7735	7017	6301	5588	4877	4168	3462	2758	2057	1358
6.7	.21 0662	9968	9276	8587	7900	7215	6533	5853	5176	4501
6.8	20 3828	3158	2490	1824	1161	0500	9841	9185	8530	7878
6.9	19 7229	6581	5936	5294	4653	4015	3379	2745	2113	1484
7.0	0.19 0856	0231	9609	8988	8370	7753	7139	6527	5917	5310
7.1	.18 4704	4101	3500	2901	2304	1709	1116	0526	9937	9351
7.2	17 8766	8184	7604	7025	6449	5875	5303	4733	4165	3599
7.3	17 3035	2473	1913	1355	0799	0245	9693	9143	8595	8049
7.4	.16 7505	6963	6422	5884	5347	4813	4280	3750	3221	2694
7.5	16 2169	1646	1124	0605	0087	9572	9058	8546	8036	7527
7.6	15 7021	6516	6013	5512	5013	4515	4020	3526	3034	2543
7.7	.15 2055	1568	1083	0599	0118	9638	9160	8683	8209	7736
7.8	14 7264	6795	6327	5861	5396	4933	4472	4013	3555	3098
7.9	14 2644	2191	1740	1290	0842	0395	9951	9508	9066	8626

x	0	1	2	3	4	5	6	7	8	9
8.0	0.13 8187	7750	7315	6881	6449	6019	5590	5162	4736	4312
8.1	.13 3889	3468	3048	2630	2213	1798	1384	0972	0561	0152
8.2	12 9744	9338	8933	8529	8127	7727	7328	6930	6534	6139
8.3	12 5746	5354	4964	4575	4187	3801	3416	3032	2650	2270
8.4	. 12 1890	1512	1136	0761	0387	0014	9643	9273	8905	8538
8.5	11 8172	7807	7444	7082	6722	6362	6004	5648	5292	4938
8.6	11 4585	4234	3883	3534	3187	2840	2495	2151	1808	1466
8.7	. 11 1126	0787	0449	0113	9777	9443	9110	8778	8447	8118
8.8	10 7790	7463	7137	6812	6489	6166	5845	5525	5206	4888
8.9	10 4572	4256	3942	3628	3316	3005	2695	2387	2079	1773
9.0	0.10 1467	1163	0859	0557	0256	99562	96573	93594	90626	87669
9.1	· 09 84722	81786	78861	75946	73041	70146	67262	64389	61525	58672
9.2	09 55829	52996	50174	47361	44558	41766	38983	36210	33448	30695
9.3	09 27951	25218	22494	19780	17076	14381	11696	09021	06355	03698
9.4	· 09 01051	98414	95785	93166	90557	87956	85365	82783	80210	77646
9.5	08 75092	72546	70010	67482	64964	62454	59953	57461	54978	52504
9.6	08 50038	47581	45133	42693	40262	37840	35426	33020	30623	28235
9.7	· 08 25855	23483	21120	18765	16418	14080	11750	09428	07114	04808
9.8	08 02510	00221	97939	95666	93400	91142	88893	86651	84417	82191
9.9	07 79972	77762	75559	73364	71176	68996	66824	64659	62502	60352
10.0	0.07 58210	56075	53948	51828	49716	47611	45513	43422	41339	39263
10.1	· 07 37194	35133	33078	31031	28991	26957	24931	22912	20900	18895
10.2	07 16897	14905	12921	10943	08973	07009	05051	03101	01157	99220
10.3	06 97290	95366	93449	91539	89635	87738	85847	83962	82084	80213
10.4	· 06 78348	76489	74637	72791	70952	69118	67291	65470	63656	61848
10.5	06 60045	58249	56459	54676	52898	51126	49361	47601	45847	44100
10.6	06 42358	40622	38892	37168	35450	33738	32031	30330	28635	26946
10.7	· 06 25263	23585	21913	20246	18585	16930	15280	13636	11997	10364
10.8	06 08737	07115	05498	03887	02281	00681	99086	97496	95912	94333
10.9	05 92759	91190	89627	88069	86516	84969	83426	81889	80357	78830
11.0	0.05 77308	75791	74280	72773	71271	69774	68283	66796	65314	63837
11.1	·05 62365	60898	59436	57978	56526	55078	53635	52197	50763	49334
11.2	05 47910	46491	45076	43666	42261	40860	39464	38073	36686	35304
11.3	05 33926	32552	31183	29819	28460	27104	25753	24407	23065	21727
11.4	·05 20394	19065	17740	16420	15104	13792	12484	11181	09882	08587
11.5	05 07297	06011	04728	03450	02177	00907	99641	98380	97122	95869
11.6	04 94620	93374	92133	90896	89663	88433	87208	85987	84769	83556
11.7	·04 82346	81140	79938	78740	77546	76356	75169	73987	72808	71633
11.8	04 70461	69294	68130	66969	65813	64660	63511	62366	61224	60085
11.9	04 58951	57820	56693	55569	54448	53332	52219	51109	50003	48900

$C_v(\text{Debye})/3R$

x	0	1	2	3	4	5	6	7	8	9
12.0	0.044 7801	6705	5613	4525	3439	2357	1279	0204	9132	8064
12.1	•043 6999	5937	4879	3824	2772	1724	0679	9637	8599	7563
12.2	042 6531	5502	4477	3454	2435	1419	0406	9397	8390	7386
12.3	041 6386	5389	4395	3404	2416	1431	0449	9470	8494	7522
12.4	•040 6552	5585	4621	3660	2703	1748	0796	9847	8901	7957
12.5	039 7017	6080	5145	4213	3285	2359	1435	0515	9598	8683
12.6	038 7771	6862	5956	5052	4151	3253	2358	1465	0575	9688
12.7	•037 8803	7921	7042	6166	5292	4421	3552	2686	1823	0962
12.8	037 0104	9249	8396	7545	6697	5852	5009	4169	3331	2496
12.9	036 1664	0834	0006	9181	8358	7538	6720	5904	5091	4281
13.0	0.035 3473	2667	1864	1063	0264	9468	8674	7883	7094	6307
13.1	•034 5523	4741	3961	3184	2409	1639	0865	0097	9331	8567
13.2	033 7805	7046	6289	5534	4782	4031	3283	2537	1793	1051
13.3	033 0312	9575	8840	8107	7376	6647	5920	5196	4474	3753
13.4	•032 3035	2319	1605	0893	0183	9475	8770	8066	7364	6665
13.5	031 5967	5272	4578	3886	3197	2509	1824	1140	0458	9779
13.6	030 9101	8425	7751	7079	6409	5741	5075	4411	3748	3088
13.7	•030 2429	1773	1118	0465	9814	9164	8517	7872	7228	6586
13.8	029 5946	5308	4671	4037	3404	2773	2144	1516	0890	0266
13.9	028 9644	9024	8405	7788	7173	6559	5948	5338	4729	4123
14.0	0.028 3518	2915	2313	1713	1115	0519	9924	9331	8739	8149
14.1	•027 7561	6975	6390	5806	5225	4645	4066	3489	2914	2341
14.2	027 1769	1198	0629	0062	9496	8932	8369	7808	7249	6691
14.3	026 6134	5579	5026	4474	3924	3375	2828	2282	1737	1194
14.4	•026 0653	0113	9575	9038	8502	7968	7436	6905	6375	5847
14.5	025 5320	4795	4271	3748	3227	2708	2190	1673	1157	0643
14.6	025 0130	9619	9109	8601	8094	7588	7083	6580	6079	5578
14.7	.024 5079	4582	4085	3590	3097	2604	2113	1624	1135	0648
14.8	024 0162	9678	9195	8713	8232	7753	7275	6798	6322	5848
14.9	023 5375	4903	4432	3963	3495	3028	2563	2098	1635	1174
15.0	0.023 0713	0253	9795	9338	8882	8428	7974	7522	7071	6621
15.1	•022 6172	5725	5279	4833	4389	3947	3505	3064	2625	2187
15.2	022 1750	1314	0879	0445	0013	9581	9151	8722	8294	7867
15.3	021 7441	7016	6592	6170	5748	5328	4909	4490	4073	3657
15.4	•021 3242	2828	2415	2004	1593	1183	0775	0367	9960	9555
15.5	020 9150	8747	8345	7943	7543	7144	6745	6348	5952	5557
15.6	020 5162	4769	4377	3985	3595	3206	2818	2430	2044	1659
15.7	•020 1274	0891	0508	0127	9747	9367	8988	8611	8234	7858
15.8	019 7484	7110	6737	6365	5994	5624	5254	4886	4519	4152
15.9	019 3787	3422	3059	2696	2334	1973	1613	1254	0896	0538

x	0	1	2	3	4	5	6	7	8	9
16.0	0.019 0182	9826	9471	9118	8765	8413	8061	7711	7361	7013
16.1	.018 6665	6318	5972	5627	5283	4939	4596	4255	3914	3574
16.2	018 3234	2896	2558	2221	1885	1550	1216	0882	0550	0218
16.3	017 9887	9556	9227	8898	8570	8243	7917	7592	7267	6943
16.4	.017 6620	6298	5976	5655	5335	5016	4698	4380	4063	3747
16.5	017 3432	3117	2803	2490	2178	1866	1555	1245	0936	0627
16.6	017 0319	0012	9706	9400	9095	8791	8488	8185	7883	7582
16.7	.016 7281	6981	6682	6383	6086	5789	5492	5197	4902	4608
16.8	016 4314	4021	3729	3438	3147	2857	2568	2279	1991	1704
16.9	016 1417	1131	0846	0561	0277	9994	9711	9429	9148	8867
17.0	0.015 8587	8308	8029	7751	7474	7197	6921	6646	6371	6097
17.1	.015 5823	5550	5278	5007	4736	4465	4196	3927	3658	3390
17.2	015 3123	2857	2591	2325	2060	1796	1533	1270	1008	0746
17.3	015 0485	0224	9964	9705	9446	9188	8931	8674	8418	8162
17.4	.014 7907	7652	7398	7145	6892	6640	6388	6137	5886	5636
17.5	014 5387	5138	4890	4642	4395	4148	3902	3657	3412	3168
17.6	014 2924	2681	2438	2196	1954	1713	1473	1233	0994	0755
17.7	.014 0516	0278	0041	9804	9568	9333	9098	8863	8629	8395
17.8	013 8162	7930	7698	7467	7236	7005	6775	6546	6317	6089
17.9	013 5861	5633	5406	5180	4954	4729	4504	4280	4056	3833
18.0	0.013 3610	3387	3165	2944	2723	2503	2283	2064	1845	1626
18.1	.013 1408	1191	0974	0757	0541	0326	0110	9896	9682	9468
18.2	012 9255	9042	8830	8618	8407	8196	7985	7775	7566	7357
18.3	012 7148	6940	6732	6525	6318	6112	5906	5700	5495	5291
18.4	.012 5087	4883	4680	4477	4275	4073	3871	3670	3470	3270
18.5	012 3070	2871	2672	2473	2275	2078	1881	1684	1487	1291
18.6	012 1096	0901	0706	0512	0318	0125	9932	9739	9547	9355
18.7	.011 9164	8973	8783	8593	8403	8214	8025	7836	7648	7460
18.8	011 7273	7086	6900	6714	6528	6342	6157	5973	5789	5605
18.9	011 5422	5239	5056	4874	4692	4511	4330	4149	3969	3789
19.0	0.011 3609	3430	3251	3073	2895	2717	2540	2363	2186	2010
19.1	.011 1834	1659	1484	1309	1135	0961	0787	0614	0441	0268
19.2	011 0096	9924	9753	9582	9411	9241	9071	8901	8732	8563
19.3	010 8394	8226	8058	7890	7723	7556	7390	7223	7057	6892
19.4	.010 6727	6562	6397	6233	6069	5906	5743	5580	5417	5255
19.5	010 5093	4932	4771	4610	4449	4289	4129	3970	3811	3652
19.6	010 3493	3335	3177	3019	2862	2705	2549	2392	2236	2081
19.7	.010 1925	1770	1616	1461	1307	1153	1000	0845	0694	0541
19.8	010 0389	0237	0085	99341	97830	96323	94819	93318	91820	90325
19.9	009 88833	87344	85858	84375	82894	81417	79943	78472	77003	75538

$C_v(\text{Debye})/3\,R$

x	0	1	2	3	4	5	6	7	8	9
20.0	0.009 74076	72616	71160	69706	68255	66807	65362	63920	62481	61044
20.1	.009 59611	58180	56752	55327	53905	52485	51069	49655	48244	46836
20.2	009 45430	44028	42628	41231	39837	38445	37056	35670	34287	32906
20.3	009 31528	30153	28781	27411	26044	24679	23317	21958	20602	19248
20.4	.009 17897	16549	15203	13860	12519	11181	09846	08513	07183	05856
20.5	009 04531	03208	01889	00572	99257	97945	96635	95328	94024	92722
20.6	008 91423	90126	88831	87539	86250	84963	83679	82397	81118	79841
20.7	.008 78566	77294	76025	74758	73493	72231	70971	69714	68459	67206
20.8	008 65956	64708	63463	62220	60980	59742	58506	57272	56041	54812
20.9	008 53586	52362	51140	49921	48704	47489	46277	45067	43859	42654
21.0	0.0084 1451	0250	9051	7855	6661	5469	4279	3092	1907	0724
21.1	.0082 9544	8366	7190	6016	4844	3675	2507	1342	0180	9019
21.2	0081 7861	6704	5550	4399	3249	2101	0956	9813	8672	7533
21.3	0080 6396	5261	4129	2998	1870	0744	9620	8498	7378	6260
21.4	.0079 5144	4031	2919	1810	0702	9597	8494	7393	6293	5196
21.5	0078 4101	3008	1917	0828	9741	8656	7573	6492	5413	4336
21.6	0077 3262	2189	1118	0049	8982	7917	6853	5792	4733	3676
21.7	0076 2621	1567	0516	9467	8419	7373	6330	5288	4248	3210
21.8	0075 2174	1140	0108	9078	8049	7022	5998	4975	3954	2935
21.9	0074 1918	0902	9889	8877	7867	6859	5853	4849	3846	2846
22.0	0.0073 1847	0850	9854	8861	7869	6879	5891	4905	3921	2938
22.1	.0072 1957	0978	0001	9025	8051	7079	6109	5140	4173	3208
22.2	0071 2245	1283	0323	9365	8409	7454	6501	5550	4600	3652
22.3	0070 2706	1762	0819	9878	8939	8001	7065	6130	5198	4267
22.4	.0069 3337	2409	1483	0559	9636	8715	7795	6878	5961	5047
22.5	0068 4134	3222	2313	1405	0498	9593	8690	7788	6888	5990
22.6	0067 5093	4197	3303	2411	1521	0632	9744	8858	7974	7091
22.7	.0066 6210	5330	4452	3576	2701	1827	0955	0085	9216	8348
22.8	0065 7483	6618	5755	4894	4034	3176	2319	1464	0610	9758
22.9	0064 8907	8058	7210	6363	5518	4675	3833	2992	2153	1316
23.0	0.0064 0480	9645	8812	7980	7150	6321	5493	4667	3843	3020
23.1	.0063 2198	1378	0559	9741	8925	8110	7297	6485	5675	4866
23.2	0062 4058	3252	2447	1643	0841	0041	9241	8443	7647	6852
23.3	0061 6058	5265	4474	3684	2896	2109	1323	0538	9755	8973
23.4	.0060 8193	7414	6636	5860	5085	4311	3539	2768	1998	1229
23.5	0060 0462	9696	8931	8168	7406	6645	5886	5128	4371	3616
23.6	0059 2861	2108	1357	0606	9857	9109	8362	7617	6873	6130
23.7	.0058 5388	4648	3909	3171	2434	1699	0965	0232	9500	8770
23.8	0057 8041	7313	6586	5860	5136	4413	3691	2970	2251	1532
23.9	0057 0815	0099	9385	8671	7959	7248	6538	5829	5121	4415
24.0	0.0056 3710									

$$C_v/3R = 77.92727/x^3 \quad \text{when} \quad x > 24.$$

Author Index

Subject Index

234

RETURN TO: CHEMISTRY LIBRARY
100 Hildebrand Hall • 510-642-3753

LOAN PERIOD	1	2 *1 Month*	3
4		5	6

ALL BOOKS MAY BE RECALLED AFTER 7 DAYS.
Renewals may be requested by phone or, using GLADIS, type **inv** followed by your patron ID number.

DUE AS STAMPED BELOW.

NOV 24		
DEC 05 JAN 11		
APR 30		
NOV 14		
DEC 0 8		